INTRODUCTION TO
ANALYTIC GEOMETRY
AND
LINEAR ALGEBRA

INTRODUCTION TO

ANALYTIC GEOMETRY
AND
LINEAR ALGEBRA

ARNO JAEGER
University of Cincinnati

HOLT, RINEHART AND WINSTON, INC.   NEW YORK

97565

IN MEMORIAM

Hermann Ludwig Schmid

1908-1956

Preface

Preliminary versions of this textbook have been used for the past several years in a course required of all prospective majors in mathematics in both the College of Arts and Sciences and the College of Education at the University of Cincinnati. The objective has been to present a modern and, at least in English, a somewhat novel treatment of fundamental analytic geometry based on groups, vector spaces, and Euclidean vector spaces, together with an introduction to these algebraic structures, at a level suitable for freshmen and sophomores.

To achieve this goal without sacrificing rigor or too much substance the discussion concentrates upon comparatively few concepts re-appearing in different or more general contexts. Further, frequent shifts of focus between analytic geometry and linear algebra produce a strong mutual motivation of the *abstract* by the *concrete* and vice versa. The level of abstraction is deliberate since it is unavoidable in contemporary mathematics, and early contact with it will be of advantage to the student. Particular attention is also paid to the explicit formulation of definitions and theorems in order to familiarize the reader with the exact language of modern mathematics. Finally, the exercises are selected to challenge the student, clarify the concepts for him, and help him develop his reasoning power and mathematical intuition.

The unfamiliar aspect of this presentation is due chiefly to its systematic construction of analytic geometry in terms of *bijections* between point and translation spaces and *isomorphisms* between translation and coordinate spaces. From this modern perspective the more advanced student will be able to infer an axiomatic treatment, as the appendix indicates. Such a construction necessitates an ordering of the subject matter by algebraic tools needed to cope with problems of increasing complexity, rather than by geometric considerations. The elementary parts of the theories of finite-dimensional vector spaces, linear equations, linear inequalities, and linear programming then become easily assimilated by-products as well as sources for many exercises. In due time the student should become convinced of the advantages of the coordinate-free *abstract* vectors and linear mappings over the *concrete* number sequences and matrices. Although such an approach to analytic geometry is unusual at this level, the concepts employed are standard in modern linear algebra; and mastery of them will enable the student to proceed earlier to more advanced courses such as algebra, projective geometry, differential equations, and several parts of theoretical physics, including quantum mechanics.

As an introduction to linear algebra, this book should fall between other texts that stress abstraction but are too advanced for the beginning student and those that treat the subject mainly as a useful shorthand for college algebra. It will be ound to complement and enrich the treatment of analytic geometry in texts which combine that subject with calculus.

Teachers may find it possible, in the light of their own experiences and requirements, to use the contents in several different courses. Apart from the computational ability resulting from a good high-school training, no especial background—such as a knowledge of calculus—and certainly no mathematical maturity is needed. Some examples and exercises, which may be omitted without harm, employ calculus and elementary differential equations and are included to show the more advanced student the key role of vectorial methods in other branches of mathematics.

The text may be used as the basis for a one-semester course (for example, by assigning only Chapters 1–7 and 15) or for a two-semester course, with the possible omission of Chapters 10, 11, or 19. As an elementary but precise exposition of modern material it should prove useful also to advanced students, industrial mathematicians, economists, and high-school teachers for self-study, review, and reference. For such purposes a chart has been included on page ix, indicating the prerequisites for each chapter.

At all stages of the book much valuable help was given to me by many of my colleagues, students, and other friends. My especial thanks go to my former students, Professors Roger Chalkley and Frank Levin, and to my students, Professor William Larkin III, Mr. David Findley, Miss Joan Meyer, and Miss Kathleen Statman, for their versatile contributions, their enthusiasm, encouragement, and patience, and their sacrifice of innumerable hours. I am greatly indebted to Professor Burton W. Jones, whose extensive comments and friendly assistance improved the text considerably. I am deeply grateful to Miss Renée Hauser for the efficient and tireless work she contributed so generously towards the preparation of this book. I wish also to express my appreciation to the Charles P. Taft Memorial Fund of the University of Cincinnati for the financial assistance in the typing. Finally I am very proud to acknowledge the helpfulness and understanding of the faculty members of our Mathematics Department. May their enthusiasm and progressive spirit be contagious!

Cincinnati, Ohio   A. J.
April, 1960

INTERDEPENDENCE OF THE CHAPTERS

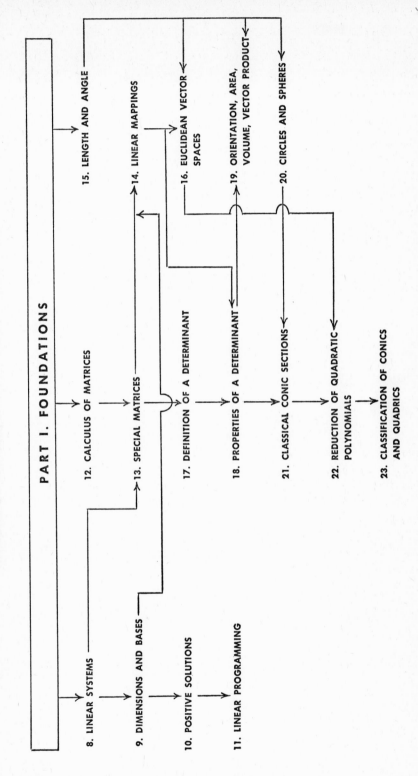

Contents

PART III: MULTILINEAR GEOMETRY AND ALGEBRA

PART IV: QUADRATIC GEOMETRY AND ALGEBRA

PART I

Foundations

Introduction

If, for the moment, we take the liberty of calling algebra the part of mathematics known to college freshmen that deals with numerical rather than geometric figures, we can roughly describe the essence of analytic geometry as follows: There exist correspondences between geometric objects, such as points, lines, curves, and algebraic objects, such as numbers, sequences of numbers, and functions on numbers. These correspondences are used to develop geometry with the help of algebra and to transform properties, problems, theorems, proofs, etc., from geometry to algebra and vice versa.

Historically analytic geometry started as a method, introduced by the French mathematician and philosopher *René Descartes* (1596–1650), of solving geometric problems by means of algebra. The fruitful interplay so initiated between geometry and algebra increased during the following centuries and stimulated both mathematical fields.

Thus the geometric method known as vector calculus, which deals with the rules of shifting positions in space, led in a natural way to its algebraic counterpart, the theory of vector spaces, which in its modern generalization is a very powerful tool in the algebra of linear polynomials. Conversely, the calculus of sequences of numbers found an imaginative interpretation (although sometimes only of an intuitive character) by clever employment of geometric terminology (such as the concepts of a four-dimensional space or of a hyperplane). More general functional relationships between numbers were seen to find very suggestive interpretations in curves or other geometric objects.

In this textbook we shall not be openly concerned with dry and possibly unmotivated geometric axioms, but shall consider as known the principal concepts and properties of elementary geometry, such as point, line, plane, distance, direction, angle, perpendicularity, and parallelism. From them some algebraic concepts and methods will be derived, which will determine the path for further investigations. In time it will become clear that analytic geometry is structurally a part of linear algebra. The appendix shows, finally, that a modern axiomatic treatment of analytic geometry is hidden in this textbook and can be obtained by a minor change, which justifies the simplified presentation chosen.

Before a formal theory can be developed we have to agree on a common *precise* language in order to be able to communicate; for vagueness could lead to confusion and error and make complete understanding impossible. Our special vocabulary is obtained by the adoption of *definitions* christening the mathematical concepts needed. Definitions can *never* be proved; they are nothing but *names for concepts*. The selection of the *concepts* depends on the theory to be developed, on pedagogical considerations, and on the taste of the expositor. The choice of the *words* given to those concepts usually depends on the inventors of the concepts; they are sometimes very suggestive and sometimes very strange, just as in a city the names of some streets make sense and others do not. To argue about definitions in mathematics is a waste of time, especially for students still learning the field in which they appear.

If a word is used in this text to designate a concept different from the usual meaning of that word in everyday life or in other books, the student should not be disturbed; every environment breeds its own language. For example, a coed speaking of a "good date" may be thinking of something entirely different from what is in the mind of a committee chairman trying to plan a meeting or of a farmer in California tasting a fruit. The word "field" will mean different things to the soldier advancing in battle, to the physicist measuring gravitation, and to the mathematician working in abstract algebra. The word "bridge" will make the dentist think of artificial teeth, the engineer of a means of crossing a waterway, or the housewife of the next meeting of the women's club.

But if a word of ordinary language is used in this textbook to designate a mathematical concept, it should be understood that that word will never be applied here in its usual sense and never should be so used by the students studying this course. This is part of the mental discipline the students should learn as soon as possible. For example, we temporarily forbid the use of the word "group," because it will soon be needed for a specific algebraic concept.

We shall usually employ letters to denote geometric, algebraic, and other concepts. The letter i will not be reserved to denote the imaginary unit $\sqrt{-1}$ *exclusively*, but frequently will stand for an arbitrary integer.

If i is meant to be an abbreviation for $\sqrt{-1}$, this will either be clear from the context or be explicitly stated. Different alphabets and letter types will be used to distinguish between different kinds of concepts. If the same letter appears in two different alphabets within a discussion, there is frequently a definite relationship between the two concepts denoted. Within one investigation the same letter type will always stand for the same concept, but different types may still be abbreviations for the same concept.

If a letter denotes an unspecified number, the student should be warned that this number may be equal to zero. This may necessitate additional arguments for this special case.

Except in algebraic equations in unknowns, equality in this text will always be meant in the sense of identity. Thus an equation $a = b$ expresses only that a and b stand for the same concept. This convention eliminates the necessity of checking whether each specific equality relation introduced is actually an equivalence relation, for the relation of identity obviously is an equivalence relation.

The point may be considered the most basic object in geometry, for any object can be expressed in terms of points. Thus we will first fix the position of a point in terms of numbers. On a plane this is generally done in the following way (Fig. 1.1): Given two straight lines, one drawn verti-

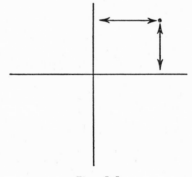

Fig. 1.1

cally and the other horizontally; any point can be described uniquely by two numbers, and any couple of numbers can be represented uniquely by a point. The absolute value of the first number gives the distance of the point in question from the vertical line, and, in case of a nonzero distance, the sign of the first number is positive or negative according to whether the point lies to the right or left of this line. Similarly, the absolute value of the second number gives the distance of the point from the horizontal line, and, in case of a nonzero distance, the sign is positive or negative according to whether the point lies above or below that line.

This "static" approach seems straightforward, but it has a number of disadvantages in the further development of analytic geometry and its connection with algebra. An alternative, more "dynamic" approach, which we shall follow here, may at first seem a bit sophisticated, especially for students with high school experience in analytic geometry, but it will prove to be far superior. The idea is quite simple. We shall describe the position of a point in terms of how to get there. This leads to the fundamental concept of a *translation*, whose properties (together with their connections with algebra) will be investigated before we build up the geometric spaces to be considered.

The journey will not be too difficult, provided the student *masters* the standard techniques taught in college algebra and trigonometry. A knowledge of calculus is *not* required. Only for the benefit of more advanced students have some examples and exercises been included that are based on calculus and elementary differential equations, to point out important connections between the subject matter of this text and other parts of mathematics. Those and other advanced applications will be marked by an asterisk and may be omitted without harm.

2

On Elementary Set Theory

Mathematics investigates not only *single* objects but, frequently, *collections* of objects. The mathematician calls every collection of distinct objects of our perception or imagination, considered as an entity, a *set*, and the objects forming that set, its *elements*. Some elements of a set may be concrete objects, whereas others of the same set may be abstract. The elements of a set may themselves be (other) sets. There are certain restrictions however, for which the student should refer to an advanced text on set theory. The idea of a set is considered to be a basic mathematical notion; therefore, its definition cannot be given within mathematics, but only in general terms of logic or philosophy.

In this text sets will often be denoted by capital italic or boldface letters A, B, $\cdots$, **A**, **B**, $\cdots$, and their elements by lower-case italic or boldface letters a, b, $\cdots$, **a**, **b**, $\cdots$. We shall employ the very useful convention that, *unless otherwise stated*, a lower-case letter stands for an element of the set that is denoted by the same capital letter of the same alphabet. If several elements of the same set are considered, we distinguish them by suffixes (subscripts) or by upper indices (enclosed in parentheses). In particular, sets of points will usually be denoted by capital English script letters $\mathfrak{A}$, $\mathfrak{B}$, $\cdots$, and their elements—that is, the points—by capital letters P, Q, $\cdots$. The abbreviation $a \; \varepsilon \; A$ is used to indicate that a is an element of the set A, or, as one frequently says, *belongs to A*. The abbreviation $b \notin A$ will mean that b is *not* an element of A.

Because of the generality of the concept of a set, there is no difficulty in giving examples. We shall introduce here some of the sets that are fundamental in analytic geometry and linear algebra, together with the names and the abbreviations chosen for them in this text.

EXAMPLES OF SETS

1. The set $\mathfrak{R}^3$ of all points of our perception, generally called *space* or *three-dimensional geometric space*.
2. The set $\mathfrak{R}^2$ of all points on a plane, generally called a *plane*. In other words, any plane will be considered to be the set of all its points.
3. The set $\mathfrak{R}^1$ of all points on a line, generally called a *line*. Thus, any line will be considered to be the set of all its points.
4. The set of all points on a line between two distinct points P, Q on this line (including P and Q), called the *line segment between P and Q*. Occasionally the requirement is dropped that $P \neq Q$; in this case a line segment might degenerate into a set consisting of a single point only.
5. The set of all points of a closed plane figure bounded by finitely many line segments, called a *(solid) polygon* (Fig. 2.1). Special types

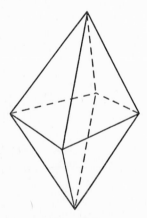

Fig. 2.1

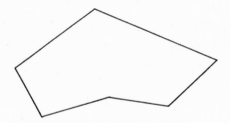

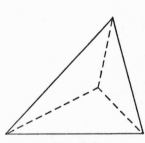

Fig. 2.2   Fig. 2.3

are the *triangles* (bounded by three line segments) and the *quadri-laterals* (bounded by four line segments).

6. The set of all points of a solid body bounded by finitely many tri-angles (in the sense of the previous definition), called a *polyhedron* (Fig. 2.2). A special type is the *tetrahedron*, which is bounded by four triangles (Fig. 2.3). (The vertices of the bounding triangles are also called vertices of the tetrahedron.)

7. The set $\mathfrak{L}_1 \cap \mathfrak{L}_2$ of all points that two given lines $\mathfrak{L}_1$, $\mathfrak{L}_2$ have in common, called *the intersection* of these lines.

8.† The sets I, I^*, I^+ of all integers (positive, negative, and zero), of all nonzero integers, and of all positive integers, respectively.

9.† The sets R, R^*, R^+ of all real numbers, of all nonzero real numbers, and of all positive real numbers, respectively.

10.† The sets C and C^* of all complex numbers and of all nonzero complex numbers, respectively.

11. The set $[\alpha,\beta]$ of all real numbers greater than or equal to a given number α and less than or equal to a given number β, called the *closed interval between α and β*.

12. The set R^2 of all couples (a_1,a_2) of two (not necessarily distinct) real numbers a_1 and a_2, called the *set of all real couples*.

13. The set R^3 of all triples (a_1,a_2,a_3) of three (not necessarily distinct) real numbers a_1, a_2, a_3, called the *set of all real triples*.

14. The set of all solutions of an algebraic equation $f(x) = 0$.

15. The set of all algebraic equations $f(x) = 0$ that have a given number a as a solution.

16. The set $A \cap B$ of all elements that two given sets A and B have in common, called the *intersection of A and B*.

17. The set $A \cup B$ of all elements that belong to either of two given sets A and B, called the *union of A and B*.

18. The set $A \times B$ of all objects (a,b) where a is an element of a given set A and b is an element of a given set B. This set is called the *(Cartesian) product* of A and B. The sets A and B are called the *left* and *right Cartesian factors*, respectively. The elements of $A \times B$ are called *(ordered) couples* or *pairs*.

The last example seems to be rather farfetched, but it plays a con-siderable role in mathematics as well as in ordinary life. For instance, let A be the set of all positive integers, and let B be the set of types of fruit (apple, plum, peach, etc.). To buy some fruit, one has to give both the number of pieces and the type. Or, the rational numbers a/b are composed of couples (a,b) where $a \, \varepsilon \, I$, and b is an element of the set I^* of all *nonzero* integers. Or, the powers a^b are defined (in a natural way) for all elements

† However, the capital italic letters I, R and C may also denote other con-cepts, but this will either be clear from the context or be explicitly stated.

(a,b) of the set $A \times B$ where A is the set of all positive rational numbers and $B = I$ is the set of all integers.

Two sets A and B are *equal* if and only if they consist of exactly the same elements. Thus a set is uniquely defined if all its elements are listed (*in an arbitrary order*). This is possible for *finite* sets, that is, sets having only finitely many elements. The list of the elements of such a set is customarily written with a comma between any two elements and with the whole enclosed by braces, in order to indicate that the collection is being considered as an entity. For example, the set S of the first three capital letters of the Latin alphabet can be written in the form $\{A,B,C\}$, or $\{B,C,A\}$, or in four other forms. Instead of $\{a_1,a_2,\cdots,a_n\}$ one writes frequently $\{a_i\}_{1 \le i \le n}$.

For infinite sets a similar notation may be used if no misunderstanding is likely. For example, $\{\cdots,-6,-3,0,3,6,\cdots\}$ can easily be interpreted as the set of all those integers that are multiples of 3. In many infinite (as well as finite) cases the following notation is convenient:

$$\{x| \text{ list of conditions that } x \text{ must satisfy}\}.$$

This expression is read: "The set of all x that satisfy $\cdots$." Thus example 11 could be abbreviated to $\{\lambda | \alpha \le \lambda \le \beta\}$, example 14 to $\{a|f(a) = 0, f(x)$ given$\}$, example 15 to $\{f(x) = 0|f(a) = 0, a$ given$\}$, and example 18 to $\{(a,b)|a \; \varepsilon \; A, \; b \; \varepsilon \; B\}$. Occasionally there is an ambiguity in this notation; therefore, it should be employed with care.

Examples 7, 11, and 16 do not always define sets. The two lines in question may be parallel, we may have $\alpha > \beta$, or the two given sets A and B may not have elements in common. In all three cases it would be correct to say that the sets do not exist. But, since the mathematician is interested in *general* statements and tries to avoid exceptional cases, he prefers a verbal statement of the kind that "the set has no elements." More precisely, the collection of *no* objects of our perception or imagination, considered as a concept of its own, is called *the empty set* or *the null set* and is denoted by the symbol "$\emptyset$." The article "the" is to indicate that we are not admitting several empty sets, such as perhaps "the empty set of points" or "the empty set of numbers" or something like that, but that there is to be only one empty set, namely, $\emptyset$. Any set different from the empty set, that is, having at least one element, is called *nonempty*. $\emptyset$ should not be confused with zero, for zero is a *number* and $\emptyset$ is a *set*.

Frequently we shall deal with a collection T of some but *not necessarily* all elements of a set S. If T is considered as an entity, in relation to S, it is called a *subset of S*, and this fact is denoted by $T \subset S$ or by $S \supset T$. It is also customary to say that S *includes* T or that T *is included in* S. Conversely, if S is considered in relation to some subset T, S is sometimes called a *superset of T*. A subset of a set need not be different from that set, just as in ordinary life a subcommittee of a committee may occasionally consist of all members of the committee. A subset of S that is different from S is called *proper*. The null set is considered to be a subset of every set.

If T is a subset of a set S and if U is a subset of T, then U is also a subset of S. If the two inclusions $U \subset T$ and $T \subset S$ are abbreviated together as the "chain" $U \subset T \subset S$, then the previous statement means that the cancellation of the middle term in such a chain leads to a correct inclusion formula. Similarly, longer chains are considered in mathematics; they may even involve infinitely many sets.

Two sets A and B are equal if and only if $A \subset B \subset A$.

EXAMPLES OF SUBSETS OF SETS

1. $\mathfrak{R}^2 \subset \mathfrak{R}^3$, $\mathfrak{R}^1 \subset \mathfrak{R}^3$.
2. If the line $\mathfrak{R}^1$ lies on the plane $\mathfrak{R}^2$, then $\mathfrak{R}^1 \subset \mathfrak{R}^2$.
3. $I \subset R \subset C$. $I^+ \subset I^* \subset I$. $R^+ \subset R^* \subset R$. $C^* \subset C$.
4. $A \supset (A \cap B)$. $B \supset (A \cap B)$.
5. If $S \subset A$ and $T \subset B$, then $(S \times T) \subset (A \times B)$.
6. $(I \times I) \subset R^2 \subset (C \times C)$.
7. If $A = \{a,b,c\}$ then the eight possible subsets of A are

$$\{a,b,c\}, \{a,b\}, \{a,c\}, \{b,c\}, \{a\}, \{b\}, \{c\}, \varnothing.$$

Sometimes not only one or a few, but *all* subsets of a given set are needed for some investigation. The set of all subsets of a given set A is called *the power set of* A and denoted by $P(A)$. The last example, for instance, shows that

$$P(\{a,b,c\}) = \{\{a,b,c\},\{a,b\},\{a,c\},\{b,c\},\{a\},\{b\},\{c\},\varnothing\}.$$

Note that, although the null set $\varnothing$ does not contain any elements, the power set $P(\varnothing)$ contains exactly one element, namely, $\varnothing$.

In all parts of mathematics connections are established among the elements of the sets under consideration. If two sets A and B are given, one may select certain couples (a,b) where $a \varepsilon A$ and $b \varepsilon B$ and *call* these selected couples *related* and all other possible couples not selected, *unrelated*. In other words, a relationship among the elements of two sets may be established by simply writing down a list of all those couples one wants to call related. More precisely, the mathematician calls any subset $\mathbf{R}$ of the Cartesian product $A \times B$ a *relation between A and B* and calls *a related to b (with respect to the relation $\mathbf{R}$)* if (a,b) ε $\mathbf{R}$, and *a not related to b* if (a,b) $\notin$ $\mathbf{R}$. The two extreme cases of a relation are $\mathbf{R} = A \times B$, and $\mathbf{R} = \varnothing$. In the first case every element of A is related to every element of B, and in the second case no element of A is related to any element of B.

In particular, such relationships may be established among the elements of one single set, namely, by taking $A = B$. In this case one speaks of a *relation in* the set A. Thus, in a set A, the relation "identity" is defined by $\mathbf{R} = \{(a,a)|a \,\varepsilon\, A)$, and the relation "distinctness" by $\mathbf{R} = \{(a,b)|a,b \,\varepsilon\, A,$ $a \neq b\}$. Among relations involving the elements of one set only, the student may already have come across *equivalence relations* and *orders*.

Any relation $\mathbf{R}$ that satisfies the three laws:

(1) $(a,a) \,\varepsilon\, \mathbf{R}$ for all $a \,\varepsilon\, A$;

(2) If $(a,b) \,\varepsilon\, \mathbf{R}$, then $(b,a) \,\varepsilon\, \mathbf{R}$;

(3) If $(a,b) \,\varepsilon\, \mathbf{R}$ and $(b,c) \,\varepsilon\, \mathbf{R}$, then $(a,c) \,\varepsilon\, \mathbf{R}$;

is called *an equivalence relation*. Instead of $(a,b) \,\varepsilon\, \mathbf{R}$ and $(a,b) \,\not\varepsilon\, \mathbf{R}$, the notations $a \equiv b$ and $a \not\equiv b$ are customary. *Equality* and *congruence* (in elementary geometry) are simple examples of equivalence relations.

Any relation $\mathbf{R}$ that satisfies the three laws:

(1) $(a,a) \,\varepsilon\, \mathbf{R}$ for all $a \,\varepsilon\, A$;

(2) If $(a,b) \,\varepsilon\, \mathbf{R}$ and $(b,a) \,\varepsilon\, \mathbf{R}$, then $a = b$;

(3) If $(a,b) \,\varepsilon\, \mathbf{R}$ and $(b,c) \,\varepsilon\, \mathbf{R}$, then $(a,c) \,\varepsilon\, \mathbf{R}$;

is called a *(partial) order*. In this case the notations $a \leq b$ and $a > b$ are customary instead of $(a,b) \,\varepsilon\, \mathbf{R}$ and $(a,b) \,\not\varepsilon\, \mathbf{R}$, respectively. For the set of all the real numbers, the relation "less than or equal" is an order; for the power set $P(S)$ of any set S, the set inclusion "$\subset$" is an order.

Among the many different kinds of relations between two sets some of the most important, within as well as outside mathematics, are those in which every element of the first set is listed exactly once. The grade list of a class, the telephone directory, the index of a book, indeed almost every list in ordinary life where two kinds of objects are brought into relationship, is of this kind. The mathematician calls every relation, M, between a set A and a set B in which every element of A is related to *one but only one* element of B, a (single-valued) *mapping of A into B*. The set A is called *the domain of definition of M*. The terminology chosen suggests a generalization of the geographical idea of assigning to every point on (some portion of) the earth a point in an atlas. The unique element of B related to some element a of A by a given mapping M is called *the image of a (under the mapping M)*, or *the M-image of a*, or *the element of B assigned to a by M*, or *the element of B on which a is mapped by M*. This visualization of a mapping is sometimes symbolized by figures involving two circles, standing for the sets A and B, and an arrow to indicate the assignment (Fig. 2.4). Frequently, to denote a mapping small letters f, g, $\cdots$ are chosen. Abbreviations like $f{:}A \to B$ or $f{:}x \to x^2 + 2$ are also used to describe mappings in general or to abbreviate the rules defining the relations if no misunderstanding is possible.

The definition of a mapping f of A into B demands only that every element of A be related to some element of B; it does not put any restrictions on the use of the elements of B. It may be that all elements of B are images under a given mapping, or only some, or only one element. The set of all images is called *the range of the mapping*. If all elements of B are f-images, then f is also called a mapping of A *onto* B (or a *surjective* mapping, or a *surjection*). Thus every mapping is a mapping onto its range. If the set B is visualized as the set of all points of the second circle in Fig. 2.4, then the word "onto" or the prefix "sur" indicates that the images "fill out the whole space."

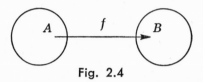

Fig. 2.4

The definition of a mapping f also does not exclude the possibility that an element of B may be the image of several elements of A. This will certainly happen if a three-dimensional geometric figure is projected on a two-dimensional sheet of paper. But if f has the important property that every element of B that is an f-image of an element of A is an f-image of *only one element*, then the relation is called a *one-to-one* (1-1) mapping (or an *injective mapping*, or an *injection*).

Mappings that are both one-to-one and onto, that is, where *every* element of the second set is an image of one and only one element, are called *one-to-one correspondences* (or *bijections*, or *bijective mappings*). In this case the elements of A and B can be paired in such a way that each element of one set has exactly one element of the other set as a partner and none is left out.

Frequently a mathematical object will be employed to define a mapping in a natural way, provided that within the context no misunderstanding is possible. The symbol for this object may sometimes serve as a deputy for the symbol of the mapping in question. In this case we shall say that the mathematical object *induces* the mapping. Thus the mapping $x \rightarrow 3x$, which assigns to every number 3 times that number, may be said to be induced by the number 3. But the mapping $x \rightarrow x + 3$ is also induced by the number 3.

EXAMPLES OF MAPPINGS

Every elementary (single-valued) function from high school or from a calculus class is a mapping of its domain of definition into the set of all (real or complex, depending on the viewpoint) numbers. In fact, many mathematicians use the words "mapping" and "function" as synonyms. We shall, in general, restrict the meaning of the word "function" to mappings from sets of *numbers* or sets of sequences of *numbers* into sets consisting of *numbers* and possibly one additional symbol ∞, called *infinity*.

1. For every set S, $x \rightarrow x$ defines a mapping of S onto itself, called the *identity mapping of S*. It is obviously a one-to-one correspondence. Although apparently trivial, it is quite important.

2. $x \rightarrow \tan x$ defines a mapping of R onto the set consisting of all real numbers and the symbol infinity. It is not one-to-one.

3. $x \rightarrow 3x + 2$, an example of a *linear polynomial function*, defines a one-to-one correspondence of R onto itself.

4. $(x,y) \rightarrow x - y$ defines a mapping of R^2 onto R, it is not one-to-one.

5. Let A be the set of all distinct couples of points of $\Re^3$ and let B be the set of all lines in $\Re^3$. The rule that assigns to each couple the line that passes through these two points defines a mapping of A onto B. It is not one-to-one.

6. Rotate all points of $\Re^2$ or $\Re^3$ about a given point (in $\Re^2$) or a given axis (in $\Re^3$) by some angle. Then the rule assigning to every point that point to which it is moved by this process is called a *rotation of $\Re^2$ or $\Re^3$*.

7. The following mapping of $\Re^3$ (or $\Re^2$) onto itself is called a *reflection about a plane $\Re^2$* (about a line $\Re^1$): Every point of $\Re^2$ (or $\Re^1$) is mapped onto itself. The image of any point P outside $\Re^2$ (outside $\Re^1$) is that point Q on the perpendicular to $\Re^2$ (to $\Re^1$) through P which has the same distance from the plane (line), but twice that distance from P.

8. Let A be the set of all circles on the surface of a sphere, and let B be the set of all planes that have at least two different points in common with the sphere. The mapping that assigns to every such circle the plane that contains this circle is both one-to-one and onto.

9. Fix on a line $\Re^1$ one point (the "origin"), one direction (the "positive direction"), and a unit length of measure. Assign to each point on $\Re^1$ the number whose absolute value gives the distance of this point from the origin and, if that number is different from zero, the positive or negative sign depending on whether or not the point in question lies in the positive direction from the origin. The mapping so obtained is one-to-one onto.

10. Let f be a mapping of a set A into a set B, not necessarily one-to-one. The rule that assigns to every element b of B the set of those elements of A that are mapped on b defines a mapping of B into $P(A)$. It is called *the inverse of f*.

11. Let c be a one-to-one correspondence of a set S onto a set T. Then the mapping of T onto S that assigns to every t that uniquely determined element s of S for which $c(s) = t$ is called the *opposite* (or *inverse*) correspondence of c. It is a one-to-one correspondence, too. The assignment is just reversed. A comparison with the previous example shows that the terminology "inverse" is ambiguous *in the*

case of one-to-one correspondences. But it will usually refer to our present concept.

12. Let $P(A)$ be the set of all subsets of a given set A. The rule that assigns to every subset S of A the subset $\{t | t \; \varepsilon \; A, \, t \; \not\varepsilon \; S\}$ is a mapping of $P(A)$ onto itself. It is called *complementation*.

13. Let $S = \{A, B, C\}$ be a set of three elements. There exist 6 one-to-one correspondences of S onto itself (usually called *permutations*).

C_1: $\{(A,A), \quad (B,B), \quad (C,C)\}$ (the identity mapping),
C_2: $\{(A,A), \quad (B,C), \quad (C,B)\}$,
C_3: $\{(A,B), \quad (B,A), \quad (C,C)\}$,
C_4: $\{(A,B), \quad (B,C), \quad (C,A)\}$,
C_5: $\{(A,C), \quad (B,A), \quad (C,B)\}$,
C_6: $\{(A,C), \quad (B,B), \quad (C,A)\}$.

If a mapping is defined explicitly, the image of every element can be expressed explicitly, too. But if we consider mappings *in general,* an abstract symbol for the image of some element may be needed. Unfortunately, no single notation is applied by mathematicians to denote images; the way to express images varies considerably from field to field and even from author to author.

NOTATIONS FOR THE IMAGE OF AN ELEMENT UNDER A MAPPING M

1. *The functional notation*: The image of the element a under the mapping m is denoted by $m(a)$. This is the most customary notation; it is frequently applied in the case of functions. Unless otherwise stated, we shall use the functional notation in all general discussions involving mappings.

2. *The left-operator notation*: The image of the element a under the mapping m is denoted by ma. A symbol m so used is called a *(left) operator.* This notation is employed, for example, in the case of trigonometric functions. We write "sin x" and not "sin (x)". Also in the mapping $a \rightarrow 3a$, the number 3 inducing this mapping is used as a left operator. In calculus the left-operator notation $\frac{d}{dx}f(x)$ is chosen frequently for derivatives, that is, images of differentiable functions under the mapping $f(x) \rightarrow \frac{d}{dx}f(x)$ (called *derivation*).

3. *The right-operator notation*: The image of the element a under the mapping m is denoted by am. A symbol m so used is called a *right operator.* For this notation it is harder to find *elementary* examples. But in the mapping $a \rightarrow a/2$ the combined symbol "$/2$" is a right operator.

4. *Superscript notations*: The image of the element a under the mapping m is denoted by m^a or by a^m. The first notation is applied in the case

of the exponential function defined by $x \rightarrow e^x$, and the second one in the mapping $x \rightarrow x^2$. In calculus the notation f' for the derivative of f is a sort of superscript notation.

5. *Suffix, or subscript notations*: The image of the element a under the mapping m is denoted by m_a or a_m. In calculus the image of a differentiable function f under the partial derivation $f \rightarrow \frac{\partial}{\partial x} f$ is frequently denoted by f_x.

6. Notation of an image by employing the same letters but a different type.

7. *A sequence (or k-tuple) of elements of a set A*: Let J be the set of all positive integers less than or equal to a fixed integer k. Every mapping s that assigns to every number j of J an element of A, written s_j, is called a *finite sequence of elements of A* or a *k-tuple of elements of A*. The elements s_i are called the *coordinates (or scalar components)* of s. The number k is called the *length* of the sequence. Usually this mapping s, which spells out the order in which the elements are to be listed, is denoted explicitly by $(s_1, \cdots, s_k)$, $(s_i)_{i \in J}$, or $(s_i)_{1 \le i \le k}$. Generally, it is more convenient to consider sequences as collections of (*not necessarily distinct*) elements *listed in a definite order, and we shall use that easier interpretation throughout the text*. If J is generalized to be the set of *all* positive integers, the corresponding mapping is called an *infinite sequence*. Infinite sequences play a considerable role in calculus.

For a fixed positive integer k, the set of all k-tuples of elements of a set A is denoted by A^k. The set A^1 is usually identified with A (that is, a 1-tuple is identified with the single element of which it is composed). The set of all k-tuples of A *of all finite lengths k* is denoted by A^∞ and called *the set of all restricted sequences of elements of A*. The set of all infinite sequences of elements of A is denoted by $\overline{A^\infty}$ and sometimes called *the set of all unrestricted sequences of elements of A*.

With the convention introduced in Chapter 1 equality of two sequences $(s_i)_{i \in J}$ and $(t_k)_{k \in K}$ means *identity*, that is, $J = K$ and $s_i = t_i$ for every $j \varepsilon J = K$. In other words, an equality $(s_1, s_2, \cdots, s_n) = (t_1, t_2, \cdots, t_m)$ is possible only if $n = m$ and is then equivalent to n equalities $s_1 = t_1$, $s_2 = t_2$, $\cdots$, $s_n = t_n$, and an equality of two infinite sequences is equivalent to (countably) infinitely many equalities of their corresponding coordinates.

Warning: The abbreviations $(s_i)_{1 \le i \le n}$ and $\{s_i\}_{1 \le i \le n}$ must be distinguished *very carefully*. In the first, which denotes a *sequence*, the elements a_i are not necessarily distinct, but the order in which they are listed matters very much. In the second, which denotes a *set*, all elements a_i must be distinct, but the order in which they are listed is not essential. In particular, the 1-*tuple* (s) is identified with the *element s*, but the *set* $\{s\}$ must always be distinguished from the *element s*.

8. *A double sequence (or matrix) of elements of a set A*: Temporarily let I be the set of all positive integers less than or equal to a fixed integer p, and let J be the set of all positive integers less than or equal to a fixed integer q *(not necessarily equal to p)*. Every mapping s that assigns to every pair (i,j) ε $I \times J$ (where the order in which i and j are listed now matters) an element of A, written s_{ij}, is called a *finite double sequence (of elements of A)*, or a *(p × q)-matrix* or a *matrix of p rows and q columns*. Usually this mapping is spelled out by listing all images in the following rectangular array:

$$\begin{bmatrix} s_{11} & s_{12} & s_{13} & \cdots & s_{1q} \\ s_{21} & s_{22} & s_{23} & \cdots & s_{2q} \\ \cdot & & \cdot & & \cdot \\ \cdot & & \cdot & & \cdot \\ \cdot & & \cdot & & \cdot \\ s_{p1} & & s_{p3} & & s_{pq} \end{bmatrix} ,$$

abbreviated $(s_{ij})_{(i,j)\,\varepsilon I\times J}$ or simply (s_{ij}). For practical purposes it is convenient to regard matrices as rectangular arrays of (not necessarily distinct) elements of a set in which the order of listing matters, and we shall do so later (see Chapter 12). If I and J are generalized to mean the set of *all* positive integers, then the corresponding generalization is called an *infinite double sequence* or an *infinite matrix*.

For fixed positive integers p and q, the set of all $(p \times q)$-matrices of elements of a set A is denoted by $A^{(p\times q)}$. The set $A^{(1\times1)}$ is usually identified with A (that is, a (1×1)-matrix is identified with the single element of which it is composed). The set of all finite matrices of elements of A with all possible numbers of rows and columns is denoted by $A^{(\infty\times\infty)}$ and called *the set of all restricted double sequences of elements of A*. The set of all infinite matrices of elements of A is denoted by $\overline{A^{(\infty\times\infty)}}$ and sometimes called *the set of all unrestricted double sequences of elements of A*.

With the convention introduced in Chapter 1 equality of two matrices $(s_{ij})_{(i,j)\,\varepsilon I\times J}$ and $(t_{kl})_{(k,l)\,\varepsilon K\times L}$ means *identity*, that is, $I = K$, $J = L$ and $s_{ij} = t_{ij}$ for every i ε I, j ε J. In other words, an equality

$$\begin{bmatrix} s_{11} & s_{12} & \cdots & s_{1q} \\ s_{21} & s_{22} & \cdots & s_{2q} \\ \cdot & \cdot & & \cdot \\ \cdot & \cdot & & \cdot \\ \cdot & \cdot & & \cdot \\ s_{p1} & s_{p2} & \cdots & s_{pq} \end{bmatrix} = \begin{bmatrix} t_{11} & t_{12} & \cdots & t_{1n} \\ t_{21} & t_{22} & \cdots & t_{2n} \\ \cdot & \cdot & & \cdot \\ \cdot & \cdot & & \cdot \\ \cdot & \cdot & & \cdot \\ t_{m1} & t_{m2} & \cdots & t_{mn} \end{bmatrix}$$

is possible *only if* $p = m$ and $q = n$ and is then equivalent to p times q equalities $s_{11} = t_{11}, \cdots, s_{1n} = t_{1n}, \cdots, s_{p1} = t_{p1}, \cdots, s_{pq} = t_{pq}$.

9. *Notations for sets of images*: Let m be a mapping of a set A into a set B, and let S be a subset of A. Then the set of all m-images of all elements of S—in functional notation, the set $\{m(s)\,|\,s \;\varepsilon\; S\}$—is a subset of B. For this image set, the notations $m(S)$, mS, or Sm, are all customary, depending on the notations employed for the images of single elements. Occasionally also, the superscript and subscript notations are generalized in a similar way.

Frequently two mappings can be combined to define a third mapping. Let f be some mapping of a set A into a set B. Let g be a mapping into some set D from a set C which *includes* the range of f (Fig. 2.5). Then

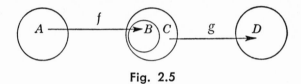

Fig. 2.5

the rule that assigns to an element $a \;\varepsilon\; A$ the element of D that is the g-image of the f-image of a defines a mapping that is called the *composite* of these two mappings. If a uniform notation is chosen, this mapping is abbreviated as follows:

$$
\begin{array}{lll}
g \circ f\!: & a \rightarrow g(f(a)) & \text{(functional notation)} \\
gf\!: & a \rightarrow g(fa) & \text{(left-operator notation)} \\
fg\!: & a \rightarrow (af)g & \text{(right-operator notation)} \\
fg \text{ (as superscript)}\!: & a \rightarrow (a^f)^g & \text{(superscript-operator notation)} \\
fg \text{ (as subscript)}\!: & a \rightarrow (a_f)_g & \text{(suffix operator notation)}
\end{array}
$$

In other words, the abbreviations $(g \circ f)(a)$, $(gf)a$, and $a(fg)$ are *defined* as follows:

$$(g \circ f)(a) = g(f(a))$$

$$(gf)a = g(fa)$$

$$a(fg) = (af)g$$

$$a^{fg} = (a^f)^g,$$

$$a_{fg} = (a_f)_g ,$$

depending on the notation chosen. If different kinds of notation are chosen for f and g, the description becomes more complicated, but we shall avoid this in this text. Note again that $g \circ f$ is to be defined *only* if $f(A) \subset C$, that is, if the domain of definition of g includes the range of f.

EXAMPLES OF COMPOSITE MAPPINGS

Define four mappings of R into R by the rules:

$$f: x \to x^2, \qquad g: x \to \sin x, \qquad h: x \to x - 2, \qquad k: x \to e^{-x}.$$

We apply functional notation.

1. $f \circ g$: $\quad x \to (\sin x)^2$.
2. $g \circ f$: $\quad x \to \sin (x^2)$.
3. $f \circ h$: $\quad x \to (x - 2)^2$.
4. $h \circ f$: $\quad x \to x^2 - 2$.
5. $f \circ k$: $\quad x \to e^{-2x}$.
6. $k \circ f$: $\quad x \to e^{-x^2}$.
7. $(f \circ g) \circ h$: $\quad x \to (\sin (x - 2))^2$
8. $f \circ (g \circ h)$: $\quad x \to (\sin (x - 2))^2$
9. $(h \circ g) \circ f$: $\quad x \to \sin (x^2) - 2$
10. $h \circ (g \circ f)$: $\quad x \to \sin (x^2) - 2$
11. If c is a one-to-one correspondence of a set S onto a set T and if $\bar{c}$ is its opposite mapping (see Example 11 of Mappings), then

$$\bar{c} \circ c \text{ is the identity mapping of } S$$

and

$$c \circ \bar{c} \text{ is the identity mapping of } T.$$

12. The composite of complementation (Example 12 of Mappings) with itself is the identity mapping.

The examples show that, if composites can be defined, the order in which the mappings are applied matters very much. Examples 7 to 10 suggest that, for "*triple composites,*" a sort of associative law may hold. To verify this we will return to the abstract definition of a mapping and check under what circumstances two mappings are equal.

A mapping of a set A into a set B is defined as the subset $\{(a,f(a)) | a \, \varepsilon \, A\}$ of $A \times B$ if we choose the functional notation. Let $g = \{(c,g(c)) | c \, \varepsilon \, C\}$ be a mapping of a set C into a set D. Suppose now that an element $a \, \varepsilon \, A$ does *not* belong to C. Then the couple $(a,f(a))$ belongs to f, but cannot belong to g. Hence in this case $f \neq g$. In other words $A = C$ is a *necessary* condition for f and g to be equal.

Now let us assume that $A = C$. Then the mappings $f = \{(a,f(a)) | a \, \varepsilon \, A\}$ and $g = \{(a,g(a)) | a \, \varepsilon \, A\}$ are obviously equal if and only if $f(a) = g(a)$ for every $a \, \varepsilon \, A$.

Hence two mappings $f: A \to B$ and $g: C \to D$ are equal if and only if their domains of definition are equal and the f-image of every element of A is equal to its g-image. Note, in particular, that B and D need not be equal. In fact, a mapping f of A into B is likewise a mapping of A into its range $f(A)$, and, if the mapping is not onto, then $f(A) \neq B$ (but, of course, $f(A) \subset B$).

Suppose now we have three mappings $p: A \rightarrow B$, $q: B \rightarrow C$, and $r:$ $C \rightarrow D$. In this case both $(p \circ q) \circ r$ and $p \circ (q \circ r)$ are mappings of A into D. Applying the definition of the composite mapping several times, for an element $a \; \varepsilon \; A$, we obtain

$$((p \circ q) \circ r)(a) = (p \circ q)(r(a)) = p(q(r(a))),$$

$$(p \circ (q \circ r))(a) = p((q \circ r)(a)) = p(q(r(a))).$$

Hence the $((p \circ q) \circ r)$-images and $(p \circ (q \circ r))$-images coincide for every $a \; \varepsilon \; A$, and, consequently, we have the important *associative law for composite mappings*:

$$(p \circ q) \circ r = p \circ (q \circ r), \tag{2.1}$$

provided that all composites in this formula are defined.

Let us now return to a single mapping f of a set A into a set B. If S is a proper subset of A, then the rule $s \rightarrow f(s)$ defines a mapping of S into B. It assigns to every element of S the same element of B as the mapping f does; thus the two mappings are very closely related because *the same rule* is applied in both cases. By the definition of equality of mappings, however, the two mappings cannot be called equal, because $A \neq S$. The most one can say is that f *induces* a mapping of S into B. This mapping $s \rightarrow f(s)$ is called *the restriction of f to* (the subset) S and is denoted by f_S. If we go back to the definition of a mapping as a relation, then we find that $f_S = f \cap (S \times B)$; that is, that f_S is a subset of f. Conversely, a mapping g of a set A into a set B is called *an extension to A* of a mapping h of $S \; (\subset A)$ into B if the restriction g_S of g to S is equal to h. Note that, for a given subset S, there exists only one restriction of a mapping, although a mapping can be extended in many different ways.

EXAMPLES OF RESTRICTIONS OF MAPPINGS

1. The identity mapping ι of a set A into itself can be restricted to the identity mapping of any subset S of A.
2. Let $\mathbf{m}$ be a rotation of $\Re^3$ by 180° about an axis $\mathfrak{A}$. If $\mathfrak{A}$ is perpendicular to a plane $\Re^2$ and intersects $\Re^2$ in the point P, then the restriction of $\mathbf{m}$ to $\Re^2$ is a rotation of $\Re^2$ about P. If $\mathfrak{A}$ belongs to $\Re^2$, then the restriction of $\mathbf{m}$ to $\Re^2$ is equal to the reflection of $\Re^2$ about the line $\mathfrak{A}$.
3. Let $\mathbf{n}$ be a reflection of $\Re^3$ about the plane $\mathfrak{H}$. If $\Re^2$ is a plane perpendicular to $\mathfrak{H}$, then the restriction of $\mathbf{n}$ to $\Re^2$ is equal to the reflection of $\Re^2$ about the line $\mathfrak{A}$ that $\mathfrak{H}$ and $\Re^2$ have in common. Together with the previous example, this shows that the restriction of a rotation to $\Re^2$ can be equal to the restriction of a reflection.
4. The rule $z = x + iy \rightarrow \sqrt{x^2 + y^2}$ defines a mapping f of C into R. The rule $z = x + iy \rightarrow |x|$ likewise defines a mapping g of C into R.

It is obvious that $f \neq g$, but we have $f_R = g_R$ if the two mappings are restricted to the set R of all real numbers. This shows also that mappings can be extended in different ways.

5. The rules $x \rightarrow + x$ and $x \rightarrow -x$ define two different mappings f^+ and f^- of the set of non-negative real numbers into R. Let 0 be the set consisting of the number zero alone. Then $f_0^+ = f_0^-$.

6. The rule $x \rightarrow \sqrt{x^2}$ defines a mapping of R into itself. The restriction of this mapping to the set of nonnegative real numbers is equal to the identity mapping (of that set into itself).

EXERCISES

1. Write down the set $\{A,B,C\}$ in five other ways by changing the order of the elements listed.

2. Write down the 16 subsets of the set $\{a,b,c,d\}$.

3. How many elements does the power set $P(A)$ of a set A of n elements have?

4. Interpret in words the following sets:
   (a) $\{x|x \text{ real}, x < 0\}$;   (b) $\{(x,y)|x/y = 1, y \neq 0\}$;
   (c) $\{(x,y)|x + y = 0\}$;   (d) $\{x|x^n = 1\}$; *(e) $\{f(x)|f'(x) = g(x)\}$;
   (f) $\{(x,y)|y = e^x\}$;   (g) $\{x|\alpha < x < \beta\}$;
   (h) $\{f|\{f(x)|x \, \varepsilon \, A\} = A\}$.

5. Write down in the compact form of the previous example the following sets: (a) the set of all even integers; (b) the set of all couples of real numbers that are inverses of each other; (c) the set of all real numbers that do not solve the equation $f(x) = 0$; (d) the set of all couples of two distinct numbers; (e) the mapping defined by the cosine function.

6. Prove that equality is both an equivalence relation and an order.

7. Prove that set inclusion defines an order for the power set of any set.

8. The following rules define mappings of the set of all real numbers into itself:
   (a) $x \rightarrow x^2 - 1$;   (b) $x \rightarrow x^2 + 1$;   (c) $x \rightarrow 1/(x^2 + 1)$;
   (d) $x \rightarrow 1 - \cos^2 x$. Determine which mappings are onto or one-to-one.

9. The following rules define mappings of R^2 into itself:
   (a) $(x,y) \rightarrow (y,x)$;   (b) $(x,y) \rightarrow (x + y, x - y)$;
   (c) $(x,y) \rightarrow (y,-x)$;   (d) $(x,y) \rightarrow (e^x, y + 1)$;
   (e) $(x,y) \rightarrow (x + y, 0)$.   Determine which of these mappings are onto or one-to-one.

10. The following rules define mappings of R^2 into R^3:

(a) $(x,y) \rightarrow (x,0,y)$; (b) $(x,y) \rightarrow (x,x,x)$;
(c) $(x,y) \rightarrow (x, x + y, x - y)$. Determine which of these mappings are onto or one-to-one.

11. Construct the two-dimensional analog of example 8 of Mappings.

12. Let f, g, h, k be the four mappings defined in the collection of examples of composite mappings. Determine $g \circ h$, $h \circ g$, $g \circ k$, $k \circ g$, $(f \circ h) \circ (g \circ k)$, $g \circ ((h \circ f) \circ k)$, $g \circ g$, and $(h \circ h) \circ h$.

13. Use the left-operator notation to prove the associative law for composite mappings.

14. The rule $x + iy \rightarrow x - iy$ defines a mapping f called *conjugation* of C onto itself. Prove that this is a one-to-one correspondence. What are the restrictions of this mapping to the set of real numbers and to the set of purely imaginary numbers? Prove also that

$$f(z_1 + z_2) = f(z_1) + f(z_2)$$

$$f(z_1 z_2) = f(z_1)f(z_2).$$

15. Describe the four different mappings of the set $\{a,b\}$ into the set $\{c,d\}$.

16. Describe the six possible one-to-one correspondences of the set $S = \{a,b,c\}$ onto itself. They are called the *permutations of S*.

17. Prove that $\emptyset = \emptyset \times A$ for any set A.

3

Translations

Suppose you arrive in New York City at Pennsylvania Station and ask someone to direct you to Grand Central Station (Fig. 3.1). Then you may receive the answer: "Go north to Times Square and then east to Park Avenue." Or you may be told: "Go three blocks east and ten blocks north." The first person describes the position of Grand Central Station relative to Pennsylvania Station by telling you an exact route to follow— namely, by defining two line segments along which you have to move. The second person tells you how to shift your position so that eventually you reach your destination.†

The first description has the disadvantage that, if a part of Seventh Avenue or 42nd Street is blocked off, you may be unable to find your way unless you inquire again. Furthermore, you will have to look for street signs all the time and you may miss one. Whereas the first description gives you one of many possible ways to go (even of equal length), the second makes it possible for you to choose your way and is, therefore, more general. You know that you can reach your destination by going, say, first seven blocks north, then three blocks east, and then another three blocks north, or, alternatively, by first going four blocks east, then ten blocks north, and finally one block west (Fig. 3.2).

But the instruction "Go 3 blocks east and 10 blocks north" is also

† In New York City, the distance between each of the numbered avenues and between Fifth and Park (Fourth) Avenues is approximately the same. Thus, for this discussion both Madison Avenue and Broadway can be ignored.

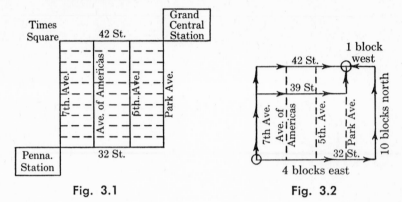

Fig. 3.1   Fig. 3.2

more general in another respect. It is meaningful for any position you have if we assume that central Manhattan with its regular net of numbered streets and avenues is extended *ad infinitum* in all directions. The instruction assigns to every point on this infinite plane another point 3 blocks east and 10 blocks north of it and, therefore, induces a mapping of this plane into (even onto) itself. This assignment can also be obtained in the following manner (Fig. 3.3): Take two transparent copies of a street map of this infinite Manhattan, put one on top of the other so that they match, and then move the upper one, as a whole, "3 blocks east and 10 blocks north." Then, after the shifting operation, every point on the upper map is the image of the point lying below it.

Obviously the above request may be generalized to the form "move m blocks east and n blocks north," where m and n can be any positive numbers, not necessarily integers. Let us abbreviate the corresponding mapping

$$mE \ \& \ nN. \tag{3.1}$$

Suppose we apply two such mappings, first $mE \ \& \ nN$ and afterward $pE \ \& \ qN$, where p and q are also nonnegative numbers. Then the composite mapping (in any order) is obviously equal to the mapping $(m + p)E \ \& \ (n + q)N$. Thus we have the formulas

$$(mE \ \& \ nN) \circ (pE \ \& \ qN) = (m + p)E \ \& \ (n + q)N \tag{3.2}$$

$$(mE \ \& \ nN) \circ (pE \ \& \ qN) = (pE \ \& \ qN) \circ (mE \ \& \ nN). \tag{3.3}$$

But perhaps one also wants to shift to the west and to the south. This is necessary, for example, to accomplish the displacement that, after (3.1) has been applied, brings everything back to the original position. Naturally, to go back one has to move m blocks west and n blocks south. If the mapping induced by this movement is abbreviated

$$(-m)E \ \& \ (-n)N \tag{3.4}$$

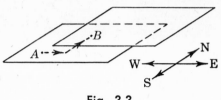

Fig. 3.3

then it is easily seen that (3.2) and (3.3) remain valid for *any* real numbers *m, n, p, q.* Thus a negative number of blocks east will mean the same number, except for a positive sign, of blocks west, etc., and the symbol $0E$ & $0N$ will stand for the instruction, "Stay where you are."

If we work on the infinite map only and do not have to worry about skyscrapers standing in our way, we can express the mapping (3.1) in a different form. On the map that I possess of New York City, 3 blocks east seem approximately as long as 10 blocks north. Thus, if one wants to go from Pennsylvania Station to Grand Central Station along a straight line, one has to go practically northeast, approximately 4000 feet. Assuming for simplicity that this is not only roughly but exactly true, the original instruction would have the same effect as the demand, "Move 4000 feet to the northeast." If directions are fixed, counterclockwise, with degree zero for north, 90° for west, etc., the mapping induced by the demand, "Move *r* thousand feet in the direction *x* degrees" can be abbreviated

$$rF \ \& \ xD. \tag{3.5}$$

Every such mapping is obviously equal to exactly one mapping of the type (3.1), and the relations between *r, x* and *m, n* can be determined by means of trigonometry if the lengths of one block in the two principal directions are given. Here *r* is a nonnegative integer, and *x* is an angle between 0° inclusive and 360° exclusive.

There is an obvious three-dimensional generalization of this type of mapping. If we define "one block up" in an appropriate fashion and abbreviate "*c* blocks up" to "*cU*" (where by negative *c* we mean "$-c$ blocks down") the three-dimensional analog of (3.1) could be abbreviated

$$aE \ \& \ bN \ \& \ cU. \tag{3.6}$$

For the corresponding generalization of (3.5) we need two angles. If the point *P* is mapped on a point $\bar{P}$ by such a three-dimensional shifting (Fig. 3.4), we construct a sphere with center *P* and radius $P\bar{P}$ and represent the direction of this shifting by the latitude "LA" and longitude "LO" of the point $\bar{P}$ on this minature globe as in geography where the "North pole" represents the direction "up." This shows that the mapping defined by such a shifting can be represented in the form

$$rF \ \& \ xLA \ \& \ yLO \tag{3.7}$$

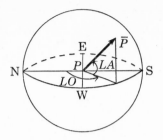

Fig. 3.4

where x and y denote suitable angles. Again the relations between a, b, c and r, x, y can be determined by means of trigonometry.

Mappings of the described kind in two and three dimensions will not only be used to express the position of points but will be employed throughout this text as the principal means to investigate geometry. They are particularly easy to define because they are determined uniquely if the image of *one* point is known. The representation (3.1) requires the knowledge of the lengths of the blocks and their principal directions. For the representation (3.5) only one reference direction (in the example, north) must be known and a scale must be given. But, whereas for the first representation the convenient rule (3.2) holds, a corresponding easy formula is obviously impossible for the second. However, (3.5) seems to be more useful for the construction of the images of the points; it also shows at once that the following two conditions are satisfied for any mapping of this type (Fig. 3.5): (1) The distance between any point and its image is constant. (2) The distance between any two points is equal to the distance between their images.

But, conversely, every mapping **m** of a plane into itself that has these two properties must be a mapping of the kind (3.5) for suitable r and x. Let us denote the **m**-images of points by overbars. If $A = \bar{A}$ for every point A, then we have the identity mapping, for which $r = 0$ and x can be chosen arbitrarily. Excluding this trival case, we shall assume that $A \neq \bar{A}$ for some point A. Let r be the distance between A and $\bar{A}$ and x an angular measure indicating the "direction from A to $\bar{A}$." Let B be a point on the line through A and $\bar{A}$ (Fig. 3.6) different from $\bar{A}$. Then,

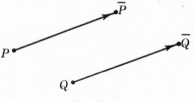

Fig. 3.5

by the first property, $\bar{B}$ must lie on the circle with center B and radius r.
By the second property, $\bar{B}$ must lie on the circle with center $\bar{A}$ and radius
equal to the distance between A and B. The two circles obviously meet
in the point C obtained by moving B along that line r units in the direction
x. But two circles can have more than one point in common, namely,
either two points or all points. Since, by the assumption $B \neq \bar{A}$, the two
circles have different centers, the second possibility is excluded. It is very
easy to prove that, if two circles with different centers have two points
of intersection, then these two points must have the same distance from
the line through the centers. Hence, in our case, the possible second point
of intersection must also lie on the line through A and $\bar{A}$—which is impossible, because the two circles have different centers. If $B = \bar{A}$, this
construction fails to work, because then the two circles coincide. But
in this case we do not take the point A for the construction, but any
other point, say, D, on this line whose image $\bar{D}$ we know from the general

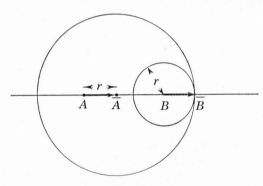

Fig. 3.6

case. This shows that the restriction of the mapping in question to the
line through A and $\bar{A}$ is equal to the restriction of rF & xD to that line.

Now let E be a point outside the line through A and $\bar{A}$ (Fig. 3.7).
Let F be the foot of the perpendicular from E on this line. Then the image
of E must lie on the intersection of the circle with radius r and center E
with the circle with center $\bar{A}$ and radius equal to the distance between
A and E. These two circles obviously meet in the point G obtained by
moving E r units in the direction x. But G cannot be the only point the
two circles have in common because G does not lie on the line through
their centers E and $\bar{A}$. Since $E \neq \bar{A}$ they have exactly two points G and
H in common. Let us assume $F \neq \bar{A}$. Then we have $\angle GE\bar{A} = \angle HE\bar{A} \neq$
$90°$; hence the line through E and H is not parallel to the line through A and
$\bar{A}$, but intersects it at a point K. Suppose now that the **m**-image of E were H.
Then, by the first part of the proof, the **m**-image of every point on the
line through E and H, in particular the image of K, would have to lie

on that line r units away. On the other hand, the image of K lies on the line through A and $\bar{A}$. This leads to a contradiction; hence, H cannot be the image of E, that is, G must be that image. If $F = \bar{A}$ this construction fails to work. In this case we do not start with the point A, but with some other point on the line through A and $\bar{A}$ whose image we know by the first part of this proof. Therefore, **m** is equal to rF & xD on the whole plane considered.

A similar proof can be given in the three-dimensional case, where a direction is determined not by one angle x but by two angles x, y.

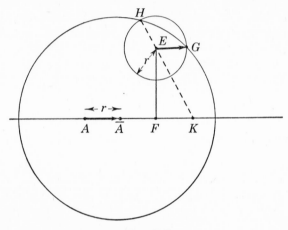

Fig. 3.7

Since the two conditions above characterize mappings by shifting of position, they will be used for the first definition of the formal theory to be developed now. They have the advantage that they do not involve the concept of direction and that not even a unit of measurement is needed, as long as it can be determined in some way whether two distances are equal or not.

Definition 3.1: A mapping **m** of $\mathfrak{R}^n$ $(n = 1,2,3)$ into itself is called a *translation* of $\mathfrak{R}^n$ if the distance between every point and its **m**-image is equal to a constant $r \geq 0$ and if the distance between any two points is equal to the distance between their respective images. The number r is called the *length* of the translation and is denoted by $|\mathbf{m}|$. A translation that assigns to a point A the image B is denoted by $\overrightarrow{AB}$. The set of all translations of $\mathfrak{R}^n$ is denoted by $\mathbf{R}^n$. The notions of parallelism and perpendicularity are applied to $\overrightarrow{AB}$ if and only if they are applied to the complete line through AB.

Note: If $A \neq B$, then $\overrightarrow{AB}$ and $\overrightarrow{BA}$ are different translations. But their composite (*in either order*) is easily seen to be the identity mapping of $\mathfrak{R}^n$.

Definition 3.2: If A and B are different points, then the set consisting (1) of all points on the (straight) line segment from A to B and (2) the direction "from A to B" is called *the directed line segment from A to B* and is denoted by AB. The distance between A and B is often called *the length* of AB and denoted by $|AB|$. A is called the *beginning* and B the *end* of AB.

Note that the symbol AB is meaningful only if $A \neq B$ and denotes a *set* consisting of points and a single direction, whereas the symbol $\overrightarrow{AB}$ is defined for any couple of points A,B and denotes a *mapping*.

The geometric results obtained above can now be expressed in the form of a theorem.

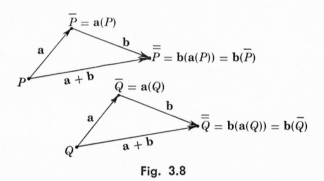

Fig. 3.8

Theorem 3.1: *If A and B are two points of $\mathfrak{R}^n$, there exists one and only one translation $\overrightarrow{AB}$ of $\mathfrak{R}^n$. If $A = B$, then the translation is the identity mapping. If $A \neq B$, then the image of any point C of $\mathfrak{R}^n$ under $\overrightarrow{AB}$ is that point D on the line through C parallel to AB whose distance from C is equal to the length of AB and for which AB and CD have the same direction.*

Thus every translation $\mathbf{m}$ of $\mathfrak{R}^n$ is uniquely defined if the image of one single point P is given. Also, every directed line segment AB determines a unique translation, different from the identity mapping, namely, that which maps the beginning A on the end B. In this way a directed line segment, which we may regard as a finite part of a straight line with an arrowhead attached to indicate direction, can be used to *represent* a translation, which cannot be "seen" (but can be constructed, as in Fig. 3.5) or marked down on a sheet of paper. Although a directed line segment AB *determines* the translation $\overrightarrow{AB}$, it is *not equal to it*. To emphasize this distinction, AB will be called *a representative* of $\overrightarrow{AB}$. There are, of course, infinitely many directed line segments that can represent the same translation; all have the same length and direction. This common direction is also frequently called *the direction of the translation*. In geometric figures the symbol for a translation is frequently placed next to one or several of its representative line segments, but the conclusion should not be drawn from this convention that this implies equality of the two concepts.

Translations are particularly interesting and useful because their composites can be seen to be translations also; this is shown by (3.2) for the two-dimensional case. Because of the construction of the right-hand side of this formula by ordinary addition of numbers, the following vocabulary is suggestive and customary:

Definition 3.3:   The composite mapping of two translations **a** and **b** is called *the sum of* **a** *and* **b** and denoted by **a** + **b**. The mapping that assigns to every couple of translations its sum is called *addition of translations*. The identity mapping, if considered as a translation, is called *the zero translation* and is denoted by **0**. If **a** + **b** = **0**, then the translation **b** is called *the negative*, or *opposite, of* **a** and is denoted by −**a**. A sum of translations of the form **c** + (−**d**) will be abbreviated **c** − **d** and called a *difference*.

The following two rules are immediate consequences of this definition.

$$\overrightarrow{AB} + \overrightarrow{BC} = \overrightarrow{AC} \tag{3.8}$$

$$\overrightarrow{AB} = -\overrightarrow{BA} \tag{3.9}$$

Theorem 3.2:   *The sum of two translations of the same space is again a translation of this space. The addition of translations satisfies the commutative law* **a** + **b** = **b** + **a** *and the associative law* **a** + (**b** + **c**) = (**a** + **b**) + **c** *for any translations* **a**, **b**, **c**.

PROOF: 1. Let P and Q be two arbitrary different points, and define $\bar{P} = \mathbf{a}(P)$, $\bar{\bar{P}} = \mathbf{b}(\mathbf{a}(P))$, $\bar{Q} = \mathbf{a}(Q)$, $\bar{\bar{Q}} = \mathbf{b}(\mathbf{a}(Q))$ (see Fig. 3.8). We consider only the case where all six points are different; the remaining parts of the proof can be supplied easily. By definition 3.1 we have to show that $|P\bar{\bar{P}}| = |Q\bar{\bar{Q}}|$ and $|PQ| = |\bar{\bar{P}}\bar{\bar{Q}}|$. The second equality is an immediate consequence of $|PQ| = |\bar{P}\bar{Q}|$ and $|\bar{P}\bar{Q}| = |\bar{\bar{P}}\bar{\bar{Q}}|$, which hold because **a** and **b** are translations. The first equality is proved by showing that the triangles $P\bar{P}\bar{\bar{P}}$ and $Q\bar{Q}\bar{\bar{Q}}$ are congruent. As $P\bar{P}$ and $Q\bar{Q}$ and, similarly, $\bar{P}\bar{\bar{P}}$ and $\bar{Q}\bar{\bar{Q}}$ have the same direction by theorem 3.1, the angles $P\bar{P}\bar{\bar{P}}$ and $Q\bar{Q}\bar{\bar{Q}}$ are equal. As $|P\bar{P}| = |Q\bar{Q}|$ and $|\bar{P}\bar{\bar{P}}| = |\bar{Q}\bar{\bar{Q}}|$ by hypothesis, the two triangles are congruent. Hence the sum of two translations is also a translation.

2. Define again $\bar{P} = \mathbf{a}(P)$ and $\bar{\bar{P}} = \mathbf{b}(\mathbf{a}(P))$. We consider only the case where $P\bar{P}\bar{\bar{P}}$ is a proper triangle (Fig. 3.9); the remaining part of the proof can be supplied easily. Construct a line through $\bar{\bar{P}}$ parallel to $P\bar{P}$ and a line through P parallel to $\bar{P}\bar{\bar{P}}$. Since $P\bar{P}\bar{\bar{P}}$ is a triangle, these two

lines cannot be parallel; hence, they must meet in a point P^*. Now $\overrightarrow{PP^*} = \mathbf{b}$ and $\overrightarrow{P^*\bar{P}} = \mathbf{a}$, by theorem 3.1; hence $\mathbf{b}(\mathbf{a}(P)) = \mathbf{a}(\mathbf{b}(P))$.

3. By formula (2.1), the associative law holds for composition of mappings in general. But translations are mappings.

The addition introduced in definition 3.3 makes it possible to construct new translations from given ones. As the commutative and associative laws hold for this addition, sums of more than two translations can be written down without the use of parentheses and without any definite order in which the translations have to be listed. For example, if $\mathbf{a}^{(1)}$, $\mathbf{a}^{(2)}$, $\mathbf{a}^{(3)}$, $\mathbf{a}^{(4)}$, $\cdots$, $\mathbf{a}^{(n-1)}$, $\mathbf{a}^{(n)}$ are translations of the same space, we might interpret the sum of these translations by the formula

$$\mathbf{a}^{(1)} + \mathbf{a}^{(2)} + \mathbf{a}^{(3)} + \mathbf{a}^{(4)} + \cdots + \mathbf{a}^{(n-1)} + \mathbf{a}^{(n)}$$
$$= ((\cdots(((\mathbf{a}^{(1)} + \mathbf{a}^{(2)}) + \mathbf{a}^{(3)}) + \mathbf{a}^{(4)}) \cdots + \mathbf{a}^{(n-1)}) + \mathbf{a}^{(n)}. \qquad (3.10)$$

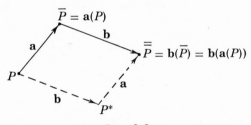

Fig. 3.9

But, by multiple application of theorem 3.2, it can be shown that any other bracketing into consecutive sums of two translations each and any change in their order yields the same result. We shall also make use of the summation sign $\sum$ by defining, as usual in mathematics,

$$\sum_{i=1}^{0} \mathbf{a}^{(i)} = \mathbf{0}, \qquad \sum_{i=1}^{1} \mathbf{a}^{(i)} = \mathbf{a}^{(1)},$$

$$\sum_{i=1}^{n} \mathbf{a}^{(i)} = \sum_{i=1}^{n-1} \mathbf{a}^{(i)} + \mathbf{a}^{(n)} \qquad \text{for } n \geq 2 \qquad (3.11)$$

in analogy with (3.10). If in (3.11) all $\mathbf{a}^{(i)}$ are equal to a translation $\mathbf{a}$ or $-\mathbf{a}$, then this sum will be abbreviated $n\mathbf{a}$ or $(-n)\mathbf{a}$, respectively. In other words, we shall define

$$\sum_{i=1}^{n} \mathbf{a} = \mathbf{a} + \mathbf{a} + \cdots + \mathbf{a} = n\mathbf{a},$$

$$\sum_{i=1}^{n} -\mathbf{a} = (-\mathbf{a}) + (-\mathbf{a}) + \cdots + (-\mathbf{a}) = (-n)\mathbf{a}, \qquad (3.12)$$

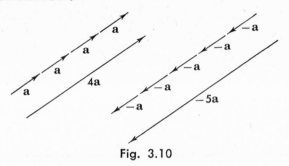

Fig. 3.10

a process that might be called *multiplication of translations by integers*.

A geometrical investigation of the "product" defined by (3.12) shows that, for **a** $\neq$ **0**, the translations n**a** and $(-n)$**a** have n times the length of **a** and the same direction as **a** or the opposite, respectively (Fig. 3.10). This process of obtaining new translations from a given translation can obviously be generalized to *any real* number, as follows.

Definition 3.4: Let **a** be a translation of a space, and let r be a real number. The translation of the same space with length $|r|\,|$**a**$|$ whose representative line segments (for $r \neq 0$) have the same direction as the representatives of **a** if $r > 0$ and the opposite direction if $r < 0$ is called *the multiple of* **a** *by the scalar* r and denoted by r**a**. Let **R**^{n} be the set of all translations of the considered space $\mathfrak{R}^n$. Then the mapping of $R \times$ **R**^{n} into **R**^{n} that assigns to every couple $(r,$**a**$)$ the scalar multiple r**a** is called *scalar multiplication of translations.*

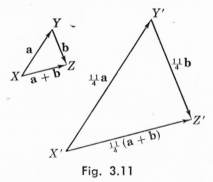

Fig. 3.11

Thus, scalar multiplication "stretches" or "shrinks" the length of any representative line segment and, in the case of negative scalars, reverses the direction. Scalar multiplication and addition of translations are related by four important laws.

Theorem 3.3: *If* **a** *and* **b** *are any two translations of a space and if* r *and* s *are two real numbers, then the following rules are satisfied:*

(1) $r(\mathbf{a} + \mathbf{b}) = r\mathbf{a} + r\mathbf{b}$ (3) $r(s\mathbf{a}) = (rs)\mathbf{a}$

(2) $(r + s)\mathbf{a} = r\mathbf{a} + s\mathbf{a}$ (4) $1\mathbf{a} = \mathbf{a}$

PROOF: 1. We consider only the case where $\mathbf{a}$ and $\mathbf{b}$ are nonzero translations *not having the same or opposite direction* and where r is positive (Fig. 3.11; here $r = 11/4$); the remaining parts of the proof can be supplied easily. Suppose that $\mathbf{a} = \overrightarrow{XY}$ and $\mathbf{b} = \overrightarrow{YZ}$; then $\mathbf{a} + \mathbf{b} = \overrightarrow{XZ}$. Suppose further that $r\mathbf{a} = \overrightarrow{X'Y'}$ and $r\mathbf{b} = \overrightarrow{Y'Z'}$; then $r\mathbf{a} + r\mathbf{b} = \overrightarrow{X'Z'}$. Since $|X'Y'| = r\,|XY|$ and $|Y'Z'| = r\,|YZ|$ and the angle at Y is equal to the angle at Y', the two triangles XYZ and $X'Y'Z'$ are similar. Hence $|X'Z'| = r|XZ|$, or $\overrightarrow{X'Z'} = r\overrightarrow{XZ} = r(\mathbf{a} + \mathbf{b})$.

2. We consider only the case where r and s are both positive and $\mathbf{a}$

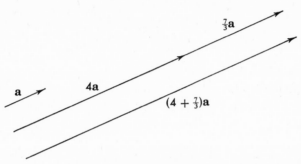

Fig. 3.12

differs from the zero translation; again the remaining parts of the proof can be supplied easily. Then $r\mathbf{a}$, $s\mathbf{a}$, $r\mathbf{a} + s\mathbf{a}$, and $(r + s)\mathbf{a}$ all have the same direction (see Fig. 3.12 for $r = 4$, $s = 7/3$). Therefore it suffices to show that $r\mathbf{a} + s\mathbf{a}$ and $(r + s)\mathbf{a}$ have the same length. Now $|r\mathbf{a} + s\mathbf{a}| = |r\mathbf{a}| + |s\mathbf{a}|$ (because the two translations involved have the same direction) $= r|\mathbf{a}| + s|\mathbf{a}|$ (by definition of scalar multiplication) $= (r + s)\,|\mathbf{a}|$ (by the distributive law for numbers) $= |(r + s)\mathbf{a}|$ (by definition of scalar multiplication).

3. Again we consider only the case where r and s are positive and $\mathbf{a}$ differs from the zero translation. Then $(rs)\mathbf{a}$ and $(rs\mathbf{a})$ have the same direction; hence it remains only to show that they have the same length. This follows from the definition of scalar multiplication.

4. Obvious.

EXERCISES

1. Suppose you go first 10 miles north, then 100 miles west, and at last 10 miles south and suddenly find yourself back at the very place

you started. If you see a bear during that trip, what will probably be the color of its fur?

2. Give *all* possible points of departure from which you would return to where you started after making the journey described in the previous exercise.

3. Which formulas of this section are proved by the preceding exercise to be invalid for shifting operations on the globe? Hence, do there exist translations on the sphere?

4. Apply the Pythagorean theorem and a suitable definition from trigonometry to compute r and x from formula (3.5) in terms of m and n from formula (3.1), and vice versa. *Caution:* The lengths of one block in the principal directions must enter the formulas as constants.

5. Compute r, x, y from formula (3.7) in terms of a, b, c from formula (3.6), and vice versa.

6. Establish the formulas corresponding to (3.2) and (3.3) in the three-dimensional case.

7. Prove (a) that, if $A \neq C$, then $\overrightarrow{AB} + \overrightarrow{BC} = \overrightarrow{AC}$; (b) that $\overrightarrow{BA}$ is the negative of $\overrightarrow{AB}$.

8. Suppose $\mathbf{a} = \overrightarrow{XY}$ and $\mathbf{b} = \overrightarrow{XZ}$. Find a representative line segment for the translation $\mathbf{a} - \mathbf{b}$.

9. Supply the omitted parts of the proof of theorem 3.2 as economically as possible.

10. Let r be a real number and let $\mathbf{a}^{(1)}$, $\mathbf{a}^{(2)}$, $\cdots$, $\mathbf{a}^{(n)}$ be translations of the same space. Prove

$$\sum_{i=1}^{n} r\mathbf{a}^{(i)} = r \sum_{i=1}^{n} \mathbf{a}^{(i)}.$$

11. Let $(\mathbf{a}_{ij})_{i=1,\cdots,m;\ j=1,\cdots,n}$ be a finite double sequence of translations of the space. Prove

$$\sum_{i=1}^{m} \left(\sum_{j=1}^{n} \mathbf{a}_{ij} \right) = \sum_{j=1}^{n} \left(\sum_{i=1}^{m} \mathbf{a}_{ij} \right)$$

by using (3.11).

12. Let r be a real number, and let $\mathbf{a}$ be a translation. Prove $(-r)\mathbf{a} = -(r\mathbf{a})$ and $-((-r)\mathbf{a}) = r\mathbf{a}$.

13. Prove that every translation is a one-to-one correspondence.

14. Supply the omitted parts of the proof of theorem 3.3 as economically as possible.

15. Prove that the composite of two reflections is not a reflection.

4

Composition Laws and Groups

The addition and scalar multiplication of translations as well as the ordinary addition and multiplication of numbers are all special cases of the very general concept of composition law.

Definition 4.1: A mapping of a Cartesian product of two sets A, B into one Cartesian factor A is called a *complete*† *composition law for A.* A mapping of a proper subset of a Cartesian product into one Cartesian factor A is called a *partial* (or *not-everywhere-defined*) *composition law for A.* The image of a couple (p,q) under a composition law is called the *composite of the couple* and may be denoted by $p * q$ in the abstract, unspecified case. Composites for which the notations $p + q$ or $p \cdot q$ are chosen are called *sums* or *products*, respectively; their respective composition laws are called *addition* or *multiplication*. The symbol between the two elements is also used as an abbreviation for the composition law. Such a law is called *internal* if $A = B$ and *external* if $A \neq B$. In the complete internal case a composition law is called *commutative* if $p * q = q * p$ and *associative* if $(p * q) * r = p * (q * r)$ for all p, q, r ε A. In the external case the set B is called *the operator set for this law,* and the mapping of A into itself that assigns to every element a the composite of a and the *operator* b is said to be *induced by b.* An operator inducing the identity mapping is called an *identity operator*.

Note: This definition does not exclude the possibility that two different

† The qualification "complete" is usually omitted if no confusion will result.

operators (that is, different elements of B) induce the same mapping. Therefore, an operator should not be identified with the symbol for the mapping that it induces.

EXAMPLES OF INTERNAL COMPOSITION LAWS

1. Ordinary addition and multiplication are complete internal composition laws for C. Their restrictions to R, R^+, and I^+ are complete. They are *commutative* and *associative*.

2. Ordinary subtraction is a complete internal composition law for C or for R, but its restrictions to R^+ or I^+ are *partial* (the difference of two positive numbers need not be positive). The composites are called *differences*. Subtraction is neither commutative nor associative.

3. Ordinary division is a partial internal composition law for C or for R. (Division by the number zero is forbidden.) The composites are called *quotients*. Division is neither commutative nor associative.

4. Definition 3.3 introduces a complete internal composition law for the set $\mathbf{R}^3$ of all translations of $\mathfrak{R}^3$. Its composites are called *sums*. It is *commutative* and *associative*.

5. Let C^k be the set of all k-tuples of complex numbers. The mapping that assigns to the couple of k-tuples $((a_1,a_2,\cdots,a_k),\ (b_1,b_2,\cdots,b_k))$ the k-tuple $(a_1 + b_1,\ a_2 + b_2,\cdots,a_k + b_k)$ is a complete internal composition law for C^k. Since the additive notation:

$$(a_1,a_2,\cdots,a_k) + (b_1,b_2,\cdots,b_k)$$

$$= (a_1 + b_1,\ a_2 + b_2,\ \cdots,\ a_k + b_k) \quad (4.1)$$

is usually chosen, this law is called *addition of k-tuples*, and the composites are called *sums*. It is both *commutative* and *associative*. We shall usually consider the restriction of this law to the real numbers.

6. Let $P(S)$ be the set of all subsets of a given set S. The mapping of $P(S) \times P(S)$ into $P(S)$ that assigns to every couple (A,B) of subsets of S the subset $A \cap B$ is a complete internal composition law which is both *commutative* and *associative*. In this case the name "intersection" is unfortunately used for both the composition law and the composite.

7. Let M be the set of all mappings of a set S into itself. Then the composition "$\circ$" of mappings is a complete internal composition law for M. In general it is not commutative, but it is associative, by (2.1).

8. Let M be a set of mappings. Then the composition "$\circ$" is an internal composition law that need not be everywhere defined; in fact, it may be "nowhere defined." This example and the preceding one explain why the term "composition of mappings" was chosen for

this particular combining of mappings. It is just a special case of a composition law.

†*9. Let S be the set of all real functions continuous in a closed interval $a \leq x \leq b$. The mapping that assigns to every couple $(f(x), g(x))$ of functions of S the function $\int_a^b f(\xi)g(x - \xi) \, d\xi$ is a complete internal composition law for S. It is obviously *not commutative*.

EXAMPLES OF EXTERNAL COMPOSITION LAWS

1. The mapping of $R^+ \times I$ into R^+ that assigns to every couple (r,i) the positive number r^i is a complete external composition law for R^+. But, since $I \subset R$, it can also be interpreted as a partial internal composition law for R. It is called *exponentiation*, and the composites are called *powers*.

2. The mapping of $\mathbf{R}^3 \times \mathfrak{R}^3$ into $\mathfrak{R}^3$ that assigns to the couple $(\mathbf{a},P)$ the point $\mathbf{a}(P)$ is a complete external composition law for $\mathfrak{R}^3$. There is no standard name for this law, but we might call it the *application of translations to points* and call the composites *translated points*.

3. Definition 3.4 introduces a complete external composition law for $\mathbf{R}^3$ with the real numbers as operators.

4. Let C^k be the set of all k-tuples of complex numbers. The mapping that assigns to every complex number r and every k-tuple $a = (a_1,a_2,\cdots,a_k)$ the k-tuple $(ra_1,ra_2,\cdots,ra_k)$ is a complete external composition law for C^k with the complex numbers as operators. Since, for this external composite, the multiplicative notation

$$r(a_1,a_2,\cdots,a_k) = (ra_1,ra_2,\cdots,ra_k) \tag{4.2}$$

is chosen generally, it is called a *scalar multiple* (for reasons that will become clear later, it is not advisable to call these scalar products). The restriction of this law to $R \times R^k$ defines a scalar multiplication of real k-tuples by real numbers.

*5. Let $P[x]$ be the set of all polynomials in one variable x, and let $Q[x]$ be the subset of all nonconstant linear polynomials. The mapping that assigns to every couple (q,p) the polynomial $\dfrac{dp}{dq} = \dfrac{dp}{dx}\dfrac{dx}{dq}$ is a complete external composition law for $P[x]$. Here every nonconstant linear polynomial q *induces* a derivation, namely, $\dfrac{d}{dq}$.

The general investigation of properties of sets with (possibly several) internal and external composition laws is the object of the branch of

---

† As noted in the introduction, examples and exercises marked with an asterisk depend on calculus or other advanced mathematics and can be omitted without harm.

modern mathematics that the research mathematician (but not the high school teacher) calls *algebra*. In this text we shall develop and apply only two special types of these sets with composition laws: those called *groups* and those called *vector spaces*, although a number of other algebraic concepts could also be used profitably to investigate geometry.

First we shall confine ourselves to a set S with one complete internal composition law and study which properties of such a law are particularly convenient. A composition law that is not associative has the great disadvantage that the notation for multiple composites, such as

$$(((a * b) * ((c * d) * e)) * f) * (g * (h * k)),$$

can become very cumbersome because of the constant need for multiple parentheses to distinguish between different possible composites among the listed elements. Therefore mathematicians often prefer to employ composition laws that are associative. One might assume that the commutative law would be just as important for avoidance of complicated notations, but the mathematician is trained to watch the order in which he writes down his symbols and, therefore, does not find it hard to condition himself to a noncommutative situation. A much more important property of some composition laws is that there exist solutions x and y *in* S for any given equations $a * x = b$ and $y * a = b$. Thus, in the case of addition of numbers, $a + x = b$ is solved by the number $b - a$. This consideration leads to the following fundamental concept:

Definition 4.2:   A nonempty set G with a complete internal associative composition law * is called a *group under that composition law* (frequently denoted by $\{G, *\}$) if, for every couple (a,b) of elements of G, there exist elements x and y in G such that $a * x = b$ and $y * a = b$ hold. A group is called *additive* or *multiplicative*, respectively, if the composition law is written† as addition or as multiplication. A group is called *commutative*† if the composition law is commutative. A nonempty subset S of a group G with composition law * is called a *subgroup of* G if it is a group under the restriction of * to S.

EXAMPLES OF GROUPS AND SUBGROUPS

1. The sets C, R, I, all *under addition*. R and I are subgroups of C, I is a subgroup of R, all *under addition*.
2. The set C^* of all nonzero complex numbers *under multiplication*, the set R^* of all nonzero real numbers *under multiplication*, the set of all nonzero rational numbers *under multiplication*, the set of all positive rational numbers *under multiplication*. Each of these groups is a subgroup of all preceding groups.

† Or *Abelian* (after the Norwegian Mathematician *Niels Henrik Abel* (1802–1829).

3. The set I_2 of all even integers, the set I_4 of all integers that are multiples of 4, the set I_{12} of all integers that are multiples of 12, the set I_{240} of all integers that are multiples of 240, the set I_0 consisting of the number zero alone, all *under addition*. Each of these groups is a subgroup of all preceding groups.

4. The set $\mathbf{R}^3$ of all translations of $\mathfrak{R}^3$ *under addition, as given in definition* 3.3. Similarly, the sets $\mathbf{R}^2$ and $\mathbf{R}^1$ *under addition of translations.* $\mathbf{R}^2$ is *not* a subgroup of $\mathbf{R}^3$, because $\mathbf{R}^2$ contains two-dimensional mappings, whereas $\mathbf{R}^3$ contains three-dimensional mappings. But the set $\mathbf{S}$ of all translations of $\mathbf{R}^3$ that map all points of a fixed plane into itself *is* a subgroup of $\mathbf{R}^3$.

5. The set C^k of all k-tuples of complex numbers *under addition,* the set R^k of all k-tuples of real numbers, the set I^k of all k-tuples of integers, all *under addition* (as defined by (4.1)). Each group is a subgroup of all preceding groups. The set of all k-tuples for which the sum of coordinates is equal to zero is also a subgroup of C^k.

6. The set G of all one-to-one correspondences of a given set S with itself (that is, the *set of all permutations* of this set) *under composition of mappings.* Any subset of the set of all one-to-one correspondences of the given set S that map one element (or several elements) of S on itself (themselves) is a subgroup of G.

7. The set $\mathbf{S}$ consisting of the identity mapping and one reflection of $\mathfrak{R}^3$ *under composition of mappings.* The only subgroup of this group is the set consisting of the identity alone.

8. The set of all rotations of $\mathfrak{R}^n$ ($n = 2, 3$) about a fixed axis or about a fixed point *under composition of mappings.*

9. Let the three points A, B, C of $\mathfrak{R}^2$ form an equilateral triangle whose center is Z. Let 0 be the identity mapping; let a, b, c be the reflections of $\mathfrak{R}^2$ about the lines through A and Z, B and Z, and C and Z, respectively; and let r, s be the rotations of $\mathfrak{R}^2$ about Z by the angles 120° and 240°, respectively. Then the set $\{0,a,b,c,r,s\}$ is a group *under composition of mappings;* it is *not commutative.*

10. The set of permutations of Example 13 of Mappings *under composition of mappings.* This group is *not commutative.*

11. The set $\{+1,-1\}$ *under multiplication.*

The definition of a group that we have given does not always provide the easiest means of checking whether a set with an internal composition law is a group. We will introduce two new notions and a criterion for being a group that is based on those notions.

Definition 4.3: An element n of a set S is called *neutral* under a composition law for S (or an *identity* or a *zero* in the multiplicative or additive case, respectively, with notation 1 or 0) if $n * s = s * n = s$ holds for every $s \,\varepsilon\, S$. An element $\bar{s}$ is called an *opposite* of the element s (or an *inverse* (s^{-1}) or a *negative* $(-s)$ of s in the multiplicative or additive case, respectively) if $s * \bar{s} = \bar{s} * s = n$. In the additive case $s_1 + (-s_2)$ is abbreviated $s_1 - s_2$.

Theorem 4.1: *A set S with an internal associative composition law is a group if and only if S has a neutral element and every element of S has an opposite in S.*

PROOF: 1. If n and $\bar{s}$ exist for every s, then the equation $a * x = b$ is solved by $x = \bar{a} * b$ (in this order), as can be seen by substitution and application of the associative law. Similarly, the equation $y * a = b$ is solved by $y = b * \bar{a}$.

2. It remains to show that, in any group, a neutral element and opposite elements exist. From definition 4.2 it follows that, for a fixed element $s \ \varepsilon \ S$, the equation

$$s * x = s$$

must have a solution; this we will denote by "n_R" (where R stands for "right"). It will be shown next that this n_R is also a solution of

$$t * x = t \tag{4.3}$$

for any $t \ (\neq s) \ \varepsilon \ S$. Let r be an element of S satisfying $r * s = t$, which must exist by definition of a group. Then

$$t * n_R = (r * s) * n_R = r * (s * n_R) = r * s = t;$$

hence n_R solves (4.3) for every $t \ \varepsilon \ S$. Similarly, an element n_L can be found that solves $y * t = t$ for every t. But, because of $n_L = n_L * n_R = n_R$, the two elements n_L and n_R are equal and neutral. Again by definition 4.2, there must exist elements $\bar{s}_L$ and $\bar{s}_R$ satisfying $\bar{s}_L * s = s * \bar{s}_R = n$ for a given $s \ \varepsilon \ S$. But, because of $s_L = s_L * (s * s_R) = (s_L * s) * s_R = s_R$, these two elements are equal and hence opposite to s.

Corollary 4.1: *A subset S of a group $\{G, *\}$ is a subgroup $\{S, *\}$ under the restricted composition law if $s_1, s_2 \ \varepsilon \ S$ implies always that $s_1 * \bar{s}_2 \ \varepsilon \ S$ for an opposite $\bar{s}_2$ of s_2.*

PROOF: From the special case $s_1 = s_2 \ \varepsilon \ S$ it follows that $s_1 * \bar{s}_1 = n \ \varepsilon \ S$. Thus S contains a neutral element. But then $n, s \ \varepsilon \ S$ implies $n * \bar{s} \ \varepsilon \ S$; that is, $\bar{s} \ \varepsilon \ S$. Hence S contains for every element an opposite element. It remains to show that the restriction of $*$ to $S \times S$ is a *composition law for S*, that is, a mapping whose images are *in* S. Since by exercise 8, part (b), any element $t_2 \ \varepsilon \ S$ is an opposite of some element $s_2 \ \varepsilon \ S$, we have $t_1 * t_2 \ \varepsilon \ S$ for any $t_1 \ \varepsilon \ S$ from the condition of the corollary.

The behavior of the composition laws of different groups can be compared by means of such mappings of one group into the other, where the composites are mapped on the corresponding composites. In this way one can establish a sort of abstract similarity and equality of groups. For this the following notions are needed:

Definition 4.4:   A mapping m of a group $\{G, *\}$ into a group $\{H, *\}$ is called *homomorphic* or a *homomorphism* (or, if $G = H$, also *endomorphic* or an *endomorphism*) if the image of the composite of any two elements g_1, g_2 of G is equal to the composite of their images:

$$m(g_1 * g_2) = m(g_1) * m(g_2). \tag{4.4}$$

A homomorphic one-to-one correspondence is also called *isomorphic* or an *isomorphism* (or, if $G = H$, also *automorphic* or an *automorphism*). Two groups are called *isomorphic* if there exists an isomorphism between them. A homomorphism is frequently called an *additive mapping* or a *multiplicative mapping* if G and H are both additive or both multiplicative, respectively.

EXAMPLES OF HOMOMORPHISMS OF GROUPS

1. The rule $z \to |z|$ defines a mapping of $\{C^*, \cdot\}$ onto $\{R^+, \cdot\}$. Both this mapping and its restriction to $\{R^*, \cdot\}$ are endomorphisms. They are multiplicative.

2. For a positive integer n, the rule $z \to nz$ defines an *automorphism* of $\{C, +\}$ and of $\{R, +\}$ but only an *endomorphism* of $\{I, +\}$ or, reinterpreted, an *isomorphism* of $\{I, +\}$ onto the additive group $\{I_n, +\}$ of all integers divisible by n. These mappings are additive.

3. The rule $z \to \bar{z}$ (*conjugation* of complex numbers) defines an automorphism of $\{C^*, \cdot\}$ and *also* an automorphism of $\{C, +\}$. The restriction of both automorphisms to R is the identity automorphism.

4. The rule $z \to z^3$ defines an *endomorphism* of $\{C^*, \cdot\}$ and an *endomorphism* of $\{R^*, \cdot\}$, but also an *automorphism* of $\{R^+, \cdot\}$.

5. The rule $x \to \log x$ defines an *isomorphism* of $\{R^+, \cdot\}$ onto $\{R, +\}$ because $\log(xy) = \log x + \log y$. Here the composition laws are multiplication in the first group and addition in the second group. Conversely, the rule $x \to e^x$ defines an *isomorphism* of $\{R, +\}$ onto $\{R^+, \cdot\}$. On these isomorphisms the practical use of logarithms is based.

6. We shall see in one of the following sections that there exists an isomorphism of $\mathbf{R}^n$ onto R^n for $n = 1, 2, 3$. This, of course, is the fundamental isomorphism of analytic geometry and the reason for the similarity of notation.

7. Examples 7 and 11 of Groups are *isomorphic*.

8. Examples 9 and 10 of Groups are *isomorphic*.

9. Let S be a subgroup of a group G. Then the identity mapping of S into G is a *homomorphism* of S into G.

10. The mapping that assigns to every element of a *commutative* group an opposite element is an *automorphism*.
11. If there exists an isomorphism of a group G *onto* a group H then there also exists an isomorphism of H onto G.

Let us return to external composition laws and introduce two notions.

Definition 4.5: If $* : B \times A \to A$ is a complete external composition law for a set A with operator set B and if b_1 and b_2 are any two operators, then the symbol $b_2 b_1$ is called the *operator product* of b_1 and b_2, and the external composition law is extended to these operator products by the definition

$$(b_2 b_1) * a = b_2 * (b_1 * a).$$

b_1 and b_2 are said to *commute* if $b_2 b_1$ and $b_1 b_2$ induce the same mapping. If there exists additionally an internal composition law $+$ for A, then the symbol $b_1 + b_2$ is called the *operator sum* of b_1 and b_2, and the external composition law is extended to these operator sums by the definition

$$(b_1 + b_2) * a = (b_1 * a) + (b_2 * a).$$

Note: These conventions may lead to confusion if a multiplication or an addition is defined for the elements of the operator set, unless the two "additions" or "multiplications" induce the same mappings.

EXAMPLES OF OPERATOR SUMS AND PRODUCTS

1. Let A be a set and let B be the set of all mappings of A into itself. Use operator notation for the images. Then the operator product induces the same mapping as the composite of the mappings induced by the same operators.
2. Define two left operators "sin" and "cos" to induce the mappings $x \to \sin x$ and $x \to \cos x$, respectively, of $\{R,+\}$ into itself. Then the operator *product* "sin cos" induces the mapping $x \to \sin (\cos x)$, and the operator *sum* "sin $+$ cos" induces the mapping $x \to \sin x + \cos x$. As $\sin (\cos x) \neq \cos (\sin x)$ in general, the two operators do not commute. Thus, strictly speaking, the concepts "sum of two functions" in calculus means their operator sum, and "function of a function" means the operator product.
*3. Define two left operators $\dfrac{\partial}{\partial x}$ and $\dfrac{\partial}{\partial y}$ to induce the two mappings $f(x,y) \to \dfrac{\partial}{\partial x} f(x,y)$ and $f(x,y) \to \dfrac{\partial}{\partial y} f(x,y)$, respectively, of the *additive* group of all functions of two variables x and y for which the mixed second derivatives exist and are continuous. Then the two operators

commute by a well-known theorem of advanced calculus. The operator *sum* induces the mapping $f(x, y) \rightarrow \dfrac{\partial}{\partial x} f(x, y) + \dfrac{\partial}{\partial y} f(x, y)$.

*4. Let $\{P, +\}$ be the *additive* group of all polynomials in one variable x. Define left operators $a_i \dfrac{d^i}{dx^i}$ for $i = 0, 1, \cdots, k$ and $a_i \ \varepsilon \ P$ to induce the mappings $f \rightarrow a_i f^{(i)}$ of this group into itself. Then the operator *product* $a_1 \dfrac{d}{dx} a_2 \dfrac{d^2}{dx^2}$ induces the mapping

$$a_1 \frac{d}{dx} a_2 \frac{d^2}{dx^2} : \qquad f \rightarrow a_1(a_2 f'')' = a_1 a_2' f'' + a_1 a_2 f'''. \qquad (4.5)$$

These two operators commute if and only if both a_1 and a_2 are constant polynomials. The symbol

$$\sum_{i=0}^{k} a_i \frac{d^i}{dx^i} \, ,$$

which is an obvious generalization of the operator *sum* of *two* operators, is defined to induce the mapping

$$\sum_{i=0}^{k} a_i \frac{d^i}{dx^i} : \qquad f \rightarrow \sum_{i=0}^{k} a_i f^{(i)}.$$

These so-called *differential operators* are applied to solve differential equations.

5. Definition 3.4 introduces an external composition law with operator set R. By theorem 3.3, the operator sum and the ordinary sum of two real numbers induce the same mapping, and the operator product and the ordinary product of two numbers induce the same mapping, too.

6. Formula (4.2) introduces an external composition law for R^n with operator set R. Let $\{R^k, +\}$ be that group in which the addition is defined by (4.1). Then it can be shown that the operator and ordinary sums of two real numbers induce the same mapping and also that the operator and ordinary products induce the same mapping.

EXERCISES

1. Prove the commutativity and associativity of Examples 4 and 5 of Internal Composition Laws.

2. Show that Examples 2 and 3 of Internal Composition Laws are neither commutative nor associative.

3. Let $P(S)$ be the set of all subsets of a set S. Show that the mapping of $P(S) \times P(S)$ into $P(S)$ that assigns to every couple of subsets

(A,B) the subset $\{s|s \ \varepsilon \ A \text{ or } s \ \varepsilon \ B\}$, called the *union* of these sets, is commutative and associative.

*4. Prove that the images of the mappings introduced in Example 5 of External Composition Laws are elements of $P[x]$.

5. Verify Examples 3 and 4 of Groups and Subgroups.

6. Determine the associativity of the composition laws, and construct a neutral element and an opposite element for every element in Examples 5 to 11 of Groups and Subgroups.

7. Prove: If n_1, n_2 are two elements of a group that are neutral, then they are equal.

8. Prove: (a) If $\bar{s}_1$, $\bar{s}_2$ are elements of a group that are opposites of s, then $s_1 = s_2$. (b) The opposite $\bar{\bar{s}}$ of the opposite $\bar{s}$ of s equals s.

9. Prove that $\bar{s}_1 * \bar{s}_2 = \overline{s_2 * s_1}$ holds in a group.

10. Write out the equations corresponding to (4.4) that verify Examples 1, 2, 3, and 4 of Homomorphisms of Groups.

11. Prove that examples 7, 8, and 10 of Homomorphisms of Groups give imomorphisms; that is, establish one-to-one correspondences defining the homomorphisms.

12. Why is the set $\{A,B\}$ with the composition law $A * A = A$, $A * B = B * A = B * B = B$ not a group?

13. Why is the set $\{A,B,C\}$ with the composition law $A * A = B * B = C * C = A$, $A * B = B * A = B * C = B$, $A * C = C * A = C * B = C$ not a group?

14. Why is $\mathbf{R}^3$, with the commutative composition law assigning to every couple of points the midpoint of the line segment joining them, not a group? Is the law associative? Prove that the set $\{A^0, A^1, A^2, A^3, A^4, A^5\}$ with the composition law (written as *multiplication*)

$$A^i A^j = \begin{cases} A^{i+j} & \text{if } i+j \le 5 \\ A^{i+j-6} & \text{if } i+j > 5 \end{cases}$$

is a *commutative* group.

15. Show that the previous example is isomorphic to the group of all rotations of $\mathbf{R}^3$ about a fixed axis *by those angles that are multiples of* $60°$.

16. Prove that the previous example is *not* isomorphic to Example 9 of Groups.

17. Prove: If a group G is isomorphic to a group H and if H is isomorphic to a group K, then G is isomorphic to K.

18. *Disprove*: If there exists a homomorphism of a group G onto a group H and a homomorphism of H onto a group K, then there also exists a homomorphism of K onto G. Make a similar statement that is correct.

19. Define for I an internal composition law $i * j = i + j - ij$. Show that the number 0 is neutral and that the number 1 does not have an opposite.

20. Prove the statements concerning equality of mappings in Examples 5 and 6 of Operator Sums and Products.

5

Vector Spaces

Additive (commutative) groups with numbers as operators are widely employed in many areas of mathematics and its applications. Although we shall later apply these types of groups mainly to geometry, we shall here study their abstract properties in general, not only for reasons of economy of thought but also to point out important structural similarities among different branches of mathematics.

Definition 5.1: An additive, commutative group with the real (or complex) numbers as multiplicative left operators is called a *real* (or *complex*) *vector space* **V** if every operator induces an endomorphism, the number 1 induces the identity mapping, the ordinary and the operator sum of any two operators induce the same mapping, and likewise the ordinary and the operator product of any two operators induce the same mapping.[†] The elements of **V** are often called *vectors*; the real or complex numbers are called *scalars*; and the external composition law is called *scalar multiplication*. A subset **S** of **V** is called a (*vector*) *subspace* of **V** if it is a vector space under the restrictions of the two composition laws.

Thus, an additive, commutative group **V** is a vector space if a multiplication of its elements with real or complex numbers is defined such

[†] This is a special case of the general definition of a vector space in which an arbitrary *field* or *division ring* in the sense of algebra can be taken as the set of scalars. But for the purpose of this elementary textbook it is sufficient to consider only R or C as possible operator sets. Most theorems about vector spaces stated here remain true in general.

that the products lie in the group and satisfy, for every $\mathbf{v}$, $\mathbf{w}$ ε $\mathbf{V}$ and every α, β ε R or ε C, the four laws:

$$\alpha(\mathbf{v} + \mathbf{w}) = \alpha\mathbf{v} + \alpha\mathbf{w} \tag{5.1}$$

$$1\mathbf{v} = \mathbf{v} \tag{5.2}$$

$$(\alpha + \beta)\mathbf{v} = \alpha\mathbf{v} + \beta\mathbf{v} \tag{5.3}$$

$$(\alpha\beta)\mathbf{v} = \alpha(\beta\mathbf{v}). \tag{5.4}$$

We shall frequently use *boldface letters* to denote vector spaces and vectors.

Remark: Some mathematicians prefer to write the multiplicative operators of a vector space *on the right*; in this case the four equations above take the form: $(\mathbf{v} + \mathbf{w})\alpha = \mathbf{v}\alpha + \mathbf{w}\alpha$; $\mathbf{v}1 = \mathbf{v}$; $\mathbf{v}(\alpha + \beta) = \mathbf{v}\alpha + \mathbf{v}\beta$; $\mathbf{v}(\beta\alpha) = (\mathbf{v}\beta)\alpha$. Others allow the operators to be written either on the left or on the right; that is, they add the rule $\alpha\mathbf{v} = \mathbf{v}\alpha$. But these changes affect only the *form* and not the *substance* of a vector space as defined above.

Note that, in any vector space $\mathbf{V}$, we have for every $\mathbf{v}$ ε $\mathbf{V}$,

$$0\mathbf{v} = 0, \tag{5.5}$$

$$(-1)\mathbf{v} = -\mathbf{v}. \tag{5.6}$$

That $0\mathbf{v}$ is neutral follows from $\mathbf{v} + 0\mathbf{v} = 1\mathbf{v} + 0\mathbf{v} = (1 + 0)\mathbf{v} = 1\mathbf{v} = \mathbf{v}$. For every $\mathbf{v}$ ε $\mathbf{V}$, that $(-1)\mathbf{v}$ is opposite to $\mathbf{v}$ follows from $\mathbf{v} + (-1)\mathbf{v} = 1\mathbf{v} + (-1)\mathbf{v} = (1 - 1)\mathbf{v} = 0\mathbf{v}$. As in the case of groups, we shall use the standard abbreviation

$$\mathbf{v} - \mathbf{w} = \mathbf{v} + (-\mathbf{w}) = \mathbf{v} + (-1)\mathbf{w} \tag{5.7}$$

for every $\mathbf{v}$, $\mathbf{w}$ ε $\mathbf{V}$.

We shall also continue to use the summation convention introduced by (3.11) for multiple sums of vectors in general.

EXAMPLES OF VECTOR SPACES AND SUBSPACES

1. The set $\mathbf{R}^3$ of all translations of $\mathfrak{R}^3$ is a real vector space under addition and scalar multiplication, as introduced by definitions 3.3 and 3.4. The set $\mathbf{P}$ of all translations of $\mathfrak{R}^3$ that map all points of some fixed plane on points of this plane is a subspace of $\mathbf{R}^3$. The set $\mathbf{L}$ of all translations of $\mathfrak{R}^3$ that map all points of some fixed line on points of this line is a subspace of $\mathbf{R}^3$, and, if this line is parallel to the above plane, also a subspace of $\mathbf{P}$. The set $\{0\}$ consisting of the zero translation alone is a subspace of all previous real vector spaces.

2. The set R^3 of all triples of real numbers is a real vector space under addition and scalar multiplication as introduced by (4.1) and (4.2). The set T of all triples of the form $(r_1, r_2, 0)$ (with r_1, r_2 ε R) is a sub-

space of R^3. The set of all triples of the form $(r,0,0)$ is a subspace of both R^3 and T. The set $\{(0,0,0)\}$ consisting of the zero triple is a subspace of all previous vector spaces of this example.

3. If all references to real numbers are replaced by references to complex numbers in example 2, we obtain the complex vector space of all complex triples and some subspaces of it. None of the vector spaces so obtained is a subspace of any vector space in example 2, because here the *complex* numbers are used as operators, but there only the *real* numbers.

4. The set $\mathbf{R}^2$ of all translations of $\mathfrak{R}^2$ is a real vector space. The set $\mathbf{M}$ of all translations of $\mathfrak{R}^2$ that map all points of a fixed line on points of that line is a subspace of $\mathbf{R}^2$. Neither of these two examples is a subspace of any of the spaces in example 1, because here we deal with translations of a *plane*, and there with translations of *three-dimensional space*.

5. The set $\mathbf{R}^1$ of all translations of $\mathfrak{R}^1$ is a real vector space.

6. The set R^n, for any positive integer n, is a real vector space under (4.1) and (4.2). Similarly, the set C^n is a complex vector space. In particular, R is a *real vector space*, and C is a *complex vector space*.

7. The set of all real polynomials in one variable x, denoted by $R[x]$, and the set of all complex polynomials in one variable x, denoted by $C[x]$, are vector spaces under ordinary addition of polynomials and ordinary multiplication of polynomials by real or complex numbers, respectively. The sets of all linear polynomials with real or complex coefficients, denoted by $R[x]_L$ and $C[x]_L$, respectively, and their subsets of all homogeneous linear polynomials (see definition 8.3), denoted by $R[x]_{LH}$ and $C[x]_{LH}$, respectively, are subspaces of the respective real or complex vector space.

8. The previous example can be extended to polynomials in several variables $x_1, x_2, \cdots, x_n$. The corresponding vector spaces are denoted either by $R[x_1,x_2,\cdots,x_n]$, $C[x_1,x_2,\cdots,x_n]$, and so forth, or, more frequently, by the same symbols used for one variable [then x stands for the n-tuple of variables $(x_1,x_2,\cdots,x_n)$].

9. A solution of an algebraic equation $f(x_1,x_2,\cdots,x_n) = 0$ or a system of algebraic equations $f_i = 0$ in several unknowns $x_1, x_2, \cdots, x_n$ is an n-tuple $s = (s_1,s_2,\cdots,s_n)$ of numbers such that the substitution $x_1 = s_1, x_2 = s_2, \cdots, x_n = s_n$ yields identities. The set of *all* solutions of a given system of *linear homogeneous* equations (see definition 8.3) is a vector space under the addition (4.1) and the scalar multiplication (4.2), which is real or complex depending on whether real or complex numbers are admitted. This vector space is a subspace either of R^n or of C^n.

10. Let $s = (s_1,s_2,\cdots,s_n)$ be a given n-tuple of (real or complex) numbers. The set of *all linear homogeneous* polynomials (real or complex)

in n variables $x_1, x_2, \cdots, x_n$ that are made zero by the substitution $x_1 = a_1, x_2 = a_2, \cdots, x_n = a_n$ is a (real or complex) vector space.

11. Exercise 8.21 will show that, to *every* vector space of n-tuples of numbers, that is, to every subspace of R^n or C^n, there corresponds the vector space of *all* the linear homogeneous polynomials (that is, a subspace of $R[x]_{LH}$ or $C[x]_{LH}$) that are made zero by the substitution $x_1 = a_1, x_2 = a_2, \cdots, x_n = a_n$. This will establish a one-to-one correspondence between the set of all subspaces (not sub*sets*) of R^n (or C^n) and the set of all subspaces (not sub*sets*) of $R[x]_{LH}$ (or $C[x]_{LH}$), which is fundamental in both algebra and geometry.

*12. The set of all real functions in one variable (or in n variables) that are m times differentiable in some region is a real vector space (often called a *function space*) if addition and multiplication by (real) numbers is defined as usual. This concept can be generalized to the complex case in the obvious way.

*13. Important subspaces of the function spaces of the previous example (defined for suitable n, m and a suitable region) are the vector spaces of *all* solutions of a given *homogeneous linear* differential equation or of a system of such equations.

*14. The set of all differential operators $\sum_{i=1}^{n} r_i \dfrac{d^i}{dx^i}$ ($r_i \; \varepsilon \; R$) of all possible orders is a vector space under operator addition and formal left-multiplication of numbers. Any subset consisting of all operators whose orders do not exceed a fixed positive integer k is a subspace. The example can be generalized to partial differential operators in the obvious way.

Future use of the preceding sets as **vector spaces** *will always be made with reference to the composition laws as defined here, respectively.*

As several of these examples show explicitly, in vector spaces one considers sums of scalar multiples. They are special cases of the following notion.

Definition 5.2: Let S be a nonempty set of elements of a vector space. Every sum $s = \alpha_1 s_1 + \alpha_2 s_2 + \cdots + \alpha_n s_n$ of scalar multiples of *finitely many different* elements $s_1, s_2, \cdots, s_n$ of S is called a *linear combination* of S (or of the elements of S) and is sometimes abbreviated $s = \sum_{i=1}^{n} \alpha_i s_i$; the scalars are called *coefficients*. A linear combination is called *trivial* if all its coefficients are equal to zero and *nontrivial* if at least one coefficient is different from zero. The set of *all* linear combinations of S is called the *span* of S and is denoted by $[S]$ or, if $S = \{s_1, s_2, \cdots\}$, by $[s_1, s_2, \cdots]$. The elements of S are called *generators* of the span and are said to *generate* or to *span* S.

Note: s, in general, is not an element of S. Hence the span of S, in general, contains S properly.

In most cases we shall consider the spans of *finite* sets $\{s_1, \cdots, s_n\}$ of vectors. In this case the span is simply the set of all possible vectors of the form $\sum_{i=1}^{n} \alpha_i s_i$.

EXAMPLES OF SPANS

1. Every nonzero vector x of $\mathbf{R}^1$ spans $\mathbf{R}^1$. In other words, if a nonzero translation x of $\mathfrak{R}^1$ is given, then every translation of $\mathbf{R}^1$ can be written in the form $r\mathbf{x}$, $r \, \varepsilon \, R$. This is only another way of saying that all non-zero translations of a line have the same or opposite direction and, therefore, differ only in their length.

2. If O, A, B are three points of $\mathfrak{R}^2$ forming a proper triangle and if translations of $\mathfrak{R}^2$ are defined by $\mathbf{a} = \vec{OA}$, $\mathbf{b} = \vec{OB}$, then $[\mathbf{a}, \mathbf{b}] = \mathbf{R}^2$. PROOF (see Fig. 5.1): Let P be a point of $\mathfrak{R}^2$. Construct lines through

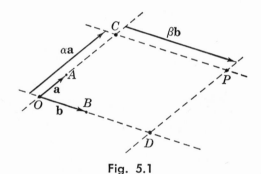

Fig. 5.1

P parallel to OA and OB. They intersect the lines through OA and through OB in two points C and D. Now $\vec{OC}$ is a multiple of $\vec{OA}$, and $\vec{CP} = \vec{OD}$ is a multiple of $\vec{OB}$; hence there exist two real scalars α, β so that $\vec{OP} = \vec{OC} + \vec{CP} = \alpha\vec{OA} + \beta\vec{OB}$. As P is arbitrary, every translation of $\mathfrak{R}^2$ is equal to some such $\vec{OP}$, hence is equal to a linear combination of $\mathbf{a}$ and $\mathbf{b}$. The span $[\mathbf{a}]$ ($\mathbf{a} \neq \mathbf{0}$) is a proper subset of $\mathbf{R}^2$, because no translation whose direction is not equal or opposite to the direction of $\mathbf{a}$ is a multiple of $\mathbf{a}$.

3. More generally, if O, A, B, C are four points of $\mathfrak{R}^3$ forming a proper tetrahedron (that is, not lying on the same plane) and if translations of $\mathfrak{R}^3$ are defined by $\mathbf{a} = \vec{OA}$, $\mathbf{b} = \vec{OB}$, $\mathbf{c} = \vec{OC}$, then these three vectors span the vector space $\mathbf{R}^3$ of all translations of $\mathfrak{R}^3$. PROOF (see Fig. 5.2): Let $\mathbf{p}$ be an arbitrary translation of $\mathbf{R}^3$, and

let P be the **p**-image of O, then $\mathbf{p} = \overrightarrow{OP}$. The line through P parallel to OC intersects the plane through OAB in exactly one point F. The line through F parallel to OB intersects the line through OA in exactly one point G. Now $\mathbf{p} = \overrightarrow{OP} = \overrightarrow{OG} + \overrightarrow{GF} + \overrightarrow{FP}$. As in the previous example, it is easy to see that $\overrightarrow{OG}$, $\overrightarrow{GF}$, and $\overrightarrow{FP}$ are multiples of $\overrightarrow{OA}$, $\overrightarrow{OB}$, and $\overrightarrow{OC}$, respectively; so every three-dimensional translation is a linear combination of $\{\mathbf{a}, \mathbf{b}, \mathbf{c}\}$.

4. The two sets $\{(1,0,0)\}$ and $\{(1,0,0), (2,0,0), (3,0,0)\}$ both span *the same subset* $\{(r,0,0)\,|\,r \;\varepsilon\; R\}$ of R^3, namely, the set of all real triples whose second and third coordinate are equal to zero.

5. The set $\{(a_1, a_2, \cdots, a_n), (b_1, b_2, \cdots, b_n), (c_1, c_2, \cdots, c_n)\}$ spans the subset of R^n of all n-tuples of the form

$$(\alpha a_1 + \beta b_1 + \gamma c_1, \alpha a_2 + \beta b_2 + \gamma c_2, \cdots, \alpha a_n + \beta b_n + \gamma c_n) \tag{5.8}$$

where α, β, and γ are any real numbers.

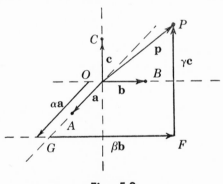

Fig. 5.2

6. The set of *all* n-tuples that have the number 1 as one coordinate and 0 as all other coordinates spans R^n (if only real scalars are admitted) and also spans C^n (for complex scalars).

    Proof: If $e^{(1)} = (1,0,\cdots,0)$, $e^{(2)} = (0,1,0,\cdots,0)$, $\cdots$, $e^{(n)} = (0,0,\cdots,0,1)$, then we have the important identity

$$\sum_{i=1}^{n} \alpha_i e^{(i)} = (\alpha_1, \alpha_2, \cdots, \alpha_n). \tag{5.9}$$

7. The set of all real polynomials of the form x^{2i} $(i = 0, 1, \cdots)$ spans the subset of $R[x]$ consisting of all *even* polynomials. The set $\{1 + x, 1 - x\}$ spans the set of all linear polynomials in x. Also, the set $\{1, 1 + x, 1 - x, 2x + 3\}$ spans the set of all linear polynomials in x.

    As an immediate consequence of definition 5.2 we have the following lemma.

Lemma 5.1:   *A linear combination of linear combinations of a subset* S *of a vector space is itself a linear combination of* S.

PROOF: We verify this lemma by showing that a scalar multiple of a linear combination of S and the sum of two linear combinations of S are again linear combinations of S.

1. If β and α_i for $i = 1, 2, \cdots, n$ are scalars and if s_i for $i = 1, 2, \cdots, n$ are vectors, then

$$\beta \sum_{i=1}^{n} \alpha_i s_i = \sum_{i=1}^{n} \beta(\alpha_i s_i) = \sum_{i=1}^{n} (\beta \alpha_i) s_i$$

by consecutive application of (5.1) and (5.4).

2. Suppose α_i (for $i = 1, 2, \cdots, m$) and β_j (for $j = 1, 2, \cdots, n$) are scalars and $s_i \; \varepsilon \; S$ (for $i = 1, 2, \cdots, m$) and $t_j \; \varepsilon \; S$ (for $j = 1, 2, \cdots, n$). Then the sum of $s = \sum_{i=1}^{m} \alpha_i s_i$ and $t = \sum_{j=1}^{n} \beta_j t_j$ is $s + t = \sum_{i=1}^{m} \alpha_i s_i + \sum_{j=1}^{n} \beta_j t_j$. If no s_i is equal to any t_j, then this expression is a linear combination of S, by definition. But if s_p is equal to t_q, then the last sum is equal to

$$\sum_{\substack{i=1 \\ i \neq p}}^{m} \alpha_i s_i + \sum_{\substack{j=1 \\ j \neq q}}^{n} \beta_j t_j + \alpha_p s_p + \beta_q t_q = \sum_{\substack{i=1 \\ i \neq p}}^{m} \alpha_i s_i + \sum_{\substack{j=1 \\ j \neq q}}^{n} \beta_j t_j + (\alpha_p + \beta_q) s_p$$

by application of the commutative and associative laws for addition and by rule (5.3). This process replaces *two* multiples of the same vector by *one* such multiple. By a sufficient number of repetitions of this process a sum of multiples of *different* vectors is obtained.

We turn now to an important criterion for a subset to be a subspace.

Theorem 5.1:   *A subset* S *of a vector space* V *is a subspace if and only if the restrictions of the two composition laws to* S *are composition laws for* S.

In other words, S is a subspace if and only if

$$s, t \; \varepsilon \; S \quad \text{and} \quad \alpha \; \varepsilon \; R(\text{or} \; \varepsilon \; C) \quad \text{imply} \quad \alpha s \; \varepsilon \; S \quad \text{and} \quad s + t \; \varepsilon \; S. \quad (5.10)$$

This is a simpler criterion than that for a subset of a group to be a subgroup.

PROOF: 1. The condition (5.10) is obviously necessary.

2. If (5.10) holds, then $t \; \varepsilon \; S$ implies $-t \; \varepsilon \; S$, by (5.6); hence $s, t \; \varepsilon \; S$ implies $s - t \; \varepsilon \; S$. Consequently, S is a subgroup, by corollary 4.1. Since the restriction of the external composition law to S is a composition law for S, by (5.10), and since the equations (5.1), (5.2), (5.3), and (5.4) certainly hold for the elements of S (because $S \subset V$), S becomes a vector space under the two restricted composition laws.

In view of lemma 5.1, theorem 5.1 implies immediately the following corollary.

Corollary 5.1:   *The span* [S] *of a set* S *of elements of a vector space* **V** *is a subspace of* **V**. [S] = [[S]]. [S] *is contained in every subspace of* **V** *that contains all elements of* S.

Among the most interesting sets S of a vector space **V** are those which span either the whole vector space **V** or a given subspace *but which contain as few elements as possible.* An analysis of the properties of these particularly useful subsets leads to the following notions.

Definition 5.3:   A nonempty subset S of a vector space **V** is called *linearly independent* if the zero vector is *not* a nontrivial linear combination of S; S is *linearly dependent* otherwise. Sometimes the (bad) terminology *"the elements of* S *are linearly independent"* is also used.

Thus the set S is linearly independent if *every* equation $\sum_{i=1}^{p} \alpha_i s_i = 0$ (with $s_i \in$ S) implies that *every* scalar α_i is equal to zero, and is linearly dependent if finitely many elements s_i *of* S *can be found* such that an equation

$$\alpha_1 s_1 + \alpha_2 s_2 + \cdots + \alpha_p s_p = 0, \qquad \alpha_1 \neq 0 \qquad (5.11)$$

holds for suitable scalars α_i. The usefulness of linear independence becomes clearer in view of the following two lemmas.

Lemma 5.2:   *A nonempty subset* S *of a vector space* **V** *is linearly dependent if and only if either* S = {0} *or there exists an element* s ε S *that is a linear combination of the set of all elements of* S *different from* s.

PROOF: 1. If S = {0}, then the nontrivial linear combination 10 (*number* 1 times zero *vector*) is equal to **0**; hence in this case S is linearly dependent. If there exists an equation $s_1 = \beta_2 s_2 + \beta_3 s_3 + \cdots + \beta_p s_p$ for $s_i \in$ S, $i = 1, \cdots, p$, and scalars β_i, then, by subtracting s_1 from both sides of this equation and applying (5.6), we obtain

$$0 = (-1)s_1 + \beta_2 s_2 + \beta_3 s_3 + \cdots + \beta_p s_p \quad \text{with} \quad -1 \neq 0;$$

that is, a nontrivial linear combination of S equal to zero. Hence S is linearly dependent in this case, too.

2. Conversely, if S is linearly dependent, then it is possible to find elements s_i in S and scalars α_i such that (5.11) is satisfied. By multiplying this equation by $1/\alpha_1$ (which exists because $\alpha_1 \neq 0$) and applying (5.1) and (5.4), we obtain

$$s_1 + \frac{\alpha_2}{\alpha_1} s_2 + \frac{\alpha_3}{\alpha_1} s_3 + \cdots + \frac{\alpha_p}{\alpha_1} s_p = 0$$

from which

$$s_1 = \left(-\frac{\alpha_2}{\alpha_1}\right)s_2 + \left(-\frac{\alpha_3}{\alpha_1}\right)s_3 + \cdots + \left(-\frac{\alpha_p}{\alpha_1}\right)s_p \qquad (5.12)$$

follows by (5.4) and (5.6). If $p > 1$ then the lemma is proved. For $p = 1$ (5.12) reduces to $s_1 = 0$, hence $\{0\} \subset S$. Now two separate cases have to be considered. Either $S = \{0\}$, and the proof is completed. Or $S \neq \{0\} = \{s_1\}$ in which case S contains an element $s \neq 0$. But then $s_1 = 0 = 0s$, that is s_1 is a linear combination of the other elements of S. *If S is finite the proof can be simplified.*

Lemma 5.3: *If S is a nonempty finite subset of a vector space containing vectors other than the zero vector, then there exists a nonempty linearly independent subset T of S that spans the same subspace as S.*

PROOF OUTLINE: If S is linearly independent, then take $T = S$. If S is linearly dependent, then consider the set $P(S)$ of all subsets of S. S contains at least one nonzero vector s, by hypothesis. Hence the set $\{s\}$ is linearly independent; that is, $P(S)$ contains at least one linearly independent set. Now choose among the *linearly independent* subsets of S a set T, which has a maximum number of elements. It can be shown without too much effort that this T (which is, in general, not unique) satisfies the lemma.

It is, of course, possible to give an easier proof of lemma 5.3 by deleting from S, if it is linearly dependent, an element that is a linear combination of the remaining elements of S, and to repeat this process until one reaches a linearly independent set. But the proof given above has the advantage that it can be generalized to the infinite case.†

EXAMPLES OF LINEAR INDEPENDENCE AND DEPENDENCE

1. If $S = \{s\}$ is a set consisting of one vector only, it is linearly independent if $s \neq 0$ and dependent if $s = 0$.
2. A set of vectors is linearly dependent if a subset of it is linearly dependent. Thus, in particular, *any set that contains the zero vector is linearly dependent.*
3. If $S = \{s_1, s_2\}$ and $s_1 \neq 0$, $s_2 \neq 0$, then S is linearly dependent if s_1 and s_2 are multiples of each other and linearly independent otherwise.
4. If $\{s_1, s_2, \cdots, s_{n-1}, s_n\}$ is linearly dependent, but $\{s_1, s_2, \cdots, s_{n-1}\}$ is linearly independent, then $s_n \varepsilon [s_1, s_2, \cdots, s_{n-1}]$.
5. In $\mathbf{R}^1$ there exists a single linearly independent element $\mathbf{a}$, namely, any nonzero translation. Since $[\mathbf{a}] = \mathbf{R}^1$, any set of two different elements of $\mathbf{R}^1$ is linearly dependent. In $\mathbf{R}^2$ there exist linearly independent sets of two different translations, for instance, $\mathbf{a}$, $\mathbf{b}$ as defined in Example 2 of Spans. Since $[\mathbf{a}, \mathbf{b}] = \mathbf{R}^2$, any set of three different elements of $\mathbf{R}^2$ is linearly dependent. In $\mathbf{R}^3$ there exist linearly independent sets of three different translations $\mathbf{a}$, $\mathbf{b}$, $\mathbf{c}$ (see Example 3 of Spans). Since

† By application of *Zorn's* lemma.

[a,b,c] $= \mathbf{R}^3$, any set of four different elements of $\mathbf{R}^3$ is linearly dependent. It can also be shown that in $\mathbf{R}^i (i = 1, 2, 3)$ *any linearly independent* set of i elements spans $\mathbf{R}^i$. Hence i is the maximum number of linearly independent elements of $\mathbf{R}^i$.

6. The n n-tuples $e^{(i)}$ of Example 6 of Spans are linearly independent.

7. The two triples (a_1,a_2,a_3) and (b_1,b_2,b_3) are linearly dependent if and only if there exist two scalars α and β, not both equal to zero, such that $(\alpha a_1 + \beta b_1, \alpha a_2 + \beta b_2, \alpha a_3 + \beta b_3) = (0,0,0)$; that is, if the three equations $\alpha a_1 + \beta b_1 = 0$, $\alpha a_2 + \beta b_2 = 0$, $\alpha a_3 + \beta b_3 = 0$ have a solution (α,β) that is not the zero couple $(0,0)$. Similarly, the four triples (a_1,a_2,a_3), (b_1,b_2,b_3), (c_1,c_2,c_3), and (d_1,d_2,d_3) are linearly dependent if and only if there exists a quadruple of numbers $(\alpha,\beta,\gamma,\delta)$ not equal to the zero quadruple which is a solution of the three equations:

$$a_i\alpha + b_i\beta + c_i\gamma + d_i\delta = 0, \qquad i = 1, 2, 3.$$

Thus, checking the linear dependence of a finite set of m n-tuples is equivalent to checking whether a certain set of linear equations has a solution different from the zero m-tuple. Exercise 18.6 will imply that a sequence of n n-tuples is linearly dependent if and only if the determinant of the double sequence is equal to zero.

8. The two couples (r_1,r_2) and (s_1,s_2) are linearly independent if and only

if $r_1s_2 - r_2s_1 \neq 0$. $\left[\text{The left-hand side is the determinant} \begin{vmatrix} r_1 & r_2 \\ s_1 & s_2 \end{vmatrix} \right.$

(see Chapter 17) $\Big]$.

*9. The three triples (r_1,r_2,r_3), (s_1,s_2,s_3), (t_1,t_2,t_3) are linearly independent if and only if

$$\begin{vmatrix} r_1 & r_2 & r_3 \\ s_1 & s_2 & s_3 \\ t_1 & t_2 & t_3 \end{vmatrix} \neq 0.$$

As in the case of groups, different vector spaces can be compared by such mappings of one vector space into the other, where *both the internal and external* composites are mapped onto the corresponding composites. For this purpose the following notions, which are generalizations of definition 4.4, are introduced.

Definition 5.4: A mapping $\mathbf{M}$ of a real vector space $\mathbf{V}$ into a real vector space $\mathbf{W}$ (or from a complex vector space into a complex vector space) is called *linear* or *homomorphic* or a *homomorphism* (or, if $\mathbf{V} = \mathbf{W}$, also *endomorphic* or an *endomorphism*) if, for every $\mathbf{v}_1$, $\mathbf{v}_2$ ε $\mathbf{V}$ and every scalar α,

$$\mathbf{M}(\mathbf{v}_1 + \mathbf{v}_2) = \mathbf{M}(\mathbf{v}_1) + \mathbf{M}(\mathbf{v}_2), \tag{5.13}$$

$$\mathbf{M}(\alpha\mathbf{v}_1) = \alpha\mathbf{M}(\mathbf{v}_1). \tag{5.14}$$

A homomorphic one-to-one correspondence is also called *isomorphic* or an *isomorphism* (or, if $\mathbf{V} = \mathbf{W}$, also *automorphic or an automorphism*). Two vector spaces are called *isomorphic* if there exists an isomorphism between them.

From conditions (5.13) and (5.14) it follows that any linear mapping maps linear combinations on corresponding linear combinations:

$$\mathbf{M}(\sum \alpha_i\mathbf{v}_i) = \sum \alpha_i\mathbf{M}(\mathbf{v}_i). \tag{5.15}$$

Note: The notions homomorphism, endomorphism, etc., of *vector spaces* have to be distinguished carefully from the corresponding notions for *groups* (definition 4.4). Both are special cases of more general concepts applicable to any couple of sets with the same numbers and kinds of internal and external composition laws. In both cases the definitions demand that the image of any composite should always be equal to the corresponding composite of the images. But while in a group we are concerned with one internal composition law only, in a vector space both the internal addition and the external multiplication have to be considered.

EXAMPLES OF LINEAR MAPPINGS

1. If $\mathbf{V}$ is any vector space and α any nonzero scalar, then $\mathbf{v} \to \alpha\mathbf{v}$ defines an automorphism.
2. $(a_1,a_2,a_3) \to (a_1,a_3)$ defines a linear mapping of R^3 into R^2.
3. $(a_1,a_2,a_3) \to (a_1,a_1,a_2,a_3)$ defines a linear mapping of R^3 into R^4.
4. $(a_1,a_2,a_3) \to (a_3,a_2,a_1)$ defines an automorphism of R^3, but $(a_1,a_2,a_3) \to (0,a_2,a_1)$ only an endomorphism of R^3.
5. If $r_{11}, r_{12}, \cdots, r_{1n}; r_{21}, r_{22}, \cdots, r_{2n}; \cdots; r_{m1}, r_{m2}, \cdots, r_{mn}$ are any m times n *given* scalars, then the mapping that assigns to the n-tuple $(a_1,a_2,\cdots,a_n)$ the m-tuple

$$(r_{11}a_1 + r_{12}a_2 + \cdots + r_{1n}a_n, r_{21}a_1 + r_{22}a_2 + \cdots r_{2n}a_n,$$

$$\cdots r_{m1}a_1 + r_{m2}a_2 + \cdots + r_{mn}a_n) \tag{5.16}$$

is a *linear* mapping of R^n into R^m.

It is not by accident that most of the above examples were chosen to involve finite sequences. For we shall see now that many vector spaces can be represented isomorphically by vector spaces of finite sequences.

Theorem 5.2:   *A (real or complex) vector space $\mathbf{V}$ that is spanned by n linearly independent elements $\mathbf{v}^{(1)}, \mathbf{v}^{(2)}, \cdots, \mathbf{v}^{(n)}$ is isomorphic to the (real or complex respectively) vector space of all n-tuples by the natural mapping* *that maps every linear combination of these elements on the sequence of its coefficients:*

$$\alpha_1 \mathbf{v}^{(1)} + \alpha_2 \mathbf{v}^{(2)} + \cdots + \alpha_n \mathbf{v}^{(n)} \to (\alpha_1, \alpha_2, \cdots, \alpha_n), \tag{5.17}$$

or (shorter)

$$\sum_{i=1}^{n} \alpha_i \mathbf{v}^{(i)} \to (\alpha_i)_{1 \le i \le n}.$$

PROOF: (5.17) certainly assigns to every *linear combination* an *n*-tuple, but that does not assure that it defines a *mapping*. That is, suppose that we had

$$\sum_{i=1}^{n} \alpha_i \mathbf{v}^{(i)} = \sum_{i=1}^{n} \beta_i \mathbf{v}^{(i)} \quad \text{with} \quad (\alpha_1, \alpha_2, \cdots, \alpha_n) \ne (\beta_1, \beta_2, \cdots, \beta_n) \tag{5.18}$$

then this element of $\mathbf{V}$, expressed as a linear combination of $(\mathbf{v}^{(i)})_{1 \le i \le n}$ *in two different ways*, would have as its "image" both $(\alpha_1, \alpha_2, \cdots, \alpha_n)$ and $(\beta_1, \beta_2, \cdots, \beta_n)$, which would contradict the definition of a mapping. But, if an equation (5.18) were true, then it would mean the same as the equation

$$\sum_{i=1}^{n} (\alpha_i - \beta_i) \mathbf{v}^{(i)} = 0 \quad \text{with} \quad (\alpha_1 - \beta_1, \alpha_2 - \beta_2, \cdots, \alpha_n - \beta_n)$$

$$\ne (0, 0, \cdots, 0).$$

Hence (5.18) would imply that a nontrivial linear combination of the $\mathbf{v}^{(i)}$ is equal to the zero vector. Since this is excluded by the hypothesis that the $\mathbf{v}^{(i)}$ are linearly independent, the situation (5.18) is impossible; therefore, (5.17) defines a mapping. That this mapping is a one-to-one correspondence is obvious by inspection; that it is linear is not hard to show.

Corollary 5.2: *For $i = 1, 2, 3$, $\mathbf{R}^i$ and R^i are isomorphic.*

PROOF: This is an immediate consequence of the last theorem, in view of the discussion of Example 5 of Linear Independence and Dependence.

These isomorphisms are the key to analytic geometry.

EXERCISES

1. Verify Examples 2, 3, and 6 of Vector Spaces and Subspaces.

*2. Let $R^\infty = \{a | a \ \varepsilon \ R^n, \ n \ \varepsilon \ I^+\}$ be the set of all finite sequences of real numbers of arbitrary length. Define addition of two *n*-tuples as before, and addition of an *n*-tuple $a = (a_1, a_2, \cdots, a_n)$ and an *m*-tuple $b = (b_1, b_2, \cdots, b_n, b_{n+1}, \cdots, b_m)$ for $m > n$ by

$$a + b = (a_1 + b_1, a_2 + b_2, \cdots, a_n + b_n, b_{n+1}, \cdots, b_m).$$

Define scalar multiplication as before. Prove that R^∞ becomes a real vector space (called the vector space of all *restricted real sequences*). Similarly, a vector space C^∞ can be defined.

*3. Let $\overline{R}^\infty$ be the set of all infinite sequences $(s_i)_{i\in I^+}$ of real numbers. Define addition and scalar multiplication as a natural extension of the definitions in the finite cases by $(s_i)_{i\in I^+} + (t_i)_{i\in I^+} = (s_i + t_i)_{i\in I^+}$ and $\alpha(s_i)_{i\in I^+} = (\alpha s_i)_{i\in I^+}$. Prove that $\overline{R}^\infty$ becomes a real vector space (called *the vector space of all unrestricted real sequences*). Similarly, a complex vector space $\overline{C}^\infty$ can be defined.

4. Verify Examples 7 and 8 of Vector Spaces and Subspaces.

5. Verify Examples 9 and 10 of Vector Spaces and Subspaces.

6. Let S be the set of all rotations of $\mathbf{R}^3$ about a given axis. Define addition of such rotations by composition of mappings, and scalar multiplication by a real number r by multiplication of the angle of rotation by r and reversal of the rotation direction if $r < 0$. Prove that S is *not* a vector space.

7. Let R^{+n} be the set of all n-tuples of positive real numbers. Then R^{+n} becomes an additive group if one defines

$$(r_1, r_2, \cdots, r_n) + (s_1, s_2, \cdots, s_n) = (r_1 s_1, r_2 s_2, \cdots, r_n s_n).$$

Define a multiplication for R^{+n} by a real scalar α by

$$\alpha(r_1, r_2, \cdots, r_n) = (e^{\alpha \log r_1}, e^{\alpha \log r_2}, \cdots, e^{\alpha \log r_n})$$

where $\log r_i$ stands for the principal value of the natural logarithm of r_i. Prove that, with these two composition laws, R^{+n} becomes a real vector space.

8. Why does R^{+n} not become a vector space if addition is defined as in the previous example but scalar multiplication is defined by $\alpha(r_1, r_2, \cdots, r_n) = (\alpha r_1, \alpha r_2, \cdots \alpha r_n)$?

9. Prove that the set of all (real) functions whose domain of definition is R and whose range is a subset of R becomes a real vector space if addition of two functions $f: x \to f(x)$ and $g: x \to g(x)$ is defined by $f + g: x \to f(x) + g(x)$ and multiplication by a real scalar α by $\alpha f: x \to \alpha f(x)$.

10. Verify that all elements of Example 5 of Spans satisfy equation (5.8).

11. Prove (5.9).

12. Give the proof of lemma 5.1 in more detail than is shown in the text and without the use of the summation sign.

13. Prove the third part of corollary 5.1.

14. Prove that the span of a set of vectors remains unaltered if one vector in this set is replaced by a nonzero multiple of this vector.

15. Let $S = \{u,v,w,\cdots\}$ be a set of vectors having at least two elements. If in S one vector, say, u, is replaced by $u + \alpha v$ (for any scalar α), the span remains unaltered.

16. Give an alternative proof of lemma 5.3.

17. Verify the statements in Examples 1 to 4 of Linear Independence and Dependence.

18. Prove that in $R^i(i = 1, 2, 3)$ any *linearly independent* set of i elements spans R^i.

19. Verify the statements in Examples 6, 7, 8 and (possibly) 9 of Linear Independence and Dependence.

20. Verify the statements in Examples 1 to 4 of Linear Mappings.

21. Prove that the mapping of R^n into R^n defined by

$$(a_1,a_2,\cdots,a_n) \rightarrow (a_1 + b_1, a_2 + b_2, \cdots, a_n + b_n)$$

is *not* linear unless $(b_1,b_2,\cdots,b_n) = (0,0,\cdots,0)$.

22. Prove that $(a_1,a_2,\cdots,a_n) \rightarrow$ (5.16) defines a linear mapping. *Hint*: Make use of (5.9) and (5.14).

23. Prove that the mapping (5.17) is linear.

24. Define a, b ε R^3 as in Example 3 of Spans. Prove that $[a]$ is isomorphic with R^1 and that $[a,b]$ is isomorphic with R^2. Why do we have isomorphy and not equality?

25. Prove that the composite of two linear mappings is also linear.

26. Prove (a) that the set of all images of a linearly independent set is also linearly independent if the mapping is an isomorphism, and (b) that the set of all homomorphic images of a linearly dependent set is linearly dependent.

27. Prove that the span of a linearly independent set of n vectors of a real vector space is isomorphic with the vector space R^n.

*28. Prove that there exists a natural one-to-one homomorphism of R^∞ (exercise 2) into $\overline{R^\infty}$ (exercise 3).

*29. Prove that R^∞ (exercise 2) is isomorphic with $R[x]$.

30. In what sense is theorem 5.1 better than definition 5.1 in reference to subspaces.

31. Let V and W be vector spaces over the same set of scalars, and let $\text{Hom}(V,W)$ be the set of all homomorphisms of V into W. Define a *sum* $M + N$ of two homomorphisms M and N of $\text{Hom}(V,W)$ by $M + N: v \rightarrow M(v) + N(v)$ [that is, apart from notation, by *operator addition*]. Define an external *product* αM of a scalar α and an endomorphism M by $\alpha M: v \rightarrow \alpha(M(v))$. Prove: (1) $M + N$ ε $\text{Hom}(V,W)$, (2) αM ε $\text{Hom}(V,W)$, (3) $\text{Hom}(V,W)$ is a *vector space* with respect to this addition and scalar multiplication.

Comment: Of considerable importance in somewhat more advanced geometry and algebra are the special cases **Hom**($\mathbf{V}, R$) for real **V** and **Hom**($\mathbf{V}, C$) for complex **V** [where R or C is regarded as a vector space over itself]. Such a vector space is called the *dual* of **V** and denoted by **V***. Its elements are called *linear forms* or *linear functionals*.

6

The Idea of Analytic Geometry

This section will discuss the fundamental one-to-one correspondences between geometric and algebraic objects on which analytic geometry is based. They will make it possible to solve geometric problems by algebraic methods and to translate algebraic questions into geometric language. Three different cases are to be distinguished: geometry on a line, on a plane, and on the whole space, and, corresponding to them, the algebra of numbers, of couples of numbers, and of triples of numbers. For a unified treatment the following terminology is introduced.

Definition 6.1: For $n = 1, 2, 3$ the *geometric* space $\mathfrak{R}^n$, the *vector* space $\mathbf{R}^n$, and the *vector* space R^n are called an n-dimensional *point space*, *translation space*, and *coordinate space*, respectively.

Note: A point space is just a *set*, whereas translation and coordinate spaces are *real vector spaces*, that is, sets in which addition and multiplication by *real* scalars are defined.

Definition 6.2: If O is a given point of $\mathfrak{R}^n (n = 1, 2, 3)$ then the translation $\overrightarrow{OP}$ from O to some point P ($\varepsilon \, \mathfrak{R}^n$) is called *the position vector of P (with respect to O)* and is denoted by $\mathbf{p}$. The point O is called *the origin* or *the coordinate system for the mapping* $P \to \mathbf{p}$.

Definition 6.3: If $(\mathbf{b}^{(i)})_{1 \leq i \leq n}$ is a sequence of n ($= 1, 2, 3$) *linearly independent* translations of $\mathbf{R}^n$, then the real n-tuple $(p_i)_{1 \leq i \leq n}$ is called the *coordinate vector* of the translation $\mathbf{p} = p_1 \mathbf{b}^{(1)} + \cdots + p_n \mathbf{b}^n$ [*with respect to* $(\mathbf{b}^{(i)})_{1 \leq i \leq n}$] and denoted by p. The sequence $(\mathbf{b}^{(i)})_{1 \leq i \leq n}$ is called the *basis* (or *base*) or *the coordinate system for the mapping* $\mathbf{p} \to$ p, and the translation $\mathbf{b}^{(i)}$ $(1 \le i \le n)$ is called the *ith base translation*.

Definition 6.4: If O is a given point of $\Re^n$ ($n = 1, 2, 3$) and if $(\mathbf{b}^{(i)})_{1 \le i \le n}$ is a given sequence of n linearly independent translations of $\Re^n$, then the real n-tuple $p = (p_i)_{1 \le i \le n}$ is called the *coordinate vector* of the point P if $\overrightarrow{OP} = p_1\mathbf{b}^{(1)} + \cdots + p_n\mathbf{b}^{(n)}$. The set consisting of the point O and the sequence $(\mathbf{b}^{(i)})_{1 \le i \le n}$ is called the *coordinate system for the mapping* $P \to p$. The line through O and $\mathbf{b}^{(i)}(O)$ is called *the ith coordinate axis*. For $n = 3$, the planes defined by two coordinate axes are called *coordinate planes*. The point $\mathbf{b}^{(i)}(O)$ is called the *ith base point*.

These definitions describe and introduce notations for the three mappings indicated in Fig. 6.1. Since all three mappings are *one-to-one onto*, the

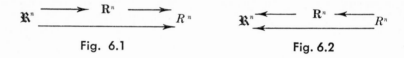

Fig. 6.1   Fig. 6.2

rules $\mathbf{p} \to P$, $p \to \mathbf{p}$, $p \to P$ likewise define mappings, which are the opposites of the preceding mappings and are indicated in Fig. 6.2. In this way points and translations can be represented (isomorphically) by sequences of numbers, and *vice versa*. Though it is an abuse of mathematical language, it is quite customary to speak of *the point* $(p_i)_{1 \le i \le n}$ or of *the translation* $(p_i)_{1 \le i \le n}$ when one really means the point or the translation *with coordinate vector* $(p_i)_{1 \le i \le n}$.

In accordance with these definitions we shall usually make the following conventions in analytic geometry: If a coordinate system is given, then *CAPITAL ITALIC TYPE*, **lower-case bold face type** and *lower-case italic type* of the same letter of the alphabet are chosen to stand respectively for the *POINT*, the **translation**, and the *n-tuple* related by these mappings. This includes the case where superscripts are added to the letter; and, for points and translations *but not for n-tuples*, it also includes the case where suffixes (subscripts) are attached. *A lower-case italic letter with a suffix will stand for a coordinate of the n-tuple that is denoted by the same letter without a suffix.* The i-th coordinate of the n-tuple $r^{(i)}$, or the ith coordinate corresponding to the translations $\mathbf{r}^{(i)}$ or $\mathbf{r}_i$ or to the points $R^{(i)}$ or R_i will always be denoted by r_{ij}. Thus, if two suffixes are chosen, the second distinguishes among different sequences and the first indicates which coordinate is to be considered. Lower-case Greek letters will represent real numbers (but real numbers are often denoted in other ways as well). Capital letters will also be employed to denote double sequences of numbers (that is, sequences of n-tuples of numbers).

The following relationships among points, translations, and their coordinate vectors make the six one-to-one correspondences of Figs. 6.1 and 6.2 extremely useful in analytic geometry.

Theorem 6.1:   *The point* $t(P)$ *has the coordinate vector* $t + p$. *The translation* $\overrightarrow{QP}$ *has the coordinate vector* $p - q$. *The translation* $\mathbf{p} + \mathbf{q}$ *has the coordinate vector* $p + q$. *The translation* $\alpha\mathbf{p}$ *has the coordinate vector* αp.

PROOF: The last two statements follow immediately from theorem 5.2. Turning to the first proposition, we have $\mathbf{t} = \overrightarrow{Pt(P)}$ and, hence, $\overrightarrow{Ot(P)} = \overrightarrow{OP} + \overrightarrow{Pt(P)} = \mathbf{p} + \mathbf{t}$ (see Fig. 6.3). Hence the coordinate vector of the point $t(P)$, which is equal to the coordinate vector of the translation $\mathbf{p} + \mathbf{t}$, is $p + t$, by the third proposition. The second proposition is true because $\overrightarrow{QP} = \overrightarrow{QO} + \overrightarrow{OP} = \overrightarrow{OP} - \overrightarrow{OQ}$ (since the translations form a group) $= \mathbf{p} - \mathbf{q}$ (see Fig. 6.4), and, by the isomorphism of theorem 5.2, the coordinate vector of this translation is $p - q$.

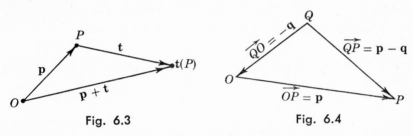

Fig. 6.3   Fig. 6.4

Corollary 6.1: $\overrightarrow{QP} = \mathbf{p} - \mathbf{q}$.

EXAMPLE OF COMPUTATION OF COORDINATE VECTORS

Suppose that an origin and a sequence of base vectors have been chosen in the three-dimensional case. Then the image of the point $(2,3,5)$ under the translation $(-1,2,2)$ is the point $(1,5,7)$. The translation that maps the point $(2,1,-1)$ on the point $(4,6,8)$ has the coordinate vector $(2,5,9)$. The translation $(9,3,1)$ is the sum of the translations $(3,1,-1)$ and $(6,2,2)$. The multiple of the translation $(3,4,5)$ by the scalar 3 is the translation $(9,12,15)$.

As the position and coordinate vectors depend very much on the coordinate system selected, there arises immediately the question of how these vectors are affected if the coordinate system is changed. If *two* coordinate systems are given, we shall, for verbal convenience, call one the *old* system and the other the *new* system. These changes may then be described as follows.

Theorem 6.2:   *If a new origin Q is introduced, then the position vector*

$\overrightarrow{QP}$ of a point P *relative to the new coordinate system is equal to* $\mathbf{p} - \mathbf{q}$. *If only the origin is changed and the sequence of the base translations is left unaltered, then* P *has the new coordinate vector* $p - q$.

PROOF: This is a restatement of the second part of theorem 6.1.

Note: Since the origin is not used to define the mapping $\mathbf{p} \to p$, a change in the origin has *no effect* on the coordinate vectors *of translations*.

Since $-\mathbf{q} = -\overrightarrow{OQ} = \overrightarrow{QO}$ equals the *new* position vector $\mathbf{0}_{new}$ of the *old* origin, theorem 6.2 can also be expressed (the notation is self-explanatory) in the form:

$$p_{new} = \mathbf{0}_{new} + p_{old}. \tag{6.1}$$

The effect that a change in the base translations has on coordinate vectors is more difficult to explain. A very convenient description can be given after the multiplication of matrices has been introduced (Chapter 12). At this stage we make only the following statements.

Theorem 6.3:   *If a new sequence* $(\mathbf{c}^{(i)})_{1 \le i \le n}$ *of base translations is introduced, then the coordinate vector of a translation* $\mathbf{p}$ *(or, if the origin is left unaltered, also of a point P) relative to the new coordinate system is obtained from the old one by a linear mapping. If the new coordinate vector of the old ith base translation is* $b_{new}^{(i)} = (b_{1i}, \cdots, b_{ni})$ $(i = 1, \cdots, n)$ *then the new coordinate vector of* $\mathbf{p}$ *(or of P) is*

$$\left(\sum_{j=1}^{n} b_{ij} p_j \right)_{1 \le i \le n}. \tag{6.2}$$

Note: This means explicitly, for $n = 2$,

$$(b_{11}p_1 + b_{12}p_2, \; b_{21}p_1 + b_{22}p_2) \tag{6.3}$$

and, for $n = 3$,

$$b_{11}p_1 + b_{12}p_2 + b_{13}p_3, \; b_{21}p_1 + b_{22}p_2 + b_{23}p_3, \; b_{31}p_1 + b_{32}p_2 + b_{33}p_3). \tag{6.4}$$

Thus, if the new base translations are given, then the new coordinates $p_i^{new}(i = 1, \cdots, n)$ of a translation (or point) are obtained as *fixed* linear combinations of the old coordinates. If the sequence *of n-tuples* $(b_{new}^{(i)})$ is abbreviated B_{new} and interpreted as a left operator inducing the mapping $p_{old} \to p_{new}$, then we can write, in formal analogy to (6.1),

$$p_{new} = B_{new} p_{old}. \tag{6.5}$$

Later, a generalization of a similar formula will define the concept of matrix multiplication.

PROOF OF THEOREM 6.3 FOR THE TWO-DIMENSIONAL CASE: 1. The rule $p_{old} \to \mathbf{p}$ defines a mapping φ, which is linear (corollary 5.2). Likewise, the mapping $\chi : \mathbf{p} \rightarrow p_{\text{new}}$ is linear. Hence, their composite mapping $\chi \circ \varphi : p_{\text{old}} \rightarrow p_{\text{new}}$ is linear, too. 2. The equations $b_{\text{new}}^{(i)} = (b_{1i}, b_{2i})$ for $i = 1, 2$ show that

$$\chi(\mathbf{b}^{(1)}) = (b_{11}, b_{21}) \quad \text{and} \quad \chi(\mathbf{b}^{(2)}) = (b_{12}, b_{22}).$$

Since χ is linear, equation (5.15) can be applied to the linear combination $p_1\mathbf{b}^{(1)} + p_2\mathbf{b}^{(2)}$. Then we have

$$(\chi \circ \varphi)(p_{\text{old}}) = \chi(\mathbf{p}) = \chi(p_1\mathbf{b}^{(1)} + p_2\mathbf{b}^{(2)}) = p_1\chi(\mathbf{b}^{(1)}) + p_2\chi(\mathbf{b}^{(2)})$$

$$= p_1(b_{11}, b_{21}) + p_2(b_{12}, b_{22}) = (b_{11}p_1 + b_{12}p_2, b_{21}p_1 + b_{22}p_2).$$

This completes the proof.

The double sequence (b_{ii}) is not quite arbitrary. As isomorphic images of the linearly independent $\mathbf{b}^{(i)}$, the n-tuples $b_{\text{new}}^{(i)}$ must, like the $\mathbf{b}^{(i)}$, be *linearly independent*. By Examples 8 and 9 of Linear Independence (Chapter 5), this means that the determinant

$$\begin{vmatrix} b_{11} & \cdots & b_{n1} \\ \vdots & & \vdots \\ b_{1n} & & b_{nn} \end{vmatrix}$$

(see Chapter 17) must be different from zero.

EXAMPLE OF CHANGE OF BASE TRANSLATIONS

Suppose an origin and a sequence of base translations $(\mathbf{b}^{(1)}, \mathbf{b}^{(2)}, \mathbf{b}^{(3)})$ have been chosen in the three-dimensional case. If new base vectors are introduced and if the old base vectors have the new coordinates $(1,2,3)$, $(2,1,0)$, $(1,0,2)$, respectively, then that translation (or point) whose old coordinates were $(2,4,6)$ has as a new coordinate vector $(1 \cdot 2 + 2 \cdot 4 + 1 \cdot 6, 2 \cdot 2 + 1 \cdot 4 + 0 \cdot 6, 3 \cdot 2 + 0 \cdot 4 + 2 \cdot 6) = (16, 8, 18)$.

Another important question is how to choose a coordinate system as conveniently as possible to attack a given problem. In the case of a graphic representation of sets of real couples or triples, the following system is chosen whenever feasible.

Definition 6.5: If the base translations of a coordinate system are perpendicular in pairs, then the coordinate system and also the coordinates with respect to it are called *rectangular*. If, in addition, the base translations have length 1, then both are called *Cartesian*†.

The Cartesian coordinates $(p_1, \cdots, p_n)$ of a point P can be determined very easily. In the two-dimensional situation, $|p_1|$ and $|p_2|$ are equal to

† After *René Descartes*

the distance of P from the second and first coordinate axes, respectively, and the sign of the coordinates is determined by the quadrant of Fig. 6.5 in which the point P lies. In the three-dimensional case, $|p_i|$ is equal to the distance of P from the plane determined by the jth and kth coordinate axes, where $j \neq k$, $i \neq j$, $i \neq k$, and the signs of the coordinates determine in which octant of Fig. 6.6 the point P lies.

If the orders of magnitude of the Cartesian coordinates of the points considered are very different—for example, if $p_1 = 10^{10}$ and $p_2 = 0.0000001$— then the base translations are chosen of different length, but still perpendicular in pairs. Then the coordinates of a point are still related to the distances described above, except that they have to be measured *in units of the respective base translations* and not in absolute units, as is usual in geometry.

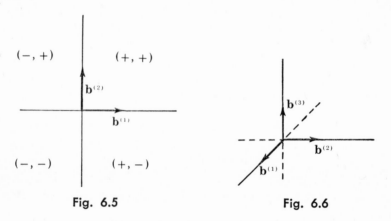

Fig. 6.5   Fig. 6.6

Cartesian and rectangular coordinate systems are very useful in the study of the behavior of functions and solutions of equations. For certain representative point sets the following terminology is customary.

Definition 6.6:   If f is a function of a variable x or of two variables x, y, then the set of all points with Cartesian or rectangular coordinates $(x,f(x))$ or $(x,y,f(x,y))$ is called *the graph of* f. The set of all points whose Cartesian coordinates are solutions of an equation or a system of equations is called *the graph of the equation* or *of the system of equations*. A two-dimensional graph of a function $x \to f(x)$ [or of an equation $g(x,y) = 0$] is called *symmetric with respect to the first coordinate axis* if it is equal to the graph of $x \to -f(x)$ [or $g(x,-y) = 0$], *symmetric with respect to the second coordinate axis* if it is equal to the graph of $x \to f(-x)$ [or $g(-x,y) = 0$], and *symmetric with respect to the origin* if it is equal to the graph of $x \to -f(-x)$ [or $g(-x,-y) = 0$]. For three-dimensional graphs, symmetries with respect to coordinate planes and with respect to the origin are similarly defined.

Note: In this definition our conventions about the use of letters are *temporarily* broken, because in calculus one usually writes $y = f(x)$ or $z = f(x,y)$ instead of $x_2 = f(x_1)$ or $x_3 = f(x_1,x_2)$, respectively.

EXAMPLES OF GRAPHS OF FUNCTIONS AND EQUATIONS

1. *The graph of any linear function* $x \to ax + b$ $(a,b \varepsilon R)$ *is a straight line.* Let x^1, x^2, x^3 be three different real numbers, and let P^i $(i = 1, 2, 3)$ be the point with coordinates $(x^i, ax^i + b)$ (see Fig. 6.7). Then the translations $\overrightarrow{P^1P^2}$ and $\overrightarrow{P^2P^3}$ have the coordinates $(x^2-x^1, a(x^2-x^1))$ and $(x^3-x^2, a(x^3-x^2))$, respectively. Hence,

$$(x^2 - x^1, a(x^2 - x^1)) = \frac{x^2 - x^1}{x^3 - x^2}(x^3 - x^2, a(x^3 - x^2)),$$

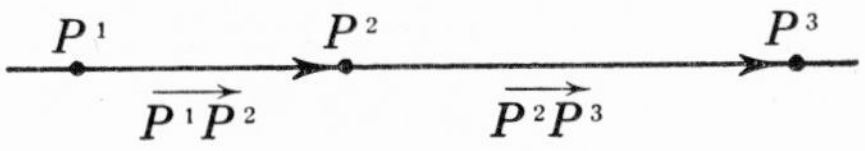

Fig. 6.7

which by the last part of theorem 6.1 means that $\overrightarrow{P^1P^2}$ is a multiple of $\overrightarrow{P^2P^3}$, and therefore any such three points lie on a line. This proof shows that the proposition remains true if the coordinate system (as defined in this text) is not rectangular.

2. *The graph of any linear equation* $\alpha x + \beta y + \gamma = 0$ $(\alpha,\beta,\gamma \varepsilon R)$ *in two unknowns is a straight line.* If $\beta \neq 0$, then, for every real x, the couple $(x, -\alpha x/\beta - \gamma/\beta)$ is a solution of the equation, and all solutions take this form. The substitution $-\alpha/\beta = a$, $-\gamma/\beta = b$ transforms this problem into the previous problem; hence, we obtain a straight line. If $\beta = 0$, then $\alpha \neq 0$ (because otherwise we would not have a *linear* equation); hence, for every real y, the couple $(-\gamma/\alpha, y)$ is a solution of this equation, and all solutions of it take this form. Now take three different real numbers y^1, y^2, y^3, and define three points P^i $(i = 1, 2, 3)$ by the coordinates $(-\gamma/\alpha, y^i)$. Then $\overrightarrow{P^1P^2}$ has the coordinates $(0, y^2-y^1)$, and $\overrightarrow{P^1P^3}$ has the coordinates $(0, y^3-y^1)$. Since the two couples are obviously multiples of each other, the three points lie on one line by the same reasoning as in the previous example. This line is the graph of the equation. Again the proposition remains true if the coordinate system is not rectangular.

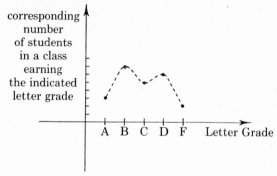

Fig. 6.8

3. The graph of a linear function of two variables is a plane, and so is that of a linear equation in three variables.

4. In the case of *empirical* functions $x \rightarrow f(x)$ whose function values are obtained by *observation*, one has only finitely many couples $(x, f(x))$. Nevertheless, the corresponding points are usually connected by some "approximating" curve whose intermediate points may or may not have any connection with the function. Thus, if a teacher has given three A's, seven B's, five C's, six D's, and two F's in a class, then this fact can be represented by the "interpolated" graph shown in Fig. 6.8. In this case the intermediate points of the curve have no meaning. But if the temperature at some place is measured hourly for a day and a graph is drawn (Fig. 6.9), then one may assume that the intermediate points of the curve give approximations of the temperature during that day at times other than the full hours.

5. If a Cartesian coordinate system is chosen, then the graph of the equation $x^2 + y^2 = 1$ is a *circle of radius* 1 about the origin (but for a non-Cartesian coordinate system it is an *ellipse*). This follows from the Pythagorean theorem. The graph is symmetric with respect to every coordinate axis and the origin. Similarly, the graph of the equation $x^2 + y^2 + z^2 = 4$ is a *sphere* of radius 2 about the origin. It is symmetric with respect to every coordinate axis and the origin.

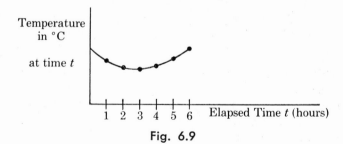

Fig. 6.9

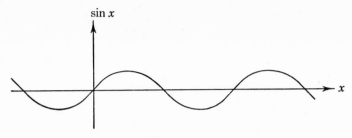

Fig. 6.10

6. The graph of the function $x \to \sin x$ (with respect to a Cartesian co-ordinate system) is the well-known sine curve sketched in Fig. 6.10. It is symmetric with respect to the origin.

7. The graph of the equation $x_1^2 + x_2^2 = -1$ is *empty*.

Some investigations are not concerned with a single graph, but with a *set* of graphs. Since graphs are geometric representations of functions or equations, which may be interpreted as elements of a vector space, it is occasionally of interest to learn how the graphs of *linear combinations* of functions or equations look. This leads to the following concepts.

Definition 6.7:   If $\mathfrak{S}$ is a set of functions $\{f_i\}_{1 \le i \le n}$ or a set of equations $\{f_i = 0\}_{1 \le i \le n}$, then the set of the graphs of all nonzero linear combinations

of $\mathfrak{S}$ is called *the span of graphs of* $\mathfrak{S}$, or, for $n = 2$, *the pencil of graphs of* $\mathfrak{S}$.

Note: A span of graphs is a set *of sets of points.*

EXAMPLES OF SPANS OF GRAPHS

1. The pencil of graphs of the set $\alpha_1 x + \beta_1 y + \gamma_1 = 0$, $\alpha_2 x + \beta_2 y + \gamma_2 = 0$ [$\alpha_i, \beta_i, \gamma_i \ \varepsilon \ R$ and $(\alpha_i, \beta_i) \ne (0,0)$] is a set of lines. It is easy to see that this set consists of sets of lines, as follows:

   a. If the two equations have exactly one common solution p, then the pencil consists of all lines passing through the point P with co-ordinates p.

   b. If the two equations do not have a common solution, then the pencil consists of all lines parallel to the graphs of these equations.

   c. If the left-hand sides of the two equations are linearly dependent, then the pencil consists of the graph of either equation.

2. If $\alpha_i x + \beta_i y + \gamma_i = 0$ $(i = 1,2,3)$ are three equations with linearly independent left-hand sides, then the span of graphs of these equations consists of all lines in $\mathfrak{R}^2$.

3. The pencil of graphs of $\{x^2 + y^2 - 1 = 0, \ x^2 + y^2 - 2 = 0\}$ consists of the graphs of all equations of the form $x^2 + y^2 - \alpha = 0$. For $\alpha > 0$, this is the set of all circles about the origin (see Fig. 6.11). For $\alpha = 0$, this is the origin itself only. For $\alpha < 0$, this is the empty graph.

In this text we shall discuss mainly the graphs of linear and quadratic functions and equations. To sketch the graphs of other algebraic and transcendental functions and equations, we refer the student to a textbook on calculus, because the methods developed there will be more satisfactory for a complete description of the curves and surfaces obtained as graphs.

Although it is evident that a Cartesian or rectangular coordinate system is convenient for the construction of graphs, it is not necessarily so advantageous for the algebraic investigation of geometric situations. In general geometric problems, involving only questions about whether

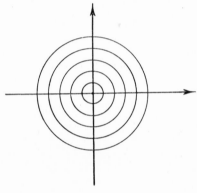

Fig. 6.11

given points lie on given lines and planes, or comparing distances along the same line, the coordinate vectors are not needed at all; position vectors and translations are sufficient. Even in geometric problems involving angular measurements and computation of absolute distances, the translation spaces should be used as long as possible; only at the end of the computation should a coordinate system be introduced, and it should then be so chosen as to make the remaining calculations as simple as possible. This suggested heavy reliance on position vectors not only reduces numerical computations to a minimum; it also provides better insight into geometric relationships. Coordinates are *artificial* and *auxiliary* tools for dealing with geometric problems; many problems are handled more naturally by using the *intrinsic* properties of geometric objects. A coordinate-free treatment is superior as well as more fruitful in the long run. Accordingly, this text is written with the intention of conditioning the student to coordinate-free thinking.

EXERCISES

1. Let $\mathbf{b}^{(1)}$, $\mathbf{b}^{(2)}$ be an old basis and $\mathbf{c}^{(1)}$, $\mathbf{c}^{(2)}$ a new basis. Find the new coordinates $(p_1^{\text{new}}, p_2^{\text{new}})$ of a point P if its old coordinates are (p_1, p_2) and the old and new bases are related by the equations:
   (a) $\mathbf{c}^{(1)} = \mathbf{b}^{(1)}$, $\mathbf{c}^{(2)} = -\mathbf{b}^{(2)}$;
   (b) $\mathbf{c}^{(1)} = \mathbf{b}^{(1)} + \mathbf{b}^{(2)}$, $\mathbf{c}^{(2)} = \mathbf{b}^{(1)} - \mathbf{b}^{(2)}$;
   (c) $\mathbf{c}^{(1)} = \mathbf{b}^{(2)}$, $\mathbf{c}^{(2)} = \mathbf{b}^{(1)}$;
   (d) $\mathbf{c}^{(1)} = \mathbf{b}^{(1)}$, $\mathbf{c}^{(2)} = \mathbf{b}^{(1)} + 2\mathbf{b}^{(2)}$.

2. Let $\mathbf{b}^{(1)}, \mathbf{b}^{(2)}, \mathbf{b}^{(3)}$ be an old basis and $\mathbf{c}^{(1)}, \mathbf{c}^{(2)}, \mathbf{c}^{(3)}$ a new basis. Find the new coordinates $(p_1^{\text{new}}, p_2^{\text{new}}, p_3^{\text{new}})$ of a point P if its old coordinates are $(p_1^{\text{old}}, p_2^{\text{old}}, p_3^{\text{old}})$ and if the old and new bases are related by the equations:
   (a) $\mathbf{c}^{(1)} = \mathbf{b}^{(2)}$, $\mathbf{c}^{(2)} = \mathbf{b}^{(3)}$, $\mathbf{c}^{(3)} = \mathbf{b}^{(1)}$;
   (b) $\mathbf{c}^{(1)} = -\mathbf{b}^{(1)}$, $\mathbf{c}^{(2)} = -\mathbf{b}^{(2)}$, $\mathbf{c}^{(3)} = -\mathbf{b}^{(3)}$;
   (c) $\mathbf{c}^{(1)} = \mathbf{b}^{(3)}$, $\mathbf{c}^{(2)} = \mathbf{b}^{(3)} + \mathbf{b}^{(2)}$, $\mathbf{c}^{(3)} = \mathbf{b}^{(3)} + 2\mathbf{b}^{(2)} + 3\mathbf{b}^{(1)}$;
   (d) $\mathbf{c}^{(1)} = \mathbf{b}^{(2)} + \mathbf{b}^{(3)}$, $\mathbf{c}^{(2)} = \mathbf{b}^{(1)} + \mathbf{b}^{(3)}$, $\mathbf{c}^{(3)} = \mathbf{b}^{(1)} + \mathbf{b}^{(2)}$.

3. Express $\mathbf{c}^{(1)}$ and $\mathbf{c}^{(2)}$ in terms of $\mathbf{b}^{(1)}$ and $\mathbf{b}^{(2)}$ if the following relations hold:
   (a) $\mathbf{b}^{(1)} = \mathbf{c}^{(1)} + \mathbf{c}^{(2)}$, $\mathbf{b}^{(2)} = \mathbf{c}^{(1)} - \mathbf{c}^{(2)}$;
   (b) $\mathbf{b}^{(1)} = 2\mathbf{c}^{(1)} + 3\mathbf{c}^{(2)}$, $\mathbf{b}^{(2)} = \mathbf{c}^{(1)} - 2\mathbf{c}^{(2)}$.

4. Express $\mathbf{c}^{(i)}$ ($i = 1, 2, 3$) in terms of $\mathbf{b}^{(i)}$ if the following equations hold:
   (a) $\mathbf{b}^{(1)} = \mathbf{c}^{(2)} + \mathbf{c}^{(3)}$, $\mathbf{b}^{(2)} = \mathbf{c}^{(1)} + \mathbf{c}^{(3)}$, $\mathbf{b}^{(3)} = \mathbf{c}^{(1)} + \mathbf{c}^{(2)}$;
   (b) $\mathbf{b}^{(1)} = \mathbf{c}^{(1)} + 2\mathbf{c}^{(2)} + 3\mathbf{c}^{(3)}$, $\mathbf{b}^{(2)} = -\mathbf{c}^{(1)} - \mathbf{c}^{(2)} + \mathbf{c}^{(3)}$, $\mathbf{b}^{(3)} = \mathbf{c}^{(1)} + 3\mathbf{c}^{(2)} - \mathbf{c}^{(3)}$.

5. Let $\mathbf{b}^{(1)}, \mathbf{b}^{(2)}$ be an old basis and $\mathbf{c}^{(1)}, \mathbf{c}^{(2)}$ a new basis. Find the new coordinates of a point if its old coordinates are (p_1, p_2, p_3) and if the old and new bases are related by the equations:
   (a) $\mathbf{b}^{(1)} = -\mathbf{c}^{(1)}$, $\mathbf{b}^{(2)} = \mathbf{c}^{(1)} - \mathbf{c}^{(2)}$;
   (b) $\mathbf{b}^{(1)} = \mathbf{c}^{(1)} + 2\mathbf{c}^{(2)}$, $\mathbf{b}^{(2)} = -\mathbf{c}^{(1)} + \mathbf{c}^{(2)}$;
   (c) $\mathbf{b}^{(1)} = \mathbf{c}^{(1)} + \mathbf{c}^{(2)}$, $\mathbf{b}^{(2)} = \mathbf{c}^{(1)} - \mathbf{c}^{(2)}$;
   (d) $\mathbf{b}^{(1)} = -\mathbf{c}^{(1)} - \mathbf{c}^{(2)}$, $\mathbf{b}^{(2)} = \mathbf{c}^{(1)} + 3\mathbf{c}^{(2)}$.
   Warning: The structure of this problem is not exactly the same as that of exercise 1.

6. Let $(\mathbf{b}^{(i)})_{1 \leq i \leq 3}$ be an old basis and $(\mathbf{c}^{(i)})_{1 \leq i \leq 3}$ a new one. If the old coordinates of a translation $\mathbf{t}$ are (t_1, t_2, t_3), what are its new ones if the two bases are related by the equations:
   (a) $\mathbf{b}^{(1)} = \mathbf{c}^{(1)}$, $\mathbf{b}^{(2)} = \mathbf{c}^{(1)} + \mathbf{c}^{(2)}$, $\mathbf{b}^{(3)} = \mathbf{c}^{(1)} + \mathbf{c}^{(2)} + \mathbf{c}^{(3)}$;
   (b) $\mathbf{b}^{(1)} = 2\mathbf{c}^{(1)}$, $\mathbf{b}^{(2)} = \mathbf{c}^{(1)} - \mathbf{c}^{(2)}$, $\mathbf{b}^{(3)} = \mathbf{c}^{(3)} - \mathbf{c}^{(1)}$?

7. Prove theorem 6.3 for the three-dimensional case.

8. In the two-dimensional case, let the old coordinates of the new

base translations be $(2,3)$, $(1,-1)$. In the three-dimensional case let the old coordinates of the new base translations be $(0,1,1)$, $(1,0,1)$, $(1,1,0)$. What are the new coordinates of the old base translations in the two cases?

9. Give a formula that expresses the new coordinates of the old base translations in terms of the old coordinates of the new base translations in the two- and three-dimensional cases.

10. Let (o_1,o_2) be the old coordinates of the new origin, and let (r_{11},r_{21}), (r_{12},r_{22}) be the old coordinates of the new base translations. What are the new coordinates of the point with old coordinates (p_1,p_2)? *Warning*: Formula (6.3) should be used with care.

11. Extend the previous exercise to the three-dimensional case.

12. Prove that the graph of a linear function of two variables is a plane. *Hint*: Call one point of the graph the *origin*, and consider position vectors of every point of this graph with respect to this origin. Show that two linearly independent position vectors can be found such that every position vector of a point of the graph is a linear combination of the two.

13. Sketch the graphs of the equations $x + y = 0$, $3x + 4y = 5$, $x^2 + y^2 = 9$, and $xy = 1$,
    (a) If a Cartesian coordinate system is chosen;
    (b) If a rectangular coordinate system is chosen such that the second base translation has four times the length of the first base translation;
    (c) If (*in a natural generalization of the concept of a graph*) a non-rectangular coordinate system is chosen where the two base translations have equal length.

14. Prove that the graph of the equation $x/\rho + y/\sigma = 1$, $\rho \neq 0$, $\sigma \neq 0$, passes through the two points with position vectors $\rho\mathbf{b}^{(1)}$ and $\sigma\mathbf{b}^{(2)}$ (see Fig. 6.12). These are the two points where the line defined by the equation "intercepts" the two coordinate axes.

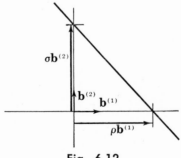

Fig. 6.12

15. Prove: The graph of the equation

$$\frac{x}{\rho} + \frac{y}{\sigma} + \frac{z}{\tau} = 1, \qquad \rho \neq 0, \quad \sigma \neq 0, \quad \tau \neq 0,$$

is the plane that passes through the three points with position vectors $\rho\mathbf{b}^{(1)}$, $\sigma\mathbf{b}^{(2)}$, $\tau\mathbf{b}^{(3)}$ (see Fig. 6.13).

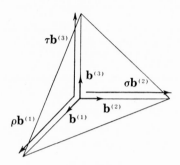

Fig. 6.13

16. Prove: If a Cartesian coordinate system is chosen, then the graph of the equation $y = ax + b$ is a line, and a is equal to the tangent of the angle α $(0 \leq \alpha < \pi)$ between the first coordinate axis and that line (Fig. 6.14).

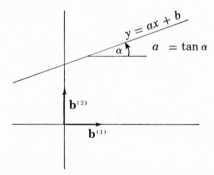

Fig. 6.14

17. If x^*, x^{**}, y^*, and y^{**} are real numbers, then the equation

$$\frac{x - x^*}{x^{**} - x^*} = \frac{y - y^*}{y^{**} - y^*},$$

if it is defined, has as its graph, the line through the points with coordinates (x^*, y^*) and (x^{**}, y^{**}) (Fig. 6.15).

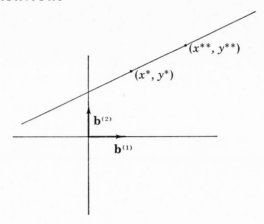

Fig. 6.15

18. Prove that, if a Cartesian coordinate system is chosen, the graph of the equation $x^2 + y^2 + z^2 = 1$ is a sphere about the origin with radius 1.

19. Define symmetry for three-dimensional graphs with respect to a coordinate plane and with respect to the origin.

20. When is the graph of $\alpha x + \beta y + \gamma = 0$ symmetric with respect to a coordinate axis or to the origin?

21. What symmetries do the graphs of the cosine, tangent, and exponential function have?

22. A solution x^* of an inequality $\sum_{i=1}^{n} a_i x_i \leq b$ is an n-tuple of (real or complex) numbers such that, by the substitution $x = x^*$, one obtains the numerical inequality demanded. Prove: (a) The graph of a linear inequality $ax + by + c \leq 0$ is a half-plane bounded by the line $ax + by + c = 0$; (b) The graph of a linear inequality $ax + by + cz + d \leq 0$ is a half-space bounded by the plane $ax + by + cz + d = 0$.

7

Lines and Planes

In this chapter we shall discuss the point sets that belong to a line, considered as a subset of $\mathfrak{R}^3$ or $\mathfrak{R}^2$, or to a plane, considered as a subset of $\mathfrak{R}^3$. Because every point in question now belongs to two point spaces simultaneously, the notion of the *position vector* becomes ambiguous. However, if O and P are both elements of the point spaces $\mathfrak{R}^i$ and $\mathfrak{R}^j$ ($i < j$) of different dimensions, then the translation $\overrightarrow{OP}$ ε $\mathbf{R}^i$ is obviously the *restriction* of the translation $\overrightarrow{OP}$ ε $\mathbf{R}^i$ *to* $\mathfrak{R}^i$; and, conversely, $\overrightarrow{OP}$ ε $\mathbf{R}^i$ is *the unique extension* of $\overrightarrow{OP}$ ε $\mathbf{R}^i$ *to* $\mathfrak{R}^j$, by theorem 3.1. Because of this simple relationship, we shall regard any translation that occurs as an element of the translation space of *larger* dimension, but omit the reference to it. If necessary, a translation may also be considered an element of the translation space of *lower* dimension. The restriction of a translation $\mathbf{u}$ of $\mathbf{R}^j$ to $\mathfrak{R}^i$ may assign to every element of $\mathfrak{R}^i$ *either* an element not belonging to $\mathfrak{R}^i$ (see Fig. 7.1) *or* an element of $\mathfrak{R}^i$. Only in the second case is the restriction a *translation* of $\mathfrak{R}^i$. If this happens, we will simply say that $\mathbf{u}$ "is" a translation of $\mathfrak{R}^i$ when we really mean that *its restriction to* $\mathfrak{R}^i$ is a translation of $\mathfrak{R}^i$.

Let us consider a line $\mathfrak{L}$ *as part of* $\mathfrak{R}^i$ ($i = 2, 3$), and choose for $\mathfrak{L}$ an origin Q and a base translation $\mathbf{b}$. Then the position vector of every point X of $\mathfrak{L}$ can be written in the form $\overrightarrow{QX} = \xi\mathbf{b}$, and every translation $\xi\mathbf{b}$ is the position vector of a point of $\mathfrak{L}$. But suppose that an origin O has been chosen in $\mathfrak{R}^i$ that is not an element of $\mathfrak{L}$ (Fig. 7.2). Then the position vector of X relative to the origin O is given by $\overrightarrow{OX} = \overrightarrow{OQ} +$

$\overrightarrow{QX} = \overrightarrow{OQ} + \xi\mathbf{b}$. Thus, by applying the conventions of the previous section to the coordinate system of $\mathfrak{R}^i$ with origin O, one obtains the following theorem.

Theorem 7.1:   *If Q is a point on a line $\mathfrak{L}$ of $\mathfrak{R}^i$ and $\mathbf{b}$ is a translation of $\mathfrak{L}$, then all points of $\mathfrak{L}$ and only those points have position vectors of the form*

$$\mathbf{x} = \mathbf{q} + \xi\mathbf{b}, \tag{7.1}$$

where ξ is a real scalar.

If a basis is introduced for $\mathbf{R}^i$, then (7.1) implies the equation

$$x = q + \xi b$$

for the coordinate vectors of X, Q, and of (the extension to $\mathfrak{R}^i$ of) $\mathbf{b}$. This establishes a relationship between the line coordinate ξ of X in $\mathfrak{L}$ and the coordinates $x = (x_1, \cdots, x_i)$ of X in $\mathfrak{R}^i$.

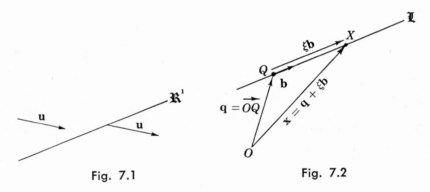

Fig. 7.1   Fig. 7.2

Note: Formula (7.1) can be memorized easily as follows: To reach a point on a line, one may first go *to* the line (that is, apply $\mathbf{q}$) and then walk *along* the line a certain distance (that is, apply $\xi\mathbf{b}$).

Corollary 7.1:   *If P and Q are distinct points on a line $\mathfrak{L}$ of $\mathfrak{R}^i$, then all points X of $\mathfrak{L}$ and only the points of $\mathfrak{L}$ have position vectors of the form*

$$\mathbf{x} = \mathbf{q} + \xi(\mathbf{p} - \mathbf{q}), \tag{7.2}$$

where ξ is a real scalar.

PROOF: If $P \neq Q$, then $\overrightarrow{QP} = \mathbf{p} - \mathbf{q}$ ($\neq 0$) can be taken as a base translation in $\mathfrak{L}$ (Fig. 7.3).

Corollary 7.2:   *If P and Q are distinct points, then all points on the line through P and Q and only the points on this line have position vectors of the form*

$$\xi\mathbf{p} + \eta\mathbf{q} \;\; \textit{with} \;\; \xi + \eta = 1. \tag{7.3}$$

PROOF: If $\xi + \eta = 1$, then

$$\xi\mathbf{p} + \eta\mathbf{q} = \mathbf{q} + \xi(\mathbf{p} - \mathbf{q}).$$

Corollary 7.3: *Three distinct points P, Q, R are collinear if and only if there exist three nonzero scalars α, β, γ with $\alpha + \beta + \gamma = 0$ such that*

$$\alpha\mathbf{p} + \beta\mathbf{q} + \gamma\mathbf{r} = \mathbf{0}. \tag{7.4}$$

PROOF: If the three points lie on a line then $1\mathbf{r} - \xi\mathbf{p} - \eta\mathbf{q} = \mathbf{0}$ with $\xi + \eta = 1$, that is, $1 - \xi - \eta = 0$, by the previous corollary. If $\xi = 0$ then $\eta = 1$ and hence $\mathbf{r} = \mathbf{q}$ contrary to the distinctness of the three

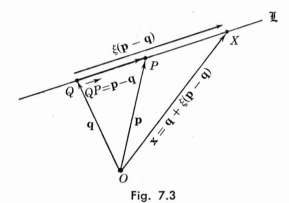

Fig. 7.3

points. Therefore, we have $\xi \neq 0$, and for a similar reason $\eta \neq 0$. If the conditions of the present corollary hold, then

$$\mathbf{r} = -\frac{\alpha}{\gamma}\mathbf{p} - \frac{\beta}{\gamma}\mathbf{q} \;\; \text{with} \;\; -\frac{\alpha}{\gamma} - \frac{\beta}{\gamma} = 1$$

because $\alpha + \beta + \gamma = 0$; hence, R lies on the line through P and Q.

We conclude the discussion of lines with the introduction of the following useful concept.

Definition 7.1: If P, Q, R are collinear points and if $P \neq Q$, then the real number ρ is called *the division ratio of R with respect to PQ* if $\overrightarrow{PR} = \rho\overrightarrow{RQ}$. If $\rho = 1$, then R is called *the midpoint of PQ*. R is also said *to divide PQ in the ratio ρ.*

$\overrightarrow{PR} = \rho\overrightarrow{RQ}$ is equivalent to $(\mathbf{r} - \mathbf{p}) = \rho(\mathbf{q} - \mathbf{r})$. If this is considered to be an equation for $\mathbf{r}$ and $\rho \neq -1$ then its solution obviously is

$$\mathbf{r} = \frac{1}{1 + \rho}(\mathbf{p} + \rho\mathbf{q}). \tag{7.5}$$

Hence, (7.5) gives the position vector of the point with the given division ratio $\rho \neq -1$ with respect to a given line segment PQ. In particular, the position vector of the midpoint of PQ is $\frac{1}{2}\,(\mathbf{p} + \mathbf{q})$.

EXAMPLES OF DIVISION RATIO

The division ratio of P with respect to PQ (see Fig. 7.4) is 0; the division ratio of Q with respect to PQ does not exist ("is equal to ∞"); and the division ratios of all other points on the line segment PQ are positive

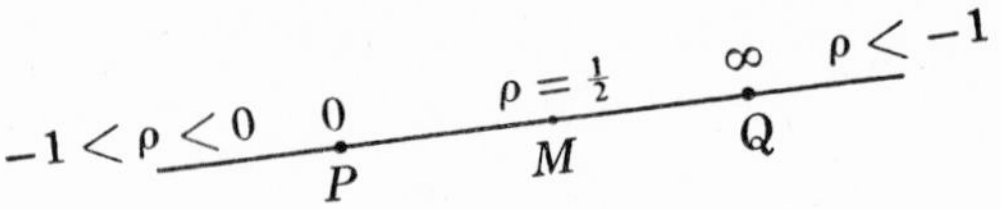

Fig. 7.4

real numbers, the larger the nearer they are to Q. If R does not belong to the line segment PQ, then the direction of PR is opposite to that of RQ; hence, in this case ρ must be negative. If $\rho < -1$, then Q lies between R and P; if $-1 < \rho < 0$, then P lies between Q and R. For negative ρ, the equality $|PR| = |RQ|$ cannot occur.

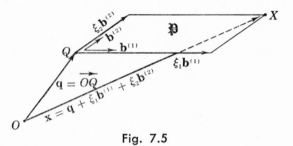

Fig. 7.5

Next let us consider a plane $\mathfrak{P}$ *as part of* $\mathfrak{R}^3$, and choose for $\mathfrak{P}$ an origin Q and base translations $\mathbf{b}^{(1)}$, $\mathbf{b}^{(2)}$. Then the position vector of every point X of $\mathfrak{P}$ can be written in the form $\overrightarrow{QX} = \xi_1\mathbf{b}^{(1)} + \xi_2\mathbf{b}^{(2)}$, and every translation $\xi_1\mathbf{b}^{(1)} + \xi_2\mathbf{b}^{(2)}$ is the position vector of a point of $\mathfrak{P}$. But suppose that in $\mathfrak{R}^3$ an origin O has been chosen that is not an element of $\mathfrak{P}$ (Fig. 7.5). Then the position vector of X relative to the origin O is given by $\overrightarrow{OX} = \overrightarrow{OQ} + \overrightarrow{QX} = \overrightarrow{OQ} + \xi_1\mathbf{b}^{(1)} + \xi_2\mathbf{b}^{(2)}$. Thus, by applying the conventions of the previous section to the coordinate system of $\mathfrak{R}^3$ with origin O, we obtain the following theorem.

Theorem 7.2:   *If Q is a point on a plane $\mathfrak{P}$ and if $\mathbf{b}^{(1)}$, $\mathbf{b}^{(2)}$ are two linearly independent translations of $\mathfrak{P}$, then all points X of $\mathfrak{P}$ and only those points have position vectors of the form*

$$x = q + \xi_1 b^{(1)} + \xi_2 b^{(2)},\tag{7.6}$$

where ξ_1 and ξ_2 are real scalars.

If a basis is introduced for $\mathbf{R}^3$, then (7.6) implies the equation

$$x = q + \xi_1 b^{(1)} + \xi_2 b^{(2)}$$

for the coordinate vectors of X and Q and of (the extension to $\mathfrak{R}^3$ of) $\mathbf{b}^{(1)}$ and $\mathbf{b}^{(2)}$. This establishes a relationship between the *plane* coordinates (ξ_1, ξ_2) of X in $\mathfrak{P}$ and the *space* coordinates $x = (x_1, x_2, x_3)$ of X in $\mathfrak{R}^3$.

Note: Formula (7.6) can be memorized easily as follows: To reach a point on a plane, one may first go *to* the plane (that is, apply $\mathbf{q}$) and then walk *along* two principal directions (which should not be opposites) certain distances (that is, apply $\xi_1 \mathbf{b}^{(1)}$ and $\xi_2 \mathbf{b}^{(2)}$).

Corollary 7.4: *If P, Q, and R are noncollinear points on a plane $\mathfrak{P}$, then all points X of $\mathfrak{P}$ and only the points of $\mathfrak{P}$ have position vectors of the form*

$$\mathbf{x} = \mathbf{q} + \xi_1(\mathbf{p} - \mathbf{q}) + \xi_2(\mathbf{r} - \mathbf{q}),\tag{7.7}$$

where ξ_1 and ξ_2 are real scalars.

PROOF: (see Fig. 7.6): If P, Q, and R are distinct and noncollinear, then $\overrightarrow{QP} = \mathbf{p} - \mathbf{q}$ and $\overrightarrow{QR} = \mathbf{r} - \mathbf{q}$ are linearly independent and so can be taken as base translations.

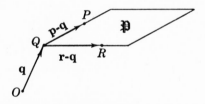

Fig. 7.6

Similarly, as in the case of lines, the following further corollaries can easily be proved.

Corollary 7.5: *If P, Q, and R are not collinear, then all points of the plane through these points and only the points on this plane have position vectors of the form*

$$\alpha \mathbf{p} + \beta \mathbf{q} + \gamma \mathbf{r} \text{ with } \alpha + \beta + \gamma = 1.\tag{7.8}$$

Corollary 7.6: *Four points P, Q, R, and S, of which no three are collinear, are coplanar if and only if there exist four nonzero scalars α, β, γ, δ with $\alpha + \beta + \gamma + \delta = 0$ such that $\alpha \mathbf{p} + \beta \mathbf{q} + \gamma \mathbf{r} + \delta \mathbf{s} = 0$.*

In this way lines and planes can be represented by equations in the position vectors or coordinate vectors of their points with the help of the additional variables ξ or ξ_1, ξ_2. To distinguish these representations from those in which no auxiliary variables are needed, the following terminology is customary.

Definition 7.2:   Equations (7.1), (7.2), (7.6), (7.7), and the corresponding equations in the coordinate vectors are called *parametric equations*, and the quantities ξ or ξ_1, ξ_2 are called *parameters*.

Although this constitutes an abuse of mathematical language, it is quite customary to speak of the line $\mathbf{x} = \mathbf{q} + \xi\mathbf{b}$ or of the plane $\mathbf{x} = \mathbf{q} + \xi_1\mathbf{b}^{(1)} + \xi_2\mathbf{b}^{(2)}$ when one really means the line or the plane whose position vectors satisfy the equation in question.

The parametric equations for lines and planes make it very easy to decide what points two lines, a line and a plane, or two planes have in common. The following three theorems give the complete answer to these questions.

Theorem 7.3:   *The lines* $\mathbf{x} = \mathbf{p} + \rho\mathbf{a}$ *and* $\mathbf{x} = \mathbf{q} + \sigma\mathbf{b}$ *have at least one point in common if and only if* $\mathbf{p} - \mathbf{q}\ \varepsilon\ [\mathbf{a},\mathbf{b}]$, *and at most one point in common if* $\mathbf{a}$ *and* $\mathbf{b}$ *are linearly independent.*

PROOF: The lines have at least one point in common if and only if there exist real numbers ρ^* and σ^* such that

$$\mathbf{p} + \rho^*\mathbf{a} = \mathbf{q} + \sigma^*\mathbf{b}, \tag{7.9}$$

that is,

$$\mathbf{p} - \mathbf{q}\ \varepsilon\ [\mathbf{a}, \mathbf{b}].$$

The solution (ρ^*,σ^*) of the vector equation is unique if $\mathbf{a}$ and $\mathbf{b}$ are linearly independent.

Note: Theorem 7.3 covers simultaneously the cases where the two lines are considered part of a plane and where they are considered part of the whole space. In the case of two-dimensional geometry, the linear independence of $\{\mathbf{a},\mathbf{b}\}$ implies always that $\mathbf{p} - \mathbf{q}\ \varepsilon\ [\mathbf{a},\mathbf{b}]$; that is, that there exists a unique point of intersection of the lines. In the three-dimensional case, the condition $\mathbf{p} - \mathbf{q}\ \varepsilon\ [\mathbf{a},\mathbf{b}]$ for a linearly independent set $\{\mathbf{a},\mathbf{b}\}$ is needed to exclude the possibility that the lines are skew.

In a similar way it can be shown that the following theorems hold.

Theorem 7.4:   *The plane* $\mathbf{x} = \mathbf{p} + \xi\mathbf{a} + \eta\mathbf{b}$ *and the line* $\mathbf{x} = \mathbf{q} + \zeta\mathbf{c}$ *have at least one point in common if and only if* $\mathbf{p} - \mathbf{q}\ \varepsilon\ [\mathbf{a},\mathbf{b},\mathbf{c}]$ *and have at most one point in common if* $\{\mathbf{a},\mathbf{b},\mathbf{c}\}$ *is linearly independent.*

Theorem 7.5:   *The planes* $\mathbf{x} = \mathbf{p} + \alpha\mathbf{a} + \beta\mathbf{b}$ *and* $\mathbf{x} = \mathbf{q} + \gamma\mathbf{c} + \delta\mathbf{d}$

have at least a line in common if and only if $\mathbf{p} - \mathbf{q} \; \varepsilon \; [a,b,c,d]$ *and have at most one line in common if* $[a,b] \neq [a,b,c,d]$.

APPLICATIONS TO ELEMENTARY GEOMETRY

Theorem 7.6: *The three medians of a triangle pass through a common point, which divides them in the ratio* 2:1.

PROOF (see Fig. 7.7): Let O, A, and B be the vertices of the triangle. Then, by corollary 7.1, the three medians satisfy, in turn, the equations

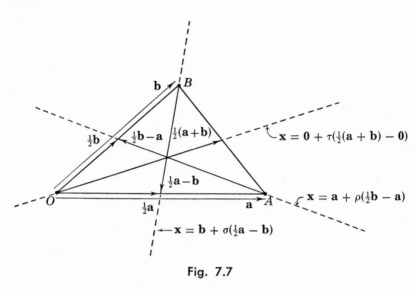

Fig. 7.7

$$\mathbf{x} = \mathbf{a} + \rho(\tfrac{1}{2}\mathbf{b} - \mathbf{a}),$$
$$\mathbf{x} = \mathbf{b} + \sigma(\tfrac{1}{2}\mathbf{a} - \mathbf{b}),$$
$$\mathbf{x} = \mathbf{0} + \tau(\tfrac{1}{2}(\mathbf{a} + \mathbf{b}) - \mathbf{0}).$$

By equating the first two of these equations, we see whether the first two medians have a point in common, and find such a point. We obtain

$$\mathbf{a} + \rho(\tfrac{1}{2}\mathbf{b} - \mathbf{a}) = \mathbf{b} + \sigma(\tfrac{1}{2}\mathbf{a} - \mathbf{b}),$$

which can be written in the form

$$(1 - \tfrac{1}{2}\sigma - \rho)\mathbf{a} - (1 - \tfrac{1}{2}\rho - \sigma)\mathbf{b} = \mathbf{0}$$

As $\mathbf{a}$ and $\mathbf{b}$ are linearly independent (otherwise we would not have a proper triangle), all the coefficients of this equation must vanish:

$$1 - \tfrac{1}{2}\sigma - \rho = 0, \quad \text{or} \quad \sigma + 2\rho = 2;$$

$$1 - \tfrac{1}{2}\sigma - \rho = 0, \quad \text{or} \quad \rho + 2\sigma = 2.$$

These two equations in the unknowns ρ and σ can be solved easily in any high-school manner. We obtain $(\tfrac{2}{3}, \tfrac{2}{3})$ as the *unique solution*. By substituting $\tfrac{2}{3}$ for ρ in the parametric equation for the first median, we obtain

$$\tfrac{1}{3}(\mathbf{a} + \mathbf{b}) \tag{7.10}$$

as the point of intersection of the first two medians. But, if we substitute $\tau = \tfrac{2}{3}$ in the parametric equation of the third median, we likewise obtain (7.10). Consequently, all three lines pass through the point (7.10). From definition 7.1 we see that this point divides the medians in the ratio

$$\frac{2/3}{1 - 2/3} = \frac{2}{1}.$$

This proof makes use of the linear independence of the translations $\mathbf{a}$ and $\mathbf{b}$ to find ordinary equations for the parameters. It is neither the shortest nor the most elegant proof for the theorem of medians, but it is straightforward. The more experienced a student is in constructing proofs involving position vectors, the more easily he will be able to give shorter alternative proofs of the same theorem. The following is an example.

ALTERNATIVE PROOF (Fig. 7.8): Let A, B, C be the three points. Then, by corollary 7.1, the equations of the medians are (with respect to *any* origin):

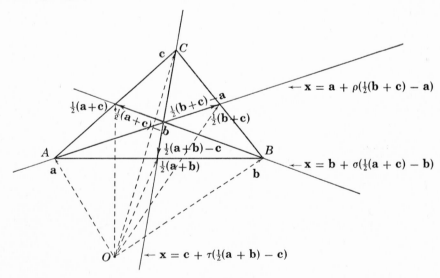

Fig. 7.8

$$x = a + \rho(\tfrac{1}{2}(b + c) - a) = (1 - \rho)a + \frac{\rho}{2}b + \frac{\rho}{2}c,$$

$$x = b + \sigma(\tfrac{1}{2}(a + c) - b) = \frac{\sigma}{2}a + (1 - \sigma)b + \frac{\sigma}{2}c,$$

$$x = c + \tau(\tfrac{1}{2}(a + b) - c) = \frac{\tau}{2}a + \frac{\tau}{2}b + (1 - \tau)c.$$

By inspection it can be seen that all three expressions are equal if $\rho = \sigma = \tau$ and if $1 - \rho = \rho/2$. The latter equation is satisfied for $2/3$; hence, the medians meet at $1/3(a+b+c)$. The division ratio follows in the same manner as before.

Theorem 7.7: (*Theorem of Ceva†*): *Let A, B, C, D be four coplanar points, no three of which are collinear. Suppose that the lines through DA and BC, through DB and CA, and through DC and AB, respectively, intersect and that their points of intersection are A', B', C', respectively. The product of the division ratios of A', B', C' with respect to BC, CA, and AB, respectively, is 1 (Fig. 7.9).*

PROOF: By corollary 7.6 there must exist four nonzero scalars α, β, γ, δ such that the position vectors of A, B, C, D must satisfy

$$\alpha a + \beta b + \gamma c + \delta d = 0 \text{ with } \alpha + \beta + \gamma + \delta = 0 \cdot \qquad (7.11)$$

If $\alpha + \beta = 0$, then $\gamma + \delta = 0$ also; in this case, (7.11) would imply

$$\alpha(a-b) + \gamma(c-d) = 0,$$

which is impossible, because the lines through BA and CD cannot be parallel, but intersect. Hence $\alpha + \beta = -\gamma - \delta \neq 0$, and, for a similar reason, $\alpha + \gamma = -\beta - \delta \neq 0$ and $\beta + \gamma = -\alpha - \delta \neq 0$.

By multiplication with $1/(\alpha + \beta) = 1/(-\gamma - \delta)$ (which exists, because $\alpha + \beta \neq 0$), we obtain from (7.11)

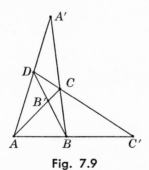

Fig. 7.9

† After the Italian mathematician *Giovanni Ceva* (1648–1734).

$$\frac{\alpha}{\alpha + \beta}\mathbf{a} + \frac{\beta}{\alpha + \beta}\mathbf{b} = \frac{\gamma}{\gamma + \delta}\mathbf{c} + \frac{\delta}{\gamma + \delta}\mathbf{d}.$$

By corollary 7.2, the point with this position vector lies on both the lines through AB and through CD, hence must be equal to C'. By exercise 7.4, the division ratio of C' with respect to $\overrightarrow{AB}$ is β/α.

Similarly it can be shown that the division ratios of B' with respect to $\overrightarrow{CA}$ and of A' with respect to BC are α/γ and γ/β, respectively. Hence their product is equal to 1.

Theorem 7.8:   (*Desargues' Theorem†*):   *Let ABC and $A'B'C'$ be two triangles such that $A \neq A'$, $B \neq B'$, $C \neq C'$, and let the lines through AA', through BB', and through CC' pass through a common point O. If each of the pairs of lines through AB and $A'B'$, through BC and $B'C'$, and through CA and $C'A'$ intersect, then the three points of intersection P, Q, R are collinear* (Fig. 7.10).

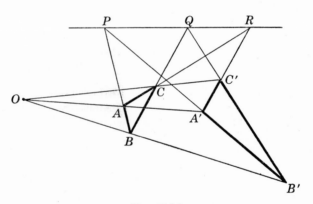

Fig. 7.10

PROOF: Let O be the origin. Then we have

$$\alpha\mathbf{a} + \alpha'\mathbf{a}' = \beta\mathbf{b} + \beta'\mathbf{b}' = \gamma\mathbf{c} + \gamma'\mathbf{c}' = \mathbf{0}$$

with

$$\alpha + \alpha' = \beta + \beta' = \gamma + \gamma' = 1$$

by corollary 7.2. By subtraction it follows that

$$\alpha\mathbf{a} - \beta\mathbf{b} = -\alpha'\mathbf{a}' + \beta'\mathbf{b}' \quad \text{with} \quad \alpha - \beta = \beta' - \alpha'. \tag{7.12}$$

If $\alpha = \beta$, then $\alpha' = \beta'$ also, and (7.12) would reduce to

$$\alpha(\mathbf{a} - \mathbf{b}) = -\alpha'(\mathbf{a}' - \mathbf{b}') \quad \text{or} \quad \alpha(\overrightarrow{BA}) = -\alpha'(\overrightarrow{B'A'})$$

† After the French mathematician *Girard Desargues* (1591–1661).

which is impossible, because the lines through AB and through $A'B'$ are not parallel by hypothesis. Hence $\alpha \neq \beta$. Similarly it can be shown that $\alpha \neq \gamma$ and $\beta \neq \gamma$.

By corollary 7.2, the position vector $\mathbf{p}$ of the point of intersection P of the lines through AB and through $A'B'$ must be *simultaneously* a linear combination of $\{\mathbf{a},\mathbf{b}\}$ and of $\{\mathbf{a'},\mathbf{b'}\}$ *with sum of coefficients equal to 1 in both cases*. But multiplication of (7.12) by $1/(\alpha - \beta) = 1/(\beta' - \alpha')$, which exists because $\alpha - \beta \neq 0$, gives

$$\frac{\alpha}{\alpha - \beta}\,\mathbf{a} - \frac{\beta}{\alpha - \beta}\,\mathbf{b} = \frac{-\alpha'}{\beta' - \alpha'}\,\mathbf{a'} + \frac{\beta'}{\beta' - \alpha'}\,\mathbf{b'}$$

that is, linear combinations of the kinds required; hence

$$\mathbf{p} = \frac{\alpha}{\alpha - \beta}\,\mathbf{a} - \frac{\beta}{\alpha - \beta}\,\mathbf{b}.$$

Similarly, one obtains

$$\mathbf{q} = \frac{\beta}{\beta - \gamma}\,\mathbf{b} - \frac{\gamma}{\beta - \gamma}\,\mathbf{c}$$

$$\mathbf{r} = \frac{\gamma}{\gamma - \alpha}\,\mathbf{c} - \frac{\alpha}{\gamma - \alpha}\,\mathbf{a}$$

as the position vectors of the other two points of intersection Q and R. But from the three equations for $\mathbf{p}$, $\mathbf{q}$, $\mathbf{r}$ it follows immediately that

$$(\alpha - \beta)\mathbf{p} + (\beta - \gamma)\mathbf{q} + (\gamma - \alpha)\mathbf{r} = \mathbf{0}.$$

Since in this equation the sum of coefficients is obviously equal to zero and since, because α, β, γ are distinct, every coefficient is different from zero, P, Q, and R are collinear, by corollary 7.3.

Note: The triangles ABC and $A'B'C'$ need not lie in the same plane. The proof is valid in $\mathfrak{R}^2$ as well as in $\mathfrak{R}^3$.

EXERCISES

1. If Q is a point with coordinates $(2,2,1)$ on a line $\mathfrak{L}$ and $\mathbf{b}$ is a translation on this line with coordinates $(3,1,2)$ (with respect to the same basis), what are the coordinates of an arbitrary point of $\mathfrak{L}$?

2. If P and Q are points with coordinates $(1,2,4)$ and $(3,2,1)$, respectively, what are the coordinates of any point on the line through P and Q?

3. Prove that (7.3) is the position vector of a point on the line segment PQ if and only if both ξ, $\eta \leq 1$.

4. Prove that (7.3) is the position vector of the point that divides PQ in the ratio η/ξ if $\xi \neq 0$.

5. Let P, Q, R be three points forming a proper triangle, and let $\mathfrak{T}^2$ be the set of all points of this closed triangle. Prove: Every $\alpha\mathbf{p} + \beta\mathbf{q} + \gamma\mathbf{r}$ with $\alpha + \beta + \gamma = 1$ and $\alpha, \beta, \gamma \geq 0$ is the position vector of a point of $\mathfrak{T}^2$; and the position vector of every point of $\mathfrak{T}^2$ can be written in this form.

6. Let P, Q, R, S be four noncoplanar points, and let $\mathfrak{T}^3$ be the set of all points of the (solid) tetrahedron $PQRS$. Prove: Every $\alpha\mathbf{p} + \beta\mathbf{q} + \gamma\mathbf{r} + \delta\mathbf{s}$ with $\alpha + \beta + \gamma + \delta = 1$ and $\alpha, \beta, \gamma, \delta \geq 0$ is the position vector of a point of $\mathfrak{T}^3$; and the position vector of every point of $\mathfrak{T}^3$ can be written in this form.

*7. Let $P^{(1)}$, $P^{(2)}$, $\cdots$, $P^{(m)}$ be the vertices of a convex polygon (or polyhedron) [see Chapter 10]. Prove: Every

$$\alpha_1\mathbf{p}^{(1)} + \alpha_2\mathbf{p}^{(2)} + \cdots \alpha_m\mathbf{p}^{(m)} \quad \text{with} \quad \sum_{v=1}^{m} \alpha_v = 1 \quad \text{and all} \quad \alpha_v \geq 0$$

is the position vector of a point of this polygon (polyhedron); and the position vector of every point of this polygon (polyhedron) can be written in this form.

8. Let $P^{(1)}$, $P^{(2)}$, $\cdots$, $P^{(m)}$ ($m > 1$) be distinct points. Prove: The set of all points whose position vectors have the form

$$\alpha_1\mathbf{p}^{(1)} + \alpha_2\mathbf{p}^{(2)} + \cdots + \alpha_m\mathbf{p}^{(m)} \quad \text{with} \quad \sum_{v=1}^{m} \alpha_v = 1 \quad \text{and all} \quad \alpha_v \geq 0$$

is a line segment (if the points are collinear) or a polygon (if the points are not collinear, but coplanar) or a polyhedron. Describe how to construct the possible point sets of this kind geometrically.

9. Prove equation (7.5).

10. Sketch the points on the line through two distinct points P and Q that divide the line segment PQ in the ratio 1, 2, $\frac{1}{2}$, $\frac{1}{3}$, $\frac{1}{4}$, $-\frac{1}{2}$, -2, $-\frac{1}{3}$, -3, respectively.

11. Prove corollaries 7.5 and 7.6.

12. Discuss all possible cases of theorem 7.3 *in detail*.

13. Let $\mathfrak{L}_1$ and $\mathfrak{L}_2$ be two lines in $\mathfrak{R}^2$ as in theorem 7.3 having precisely one point in common. Determine its coordinate vector *explicitly*.

14. Prove theorems 7.4 and 7.5.

15. Discuss all possible cases of theorems 7.4 and 7.5 *in detail*.

16. Define points A, B, C, D as in the theorem of Ceva. Prove that the sum of the division ratios of A', B', C' with respect to DA, DB, DC, respectively, is equal to -1.

17. Define points as in Desargues' theorem. Prove: If the lines through AB and $A'B'$ are parallel and if the lines through BC and $B'C'$ are likewise parallel then the lines through CA and $C'A'$ are also parallel.

18. Define points as in Desargues' theorem. Prove: If the lines through AB and $A'B'$ are parallel and if the lines through BC and $B'C'$ intersect in a point Q, then the lines through CA and $C'A'$ intersect in a point that lies on the line through Q parallel to AB.

19. Prove: The midpoints of the sides of a quadrilateral are vertices of a parallelogram (Fig. 7.11).

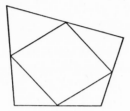

Fig. 7.11

20. Prove that the inner bisectors of the three angles of a triangle pass through a point.

Hint: Make use of the theorem that these bisectors divide the opposite sides in line segments whose lengths have the same ratio as that of the adjacent sides.

21. Let P_1, P_2, P_3 be three distinct points on a given line. Suppose that the division ratio of P_1 with respect to $P_2 P_3$ is ρ. Prove: If i, j, k ($i \neq j$, $i \neq k$, $j \neq k$) are the integers 1,2,3 in *any* order, then the division ratio of P_i with respect to $P_j P_k$ can only have the values

$$\rho, \quad \frac{1}{\rho}, \quad -1 - \rho, \quad \frac{1}{-1 - \rho}, \quad \frac{\rho}{-1 - \rho}, \quad \frac{-1 - \rho}{\rho}$$

(if defined).

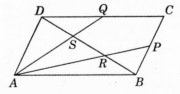

Fig. 7.12

22. Let $ABCD$ be a parallelogram, and let P, Q be the midpoints of BC and CD, respectively. Let R be the point of intersection of the diagonal through BD and the line through AP, and let S be the point of intersection of this diagonal and the line through AQ (see Fig. 7.12). Prove: $|BR| = |RS| = |SR|$.

Linear Geometry and Algebra

Part II will investigate geometric and algebraic concepts and properties connected with linear polynomials and linear equations. The number n of variables or unknowns is left unspecified, not only to obtain a unified treatment but also to cover higher-dimensional situations. Although, for $n > 3$, a direct representation of algebraic results is not possible in point and translation spaces of our perception, geometric ideas are generalized to these cases. The abstract geometric language introduced also will permit an interpretation of many higher-dimensional results or certain features of them in $\Re^3$.

8

Linear Systems

As the student may remember from high school or college algebra, there are various methods of solving systems of linear equations. Some techniques are particularly suited for special situations; others may work satisfactorily anywhere. The method that will be developed and analyzed in this chapter is not always the shortest to use, but it requires relatively little technical skill.

Every system of linear equations will be so written that on the right-hand sides there will be only zeros:

$$a_{11}x_1 + a_{12}x_2 + \cdots + a_{1n}x_n + b_1 = 0$$
$$a_{21}x_1 + a_{22}x_2 + \cdots + a_{2n}x_n + b_2 = 0 \qquad (8.1)$$
$$\cdots\cdots\cdots\cdots\cdots\cdots\cdots\cdots\cdots\cdots\cdots\cdots$$
$$a_{m1}x_1 + a_{m2}x_2 + \cdots + a_{mn}x_n + b_m = 0,$$

or, abbreviated,

$$\sum_{j=1}^{n} a_{ij}x_j + b_i = 0 \quad \text{for} \quad i = 1, 2, \cdots, m. \qquad (8.2)$$

The number n of unknowns does not need to be equal to the number m of equations. The suffixes of the a_{ij}'s are chosen so that the first suffix i indicates the ith equation and the second suffix j indicates that the element is the coefficient of the jth unknown. The a_{ij}'s and the b_i's are assumed to be all real (or all complex) numbers.

Instead of working with equations (8.1) or (8.2), it is often advisable
to use only the *system of linear polynomials*, abbreviated f_i or $f_i(x)$ or
$f_i(x_1, x_2, \cdots, x_n)$, on the left-hand sides of these equations:

$$f_1 = a_{11}x_1 + a_{12}x_2 + \cdots + a_{1n}x_n + b_1$$

$$f_2 = a_{21}x_1 + a_{22}x_2 + \cdots + a_{2n}x_n + b_2$$

$$\cdots\cdots\cdots\cdots\cdots\cdots\cdots\cdots\cdots\cdots\cdots\cdots\cdots \qquad (8.3)$$

$$f_m = a_{m1}x_1 + a_{m2}x_2 + \cdots + a_{mn}x_n + b_n,$$

or (shorter),

$$f_i = \sum_{j=1}^{n} a_{ij}x_j + b_i \quad \text{for} \quad i = 1, 2, \cdots, m. \qquad (8.4)$$

A solution $(x_1, x_2, \cdots, x_n) = x$ of (8.1) or (8.2) is, then, an n-tuple
for which $f_i(x_1, x_2, \cdots, x_n) = 0$ for $i = 1, 2, \cdots, m$; that is (in the language
of calculus), for which the polynomial $f_i(x)$ vanishes. This is a special
case of the following much more general situation.

Definition 8.1:   An n-tuple $x^* = (x_1^*, x_2^*, \cdots, x_n^*)$ of real (or complex)
numbers is called a *zero of a function f* in n variables (or *of a set S of functions*)
if the f-image of x^* (for every $f \varepsilon S$) vanishes.

Thus to be a *zero* of the function $f(x_1, x_2, \cdots x_n)$ in n *variables* $x_1, x_2, \cdots, x_n$
is the same as to be a *solution* of the equation $f(x_1, x_2, \cdots, x_n) = 0$ in n
unknowns $x_1, x_2, \cdots, x_n$.

Note: A function that maps every n-tuple whatsoever on the same
number b—in the language of the calculus, "a constant"—has either
every n-tuple as a zero, if $b = 0$, or *no* n-tuple as a zero, if $b \neq 0$. This
fact will be needed, because a polynomial $a_1x_1 + a_2x_2 + \cdots + a_nx_n + b$
collapses to the constant polynomial b if $a_1 = a_2 = \cdots = a_n = 0$.

Lemma 8.1:   *A joint zero x^* of two functions $f(x)$ and $g(x)$ is also a
zero of $\alpha f(x) + \beta g(x)$ for every $\alpha, \beta \varepsilon R$ (or C).*

PROOF: If $f(x^*) = 0$ and $g(x^*) = 0$, then obviously $\alpha f(x^*) + \beta g(x^*) = 0$, also.

The corresponding proposition for equations is : If x^* is a solution
of two equations, then it is also a solution of every equation obtained
from these two by multiplication by a number and subsequent addition.
Similarly, *every* theorem about zeros of functions can be translated into
a theorem about solutions of equations, and *vice versa*. But we shall prefer
the language of polynomials and their zeros for solving linear equations,
because this language is better suited to the application of the ideas
and theorems of vector spaces.

Definition 8.2: If x_j appears with the coefficient *zero* in $f_i + \alpha f_k$, then the replacement of f_i by the linear combination $f_i + \alpha f_k (k \neq i,$ $\alpha \; \varepsilon \; R$ (or C)), is called the *elimination of x_j in the ith polynomial by means of the kth polynomial.* The multiplication of f_i by the real (or complex) number α is called *the normalization of f_i with respect to x_j* if the coefficient of x_j in αf_i is equal to 1. The renumbering of two x_j (as well as their coefficients) in *all* polynomials of a system, or the renumbering of two polynomials are called *exchanges* of the involved x_j or f_i, respectively. These names are also used for the corresponding processes in systems of equations.

EXAMPLES OF ELIMINATION, NORMALIZATION, AND EXCHANGES

1. To *eliminate* x_2 in the polynomial

$$f = 3x_1 + 2x_2 + 6x_3 - 4x_4$$

by means of the polynomial

$$g = 2x_1 + 3x_2 - 2x_3 + x_4$$

multiply g by $-\dfrac{2}{3}$ and add $-\dfrac{2}{3} g$ to f:

$$f - \frac{2}{3} g = \frac{5}{3} x_1 + 0x_2 + \frac{22}{3} x_3 - \frac{14}{3} x_4.$$

2. To *normalize*

$$f = 2x_1 - 3x_2 + 4x_4$$

with respect to x_2, multiply f by $-\dfrac{1}{3}$:

$$-\frac{1}{3} f = -\frac{2}{3} x_1 + x_2 - \frac{4}{3} x_4.$$

Note: Normalization of f with respect to x_3 is *not possible.*

3. To *exchange* x_2 and x_5 in the polynomial

$$f = 2x_1 - 3x_2 + 2x_3 - x_4 + 6x_5,$$

interchange the suffixes 2 and 5 and reorder; the result is

$$2x_1 + 6x_2 + 2x_3 - x_4 - 3x_5.$$

4. To *exchange* f_1 and f_3 in the system

$$2x_1 - 4x_2 + 3x_3 - x_4$$

$$x_1 + x_2 - 2x_3 + x_4$$

$$8x_1 - 7x_2 + x_3 + x_4,$$

rewrite this system in the following order:

$$8x_1 - 7x_2 + x_3 + x_4$$
$$x_1 + x_2 - 2x_3 + x_4$$
$$2x_1 - 4x_2 + 3x_3 - x_4.$$

Lemma 8.2:   *Elimination and normalization do not affect the zeros of a system of linear polynomials.*

In other words, a new system of linear polynomials obtained from a given system by a succession of the alterations introduced in definition 8.2 has the same zeros, except possibly for rearranged coordinates.

PROOF: By lemma 8.1, every zero of the system of two polynomials f_i and f_k is also a zero of the system of the two polynomials $g = f_i + \alpha f_k$ and f_k. But the new system may have additional zeros. To exclude this possibility, we observe that, by the definition of the new polynomial g, we have $f_i = g - \alpha f_k$; hence, again by lemma 8.1, every zero of the second system is a zero of the first system, which means that the second system does not have any additional zeros. This completes the proof for the process of elimination. That normalization does not change the zeros is likewise an immediate consequence of lemma 8.1.

Corollary 8.1:   *The zero polynomial 0 can be omitted from any system of linear polynomials.*

PROOF: Take $f_i = 0$ in the previous proof and $\alpha = 1$. Then $\{0, f_k\}$ can be replaced by $\{f_k, f_k\}$, which obviously has the same zeros as f_k alone. Thus, 0 can be omitted.

Having made these terminological preparations, we are now ready to describe a method that will make it easy to find the zeros of a system (8.3) of linear polynomials; that is, to find the solutions of a system (8.1) of linear equations. This method is called the *reduction of a linear system to echelon form.*

REDUCTION OF A LINEAR SYSTEM TO ECHELON FORM

First omit all zero polynomials in the system (these are unlikely to occur in a concrete problem with numbers). Then normalize the first (remaining) polynomial with respect to x_1; or, if this is impossible, exchange the variable x_1 with some other variable occurring with a nonzero coefficient in the first polynomial and normalize this polynomial with respect to the new x_1. Next eliminate the (possibly new) variable x_1 from all following polynomials by means of the first polynomial. The new system of linear polynomials so obtained has the property that the first variable appears in the first polynomial with the coefficient 1, but in all other polynomials with the coefficient zero. If the first polynomial is left aside temporarily, the remaining polynomials can be considered as polynomials in x_2, x_3, $\cdots$, x_n alone. Repeat for the system of these remaining polynomials the procedure described above, with respect to x_2; that is, omit all zero polynomials (which may now have entered the picture), normalize the first remaining polynomial with respect to x_2 (if necessary, after an exchange of variables) and use that polynomial to eliminate x_2 in all further polynomials. If the first polynomial, which was left aside, is now brought back, then the new system has the property that the first variable appears in the first polynomial with the coefficient 1 and in all other polynomials with the coefficient 0 and that the second variable appears in the second polynomial with the coefficient 1 and in all later polynomials with the coefficient 0. By repeating this process, *mutatis mutandis*, one might arrive at a system of polynomials in which, for every $i = 1$, 2, $\cdots$, p, the variable x_i appears in the ith polynomial with the coefficient 1 and in all later polynomials with the coefficient zero (the number of polynomials may have decreased because of possible cancellations of zero polynomials en route).

$$x_1 + \bar{a}_{12}x_2 + \bar{a}_{13}x_3 + \bar{a}_{14}x_4 + \cdots + \bar{a}_{1n}x_n + d_1$$
$$x_2 + \bar{a}_{23}x_3 + \bar{a}_{24}x_4 + \cdots + \bar{a}_{2n}x_n + d_2$$
$$x_3 + \bar{a}_{34}x_4 + \cdots + \bar{a}_{3n}x_n + d_3 \qquad (8.5)$$
$$\dots\dots\dots\dots\dots\dots\dots$$
$$x_p + \cdots + \bar{a}_{pn}x_n + d_p$$

But it may also happen that, as a result of one of these steps, a polynomial is obtained that is a nonzero constant d. Since every zero of the original system must also be a zero of d and since d does not have any zeros, the system cannot have a zero. But, if the nonexistence of zeros (that is, the unsolvability of corresponding equations) is known, no further computation is necessary. Apart from this *exceptional case*, the form (8.5) can be reached; in many cases, p may be equal to n.

The second part of the reduction process consists in the successive elimination of the first p variables in each polynomial, except for that variable with respect to which the polynomial was normalized. The result of this process, which can *always* be applied to every system of the form (8.5), is the system

$$x_1 + \qquad\qquad + c_{1p+1}x_{p+1} + c_{1p+2}x_{p+2} + \cdots + c_{1n}x_n + d_1$$
$$x_2 + \qquad \mathbf{O} \quad + c_{2p+1}x_{p+1} + c_{2p+2}x_{p+2} + \cdots + c_{2n}x_n + d_2$$
$$x_3 + \qquad\quad + c_{3p+1}x_{p+1} + c_{3p+2}x_{p+2} + \cdots + c_{3n}x_n + d_3 \qquad (8.6)$$
$$x_4 + \quad + c_{4p+1}x_{p+1} + c_{4p+2}x_{p+2} + \cdots + c_{4n}x_n + d_4$$
$$\dots\dots\dots\dots\dots\dots\dots\dots\dots\dots\dots\dots$$
$$\mathbf{O} \qquad\qquad x_p + c_{pp+1}x_{p+1} + c_{pp+2}x_{p+2} + \cdots + c_{pn}x_n + d_p.$$

The big circles are to indicate that, in (8.6), which is called *an echelon system*, no parts are left out by a printer's error. The system is obtained from (8.5) by first using the last polynomial to eliminate x_p in all earlier polynomials, then using the second-to-last polynomial to eliminate x_{p-1} in all earlier polynomials, and so forth. This completes the reduction process. In the special case $p = n$ no c's occur in the echelon form (8.6).

Note: If the coefficients of the polynomials of the original system were real, then (8.6) has real coefficients, too.

The zeros of (8.6) can be found easily by inspection. If, for all but the first p variables, arbitrary real (or complex) numbers t_i ($i = 1, \cdots, n-p$) are chosen at will, then (8.6) reduces to the system

$$
\begin{aligned}
&x_1 + e_1 \\
&x_2 + e_2 \\
&x_3 + e_3 \\
&\cdots\cdots \\
&x_p + e_p
\end{aligned}
\tag{8.7}
$$

where the e_i's are real (or complex) numbers. If this is regarded as a system *in the variables* $x_1, \cdots, x_p$ alone, it obviously has the *unique* zero $x^* = (-e_1, -e_2, -e_3, \cdots, -e_p)$. But, if the e_i's are expressed in terms of the chosen real (or complex) numbers t_i, then (8.6) has the zero

$$
\begin{aligned}
x_1^* &= -c_{1p+1}t_1 - c_{1p+2}t_2 - \cdots - c_{1n}t_{n-p} - d_1 \\
x_2^* &= -c_{2p+1}t_1 - c_{2p+2}t_2 - \cdots - c_{2n}t_{n-p} - d_2 \\
x_3^* &= -c_{3p+1}t_1 - c_{3p+2}t_2 - \cdots - c_{3n}t_{n-p} - d_3 \\
&\cdots\cdots\cdots\cdots\cdots\cdots\cdots\cdots\cdots\cdots \\
x_p^* &= -c_{pp+1}t_1 - c_{pp+2}t_2 - \cdots - c_{pn}t_{n-p} - d_p \\
x_{p+1}^* &= \quad t_1 \\
x_{p+2}^* &= \qquad\qquad t_2 \\
&\cdots\cdots\cdots\cdots\cdots\cdots\cdots\cdots\cdots\cdots \\
x_n^* &= \qquad\qquad\qquad\qquad t_{n-p}
\end{aligned}
$$

or, shorter and differently written,

$$
\begin{aligned}
x^* = \ &t_1(-c_{1p+1}, -c_{2p+1}, \cdots, -c_{pp+1}, 1, 0, \cdots, 0) \\
+ \ &t_2(-c_{1p+2}, -c_{2p+2}, \cdots, -c_{pp+2}, 0, 1, \cdots, 0) \\
&\cdots\cdots\cdots\cdots\cdots\cdots\cdots\cdots\cdots\cdots\cdots \\
+ \ &t_{n-p}(-c_{1n}, -c_{2n}, \cdots, -c_{pn}, 0, 0, \cdots, 1) \\
- \ &(d_1, d_2, \cdots, d_p, 0, 0, \cdots, 0).
\end{aligned}
\tag{8.8}
$$

We repeat: For every choice of the real (or complex) numbers $t_1, t_2, \cdots, t_{n-p}$ (8.8) gives a zero of the echelon system (8.6). That, conversely, every zero of (8.6) can be written in the form (8.8) can be seen as follows: Suppose $y^* = (y_1^*, y_2^*, \cdots, y_p^*, y_{p+1}^*, y_{p+2}^*, \cdots, y_n^*)$ is a zero of (8.6). Put $t_1 = y_{p+1}^*$, $t_2 = y_{p+2}^*, \cdots, t_{n-p} = y_n^*$. Then (8.6) reduces to (8.7). That is, the first p coordinates of the zero in question are *uniquely* determined; hence, $x_1^* = y_1^*$, $x_2^* = y_2^*, \cdots, x_p^* = y_p^*$.

By lemma 8.2, every zero of the echelon system is also a zero of the original system, except that, if variables have been transposed during the reduction, the order of the coordinates has changed, and this has to be reversed.

Note: These zeros are real if the coefficients of the original system were real, but may be complex if the original coefficients were complex.

EXAMPLES OF REDUCTION TO ECHELON FORM

1. In

$$-x_1 + x_2 + x_3 - x_4$$
$$2x_1 - x_2 - 5x_3 + 4x_4 - 1$$
$$x_1 - 2x_2 + 2x_3 \qquad - 3$$
$$-x_1 + 3x_2 - 3x_3 + 5x_4 - 16$$

the first polynomial is normalized with respect to x_1 by multiplication by -1. By elimination of x_1 in the second, third, and fourth polynomials through use of the first polynomial, one obtains

$$x_1 - x_2 - x_3 + x_4$$
$$x_2 - 3x_3 + 2x_4 - 1$$
$$-x_2 + 3x_3 - x_4 - 3$$
$$2x_2 - 4x_3 + 6x_4 - 16.$$

By elimination of x_2 through use of the second polynomial, one obtains

$$x_1 - x_2 - x_3 + x_4$$
$$x_2 - 3x_3 + 2x_4 - 1$$
$$x_4 - 4$$
$$2x_3 + 2x_4 - 14.$$

By exchanging the third and fourth variable, one obtains

$$x_1 - x_2 + x_3 - x_4$$
$$x_2 + 2x_3 - 3x_4 - 1$$
$$x_3 \qquad - 4$$
$$2x_3 + 2x_4 - 14.$$

Elimination of x_3 in the last polynomial, followed by normalization with respect to x_4, yields

$$x_1 - x_2 + x_3 - x_4$$
$$x_2 + 2x_3 - 3x_4 - 1$$
$$x_3 \qquad - 4$$
$$x_4 - 3,$$

which has the form (8.5). Elimination of x_4 in the first three polynomials, through use of the last polynomial, gives

$$x_1 - x_2 + x_3 \qquad - 3$$
$$x_2 + 2x_3 \qquad - 10$$
$$x_3 \qquad - 4$$
$$x_4 - 3.$$

Elimination of x_3 in the first two polynomials, through use of the third polynomial, gives

$$x_1 - x_2 \qquad + 1$$
$$x_2 \qquad - 2$$
$$x_3 \qquad - 4$$
$$x_4 - 3.$$

And the final elimination of x_2 gives

$$x_1 - 1$$
$$x_2 - 2$$
$$x_3 - 4$$
$$x_4 - 3.$$

The last system obviously has the zero $x^* = (1,2,4,3)$. Since we had interchanged the third and fourth variables during this process, the original system has the *unique* zero $x^* = (1,2,3,4)$.

2. The system

$$x_1 + x_2 + 2$$
$$x_1 + x_2 + 3$$

has *no* zeros, because elimination of x_1 in the second polynomial gives the non-zero constant polynomial 1.

3. The system

$$x_1 + 2x_4 + 3x_5 + 2$$
$$x_2 + x_4 - x_5 + 1$$
$$x_3 - x_4 + 2x_5 - 1$$

has the zeros

$$x^* = t_1(-2,-1,1,1,0) + t_2(-3,1,-2,0,1) + (-2,-1,1,0,0)$$

for every choice of numbers t_1, t_2.

For the exceptional case in which a system has no zeros, the following necessary and sufficient condition is an easy consequence of our results above.

Theorem 8.1: *A system of linear polynomials* (8.3) *has a zero if and only if 1 is not a linear combination of the polynomials of the system.*

PROOF: If 1 is a linear combination of the polynomials, then there cannot exist a zero, by lemma 8.1. If 1 is not a linear combination, then the exceptional case cannot occur; hence there must exist a zero.

This chapter will be concluded with the discussion of an important type of system of linear polynomials for which this exceptional case is impossible.

Definition 8.3: A linear polynomial $f(x_1,x_2,\cdots,x_n) = a_1x_1 + a_2x_2 + \cdots + a_nx_n$ without constant term is called *homogeneous*. A system of linear polynomials is called *homogeneous* if every polynomial in it is homogeneous. Also, the corresponding equation $a_1x_1 + a_2x_2 + \cdots + a_nx_n = 0$ and every system of such equations are called *homogeneous*. A homogeneous linear polynomial, a homogeneous linear equation, and any system of either of these is called *associated* with a linear polynomial, a linear equation, or a system of either of these, respectively, if it is obtained from the latter by cancellation of all constant terms.

EXAMPLE OF AN ASSOCIATED HOMOGENOUS SYSTEM

The homogeneous system

$$3x_1 - 4x_2 + 6x_3$$
$$2x_1 + 3x_2 - x_3$$

is associated with the nonhomogeneous system

$$3x_1 - 4x_2 + 6x_3 + 5$$
$$2x_1 + 3x_2 - x_3 + 1.$$

As indicated in Example 9 of Vector Spaces and Subspaces and as proved in exercise 5.5, homogeneous systems have the following important property.

Theorem 8.2:   *The set of all zeros of a system of linear homogeneous polynomials is a vector space, which is real or complex depending on whether the coefficients of the system are real or complex.*

Note: This implies the existence of at least one zero, namely, the zero vector.

Since the difference of two zeros of a nonhomogeneous system is a zero of the associated homogeneous system (see exercise 8.5), theorem 8.2 implies the following corollary.

Corollary 8.2:   *If x is a zero of a nonhomogeneous system and if H is the vector space of all zeros of the associated homogeneous system, then $x + H = \{x + h | h \ \varepsilon \ H\}$ is the set of all zeros of the nonhomogeneous system.*

If theorems 7.1 and 7.2 are reinterpreted in terms of coordinate vectors, then, in conjunction with corollary 8.2, they show that the graph of a system of linear equations in two or three unknowns may be a line or a plane. Corollaries 7.2 and 7.5 have demonstrated that the coordinate vectors of lines and planes may also be obtained in a more symmetric way. This suggests the characterization of the zeros of a linear system in a similar manner. In preparation we introduce a definition.

Definition 8.4:   A linear combination $\alpha_1 s_1 + \alpha_2 s_2 + \cdots + \alpha_n s_n$ of elements of a vector space is called a *flock combination* if the sum of coefficients is equal to 1; that is, if $\sum_{i=1}^{n} \alpha_i = 1$. A subset S of a vector space is called a *flock* if, for any two elements of S, every flock combination of these elements also belongs to S.

Note: According to this definition, the empty set and every set consisting of a single vector are flocks, because the condition is vacuous in the first case and trivial in the second.

Theorem 8.3:   *The set of all zeros of a linear system is a flock.*

PROOF: By the preceding note, this is true if there are no zeros or if there is a unique zero. Thus, let us suppose that a system (8.4) has two distinct zeros $y^* = (y_1^*, y_2^*, \cdots, y_n^*)$ and $z^* = (z_1^*, z_2^*, \cdots, z_n^*)$. Then

$$\sum_{j=1}^{n} a_{ij} y_j^* + b_i = 0 \qquad \text{for} \quad i = 1, \cdots, m,$$

$$\sum_{j=1}^{n} a_{ij} z_j^* + b_i = 0 \qquad \text{for} \quad i = 1, \cdots, m.$$

Choose two real (or complex) numbers α and β such that $\alpha + \beta = 1$. For every $i = 1, \cdots, m$, multiply the first equation by α and the second equation by β, and add the results. Then we have, for every $i = 1, \cdots, m$,

$$0 = \alpha\left(\sum_{j=1}^{n} a_{ij}y_j^* + b_i\right) + \beta\left(\sum_{j=1}^{n} a_{ij}z_j^* + b_i\right)$$

$$= \sum_{j=1}^{n} a_{ij}(\alpha y_j^*) + \sum_{j=1}^{n} a_{ij}(\beta z_j^*) + (\alpha + \beta)b_i = \sum_{j=1}^{n} a_{ij}(\alpha y_j^* + \beta z_j^*) + b_i,$$

which shows that $\alpha y^* + \beta z^*$ is also a zero of the system.

EXERCISES

1. Find solutions of the following systems of linear equations:

(a)
$$2x_1 - x_2 + x_3 + x_4 = 4$$
$$x_1 - 3x_2 + x_3 + 8x_4 = 5$$
$$3x_1 \quad\quad - x_3 + 5x_4 = 0$$
$$x_1 + x_2 - x_3 + 2x_4 = 5;$$

(b)
$$3x_1 - x_2 + 3x_3 - x_4 = 4$$
$$x_1 - 3x_2 + x_3 + x_4 = 0$$
$$2x_1 + 2x_2 - 3x_3 + 2x_4 = 3$$
$$-x_1 - 2x_2 + 3x_3 + 3x_4 = 3;$$

(c)
$$2x_1 + 3x_2 - 4x_3 + 24x_4 - 2x_5 = 0$$
$$3x_1 - 2x_2 + x_3 - 6x_4 + 2x_5 = 5$$
$$-2x_1 + x_2 + 13x_3 - 3x_4 + 3x_5 = 1$$
$$2x_2 - 3x_3 - 2x_4 + 4x_5 = 4$$
$$x_1 \quad\quad\quad\quad + x_5 = 2;$$

(d)
$$3x_1 - 2x_2 + 4x_3 = 12$$
$$4x_1 + 5x_2 + 6x_3 = 8$$
$$7x_1 + 3x_2 + 10x_3 = 20;$$

(e)
$$4x_1 + 2x_2 + 8x_3 + 9x_4 + 7x_5 + 3 = 0$$
$$6x_1 - 7x_2 + 3x_3 + x_4 - 2x_5 + 2 = 0$$
$$x_1 + x_2 + x_3 + x_4 - x_5 \quad\quad = 0;$$

(f)
$$2x_1 - 3x_2 + 3x_3 = 5$$
$$4x_1 - x_2 + x_3 = 5$$
$$x_2 + x_3 = 5$$
$$3x_1 + x_2 = 5;$$

(g)
$$x_1 + x_2 + x_3 + x_4 + x_5 = 0.$$

2. Let $i = +\sqrt{-1}$. Find the zeros of the following systems of linear polynomials:

(a)
$$ix_1 + x_2 + ix_3 = 1$$
$$2x_1 + 3x_2 + 2x_3 = 3$$
$$ix_1 + x_2 = 0;$$

(b)
$$(1 - i)x_1 + x_2 + (1 + i)x_3 = 0$$
$$x_1 + (1 + i)x_2 + x_3 = 1$$
$$(1 + i)x_1 + ix_2 + (i - 1)x_3 = 2;$$

(c)
$$ix_1 + x_2 + x_3 = 0$$
$$x_1 + ix_2 + x_3 = 0$$
$$x_1 + x_2 + ix_3 = 0.$$

3. Prove: Every zero of a system $\{f_i\}_{1 \le i \le m}$ of (not necessarily linear) polynomials is a zero of every polynomial of the span $[f_i]_{1 \le i \le m}$ of these polynomials.

4. Let $f: x \to f(x)$ and $g: x \to g(x)$ be polynomials in one variable x. Prove: Every zero x^* of f is also a zero of $g \circ f$, but in general not of $f \circ g$, provided that g does not have a constant term.

5. Prove corollary 8.2 by showing that the difference between two zeros of a linear system is a zero of the associated homogeneous system.

6. If f and g are linearly independent (strictly) linear polynomials in two variables, their graphs are straight lines (see Chapter 7). How do we characterize geometrically the lines that are graphs of a polynomial of the span $[f,g]$.
Hint: There are two separate cases.

7. If f and g are linearly independent (strictly) linear polynomials in three variables, how can the graphs of all polynomials of the span $[f,g]$ be characterized geometrically?

8. Find algebraic conditions for three lines to pass through a common point or to be parallel.
Hint: Make use of theorem 8.1 for the second part. Generalize the results to planes in $\mathbf{R}^3$.

9. Prove: The set of all (*not necessarily linear*) polynomials that have a given n-tuple z^* as a zero is a vector space.

10. Express the number of t_i's in (8.7) in terms of the number m of polynomials, the number n of variables, and the total number of polynomials "0" canceled during the reduction process.

11. The process of reduction to echelon form can be changed in the following way: Instead of eliminating a variable x_k in all polynomials below the kth polynomial, one may eliminate x_k *simultaneously* in all but the kth polynomial. In this way the echelon form (8.6) is apparently reached faster. Why is this process more cumbersome in practice?

12. Prove that the $n - p$ n-tuples

$$(-c_{1p+1}, -c_{2p+1}, \cdots, -c_{p,p+1}, 1, 0, \cdots, 0),$$

$$(-c_{1p+2}, -c_{2p+2}, \cdots, -c_{p,p+2}, 0, 1, \cdots, 0),$$

$$\cdots\cdots\cdots\cdots\cdots\cdots\cdots\cdots\cdots\cdots\cdots\cdots$$

$$(-c_{1n}, -c_{2n}, \cdots, -c_{pn}, 0, 0, \cdots, 1)$$

are linearly independent.

13. Prove that the polynomials of (8.6) are linearly independent.

14. Prove: A system of homogeneous linear polynomials in which the number of variables exceeds the number of polynomials always has a zero different from the zero vector $(0, 0, \cdots, 0)$.

15. Prove: A flock combination $\sum_{i=1}^{p} \beta_i \mathbf{b}^i$ of flock combinations $\mathbf{b}^i = \sum_{j=1}^{q} \alpha_{ij} \mathbf{a}^j$ of $\mathbf{S} = \{\mathbf{a}^i\}_{1 \le i \le q}$ is a flock combination of $\mathbf{S}$.

16. Prove: A subset $\mathbf{S}$ of a vector space is a flock if and only if it has the following property: If $\mathbf{a}, \mathbf{b}, \mathbf{c} \ \varepsilon \ \mathbf{S}$, then, for every scalar λ,

$$\mathbf{a} + \lambda(\mathbf{b} - \mathbf{c}) \ \varepsilon \ \mathbf{S}.$$

17. What are the possible graphs of the solutions of any system of linear equations in at most three unknowns?
    Hint: Find all possible flocks of solutions.

18. Prove: A flock that contains the zero vector is a subspace.

19. Prove: The set of all differences of elements of a nonempty flock $\mathbf{F}$ is a subspace $\mathbf{S}$. If $\mathbf{f}$ is a fixed element of the nonempty $\mathbf{F}$, then $\mathbf{F} = \{\mathbf{f} + \mathbf{s} | \mathbf{s} \ \varepsilon \ \mathbf{S}\}$. Because of this close relationship, $\mathbf{S}$ is sometimes called the *associated subspace* of $\mathbf{F} \ne \varnothing$.

*20. Prove: The set of all solutions of a linear differential equation is a flock. If y^* is a solution of a linear differential equation and if H is the vector space of all solutions of the associated homogeneous differential equation (defined analogously to definition 8.3) then

$\{y^* + h | h \ \varepsilon \ H\}$ is the set of all solutions of the original differential equation.

21. Let $\mathcal{F}$ be the set of all flocks $\neq \varnothing$ of R^n, and let $\mathcal{T}$ be the set of all subspaces of the vector space $R[x_1, x_2, \cdots, x_n]_L$ of all linear polynomials in n variables with real coefficients. Assign to every flock $F \neq \varnothing$ of R^n the subspace of all linear polynomials that have all elements of F as zeros. Prove: The mapping so defined is one-to-one, but not onto. Which subspaces of linear polynomials are not images under this mapping? Prove also: The restriction of this mapping to the set $\mathcal{S}$ of all subspaces of R^n is a one-to-one correspondence onto the set $\mathcal{H}$ of all subspaces of the vector space $R[x_1, x_2, \cdots, x_n]_{LH}$ of all linear *homogeneous* polynomials in n variables with real coefficients.

22. Solve the following system of ordinary linear differential equations in four unknown functions $y_1(x)$, $y_2(x)$, $y_3(x)$, $y_4(x)$:

$$y_1' - 3y_2' + 2y_3' + \quad y_4' = 0$$
$$2y_1' + 3y_2' + \quad y_3' - 10y_4' = 0$$
$$y_1' + \quad y_2' - 3y_3' - \quad y_4' = 0$$
$$y_1' - 2y_2' + \quad y_3' \qquad\quad = 0.$$

9

Dimension and Bases of a Vector Space

The previous chapter left one problem open: Suppose that a solvable system of linear polynomials is reduced to echelon form *in two different ways* (for example, by the application of different exchanges). Is it then possible that the two corresponding formulas (8.8) describing all possible zeros may contain a *different* number of t's? This question will be answered in the negative in this chapter. It is a special case of a much more general problem, namely, how to describe the elements of a vector space in a unique way.

In Chapter 5 it has been indicated that, in the translation space $\mathbf{R}^n (n = 1, 2, 3)$, *at most* n vectors can be linearly independent, any $n + 1$ vectors must be linearly dependent, and any vector can be expressed uniquely as a linear combination of n linearly independent vectors. In the vector space R^n of all real n-tuples, we have a similar situation. In Example 6 of Spans it was proved that every real n-tuple can be expressed as a linear combination of the $e^{(i)}$, and (5.9) shows that the n $e^{(i)}$'s are linearly independent. But n is the maximum number of linearly independent n-tuples. For suppose we had $n + 1$ linearly independent n-tuples:

$$a^{(1)} = (a_{11}, a_{12}, \cdots, a_{1n})$$
$$= a_{11}e^{(1)} + a_{12}e^{(2)} + \cdots + a_{1n}e^{(n)} = \sum_{j=1}^{n} a_{1j}e^{(i)}$$
$$a^{(2)} = (a_{21}, a_{22}, \cdots, a_{2n})$$
$$= a_{21}e^{(1)} + a_{22}e^{(2)} + \cdots + a_{2n}e^{(n)} = \sum_{j=1}^{n} a_{2j}e^{(i)}$$

$$a^{(n+1)} = (a_{n+1,1}, a_{n+1,2}, \cdots, a_{n+1,n})$$

$$= a_{n+1,1}e^{(1)} + a_{n+1,2}e^{(2)} + \cdots + a_{n+1,n}e^{(n)} = \sum_{j=1}^{n} a_{n+1,j}e^{(j)}. \quad (9.1)$$

Then there would *not* exist a set of $n + 1$ numbers $k_1, k_2, \cdots, k_{n+1}$, not all equal to zero, such that

$$k_1 a^{(1)} + k_2 a^{(2)} + \cdots + k_{n+1} a^{(n+1)} = 0, \text{ or (shorter) } \sum_{i=1}^{n+1} k_i a^{(i)} = 0. \quad (9.2)$$

This, because of (9.1), means the same as

$$k_1(a_{11}e^{(1)} + a_{12}e^{(2)} + \cdots + a_{1n}e^{(n)}) + k_2(a_{21}e^{(1)} + \cdots + a_{2n}e^{(n)}) + \cdots$$
$$+ k_{n+1}(a_{n+1,1}e^{(1)} + \cdots + a_{n+1,n}e^{(n)}) = 0$$

or, after rewriting the left-hand side as a linear combination of the $e^{(i)}$'s

$$(k_1 a_{11} + k_2 a_{21} + \cdots + k_{n+1}a_{n+1,1})e^{(1)} + (k_1 a_{12} + k_2 a_{22} + \cdots$$
$$+ k_{n+1}a_{n+1,2})e^{(2)} + \cdots + (k_1 a_{1n} + k_2 a_{2n} + \cdots \quad (9.3)$$
$$+ k_{n+1}a_{n+1,n})e^{(n)} = 0.$$

Since the $e^{(i)}$'s are linearly independent, equation (9.3) implies the following n equations for the $n + 1$ quantities $k_1, k_2, \cdots, k_{n+1}$:

$$a_{11}k_1 + a_{21}k_2 + \cdots + a_{n+1,1}k_{n+1} = 0 \qquad \sum_{i=1}^{n+1} a_{i1}k_i = 0$$

$$a_{12}k_1 + a_{22}k_2 + \cdots + a_{n+1,2}k_{n+1} = 0 \qquad \overset{\text{or}}{\underset{\text{(shorter)}}{}} \qquad \sum_{i=1}^{n+1} a_{i2}k_i = 0 \quad (9.4)$$

$$\cdots\cdots\cdots\cdots\cdots\cdots\cdots\cdots \qquad\qquad \cdots\cdots\cdots\cdots$$

$$a_{1n}k_1 + a_{2n}k_2 + \cdots + a_{n+1,n}k_{n+1} = 0 \qquad \sum_{i=1}^{n+1} a_{in}k_i = 0.$$

As the equations (9.4) are homogeneous in the k's, there exists at least one zero (namely, the zero vector). As the number n of equations in (9.4) is less than the number $n + 1$ of unknowns k_i, there must also exist a zero different from the zero vector (see exercise 8.14), that is, an $(n + 1)$ tuple $(k_1, k_2, \cdots, k_{n+1})$ with at least one $k_i \neq 0$. But this contradicts the linear independence of the $a^{(i)}$'s. Hence, every set of $n + 1$ n-tuples is *linearly dependent*.

The maximum number of linearly independent elements of a vector space, provided that such a number exists, and the unique expressibility of any element of that space by a linear combination of certain distinguished elements are very closely connected. Before we investigate this relationship, we first introduce two fundamental definitions.

Definition 9.1: If, in a vector space **V**, there exists a maximum number d of linearly independent elements, then d is called *the dimension of* **V**, denoted by dim **V**, and **V** is called *finite-dimensional*. If d does not exist, then **V** is said to be *infinite-dimensional*, and this is denoted by dim **V** $= \infty$.

Note: Not every vector space is finite-dimensional. For example, it can be shown that the vector space of *all* polynomials in one variable (*not* only that of the linear polynomials) is infinite-dimensional.

Definition 9.2: If every element of a vector space **V** can be expressed *uniquely* as a linear combination of a subset **S** of **V**, then **S** is called *a basis* (or *coordinate system*) *of* **V** and its elements *base vectors*.

Note: It is not required that the set forming a basis be *finite*. For example, the elements $1, x, x^2, \cdots, x^n, \cdots$ (that is, all positive powers of x) form a basis for the vector space of all polynomials in x. It is possible to show that *every* vector space has a basis, but the proof of this for infinite-dimensional vector spaces requires some knowledge of set theory. For finite-dimensional vector spaces, however, we can construct bases without much difficulty.

Theorem 9.1: *Let* **V** *be a vector space of dimension* d. *Then any basis of* **V** *consists of* d *linearly independent elements of* **V**, *and any* d *linearly independent elements of* **V** *form a basis of* **V**.

PROOF: The set of elements of **V** forming a basis must be linearly independent, for, if these elements were linearly dependent, then the element **0** could be expressed *in several ways* as a linear combination of them. Hence the number of elements of a basis can be *at most* d.

Suppose we have d linearly independent elements $\mathbf{a}^{(1)}, \mathbf{a}^{(2)}, \cdots, \mathbf{a}^{(d)}$ and an additional arbitrary element **b** of **V**. Then the set $\{\mathbf{a}^{(1)}, \mathbf{a}^{(2)}, \cdots, \mathbf{a}^{(d)}, \mathbf{b}\}$ is linearly dependent; that is, there exists a relationship of the form

$$k_1\mathbf{a}^{(1)} + k_2\mathbf{a}^{(2)} + \cdots + k_d\mathbf{a}^{(d)} + k_{d+1}\mathbf{b} = \mathbf{0} \tag{9.5}$$

where $k = (k_1, k_2, \cdots, k_{d+1})$ is a $(d + 1)$-tuple of numbers different from the zero-tuple. In particular, k_{d+1} must be different from zero, for otherwise (9.5) would imply that the a's are linearly dependent. Therefore, we can conclude from (9.5) that

$$\mathbf{b} = h_1\mathbf{a}^{(1)} + h_2\mathbf{a}^{(2)} + \cdots + h_d\mathbf{a}^{(d)} \tag{9.6}$$

with

$$h_1 = -\frac{k_1}{k_{d+1}}, \qquad h_2 = -\frac{k_2}{k_{d+1}}, \cdots, h_d = -\frac{k_d}{k_{d+1}}.$$

Thus, every element **b** of **V** can be represented as a linear combination of the a's in *some* way.

Suppose next that **b** could also be represented as a linear combination of the **a**'s in some way *different* from (9.6), for example, by

$$\mathbf{b} = g_1 \mathbf{a}^{(1)} + g_2 \mathbf{a}^{(2)} + \cdots + g_d \mathbf{a}^{(d)} \tag{9.7}$$

so that the two sequences of coefficients are not equal; that is,

$$h = (h_1, h_2, \cdots, h_d) \neq (g_1, g_2, \cdots, g_d) = g. \tag{9.8}$$

Then we subtract (9.6) from (9.7) and obtain

$$\mathbf{0} = (g_1 - h_1)\mathbf{a}^{(1)} + (g_2 - h_2)\mathbf{a}^{(2)} + \cdots + (g_d - h_d)\mathbf{a}^{(d)}.$$

Since the **a**'s are linearly independent, all coefficients of the right-hand side must vanish:

$$g_1 - h_1 = 0, \qquad g_2 - h_2 = 0, \cdots, g_d - h_d = 0.$$

But this contradicts (9.8). Thus *two different* representations of **b** as a linear combination of the **a**'s are *not possible*. This proves that the d elements $\mathbf{a}^{(1)}, \mathbf{a}^{(2)}, \cdots, \mathbf{a}^{(d)}$ form a basis of **V**.

To conclude the proof, we have still to show that *fewer* than d linearly independent elements can *never* form a basis of a vector space of dimension d. For, suppose the set $\{\mathbf{c}^{(1)}, \mathbf{c}^{(2)}, \cdots, \mathbf{c}^{(e)}\}$ of e linearly independent elements (with $e < d$) were also a basis of **V**. Then every element of the first basis $\{\mathbf{a}^{(1)}, \mathbf{a}^{(2)}, \cdots, \mathbf{a}^{(d)}\}$ could be expressed in terms of the **c**'s:

$$\mathbf{a}^{(1)} = \sum_{j=1}^{e} a_{ij} \mathbf{c}^{(j)}$$

$$\mathbf{a}^{(2)} = \sum_{j=1}^{e} a_{2j} \mathbf{c}^{(j)}$$

. . . .

$$\mathbf{a}^{(d)} = \sum_{j=1}^{e} a_{dj} \mathbf{c}^{(j)}.$$

Now, any linear combination of the **a**'s can also be expressed as a linear combination of the **c**'s:

$$\sum_{i=1}^{d} k_i \mathbf{a}^{(i)} = \sum_{i=1}^{d} k_i \sum_{j=1}^{e} a_{ij} \mathbf{c}^{(j)} = \sum_{j=1}^{e} \left(\sum_{i=1}^{d} a_{ij} k_i \right) \mathbf{c}^{(j)}. \tag{9.9}$$

The transformation in (9.9) can be obtained in a similar way as the transition from (9.2) to (9.3).

For suitable choices of the k's, (9.9) is equal to the zero vector, namely, if $k = (k_1, k_2, \cdots, k_d)$ is a common zero of the e linear homogeneous polynomials

$$\sum_{i=1}^{d} a_{i1} k_i, \sum_{i=1}^{d} a_{i2} k_i, \cdots, \sum_{i=1}^{d} a_{ie} k_i.$$

Since this is a homogeneous system, it always has zeros, and it has more than one zero [that is, more than the zero $(0,0,\cdots,0)$] because the number of variables exceeds the number of polynomials (see exercise 8.14). But, if we have a zero $k \neq (0,0,\cdots,0)$, then for this d-tuple k the expression (9.9) is $\mathbf{0}$, *contradicting* the assumption that the $\mathbf{a}$'s are *linearly independent*. Therefore, fewer than d elements of $\mathbf{V}$ cannot form a basis of $\mathbf{V}$.

From theorem 9.1 and theorem 5.2 we have immediately the following corollary.

Corollary 9.1: *Every real or complex vector space of dimension n is isomorphic with R^n or C^n, respectively.*

Hence we always have easy concrete models of finite-dimensional vector spaces $\mathbf{V}$. The elements of $\mathbf{V}$ may be expressed as linear combinations of a given basis and represented by the sequences of their coefficients (see Chapter 14).

Theorem 9.1 also gives an important characterization of the dimension of a vector space and every subspace of it. As an immediate consequence we have a corollary.

Corollary 9.2: *The dimension of every proper subspace of a finite-dimensional vector space $\mathbf{V}$ is less than the dimension of $\mathbf{V}$.*

It is advisable to extend the concept of dimension to flocks in the following manner.

Definition 9.3: If $\mathbf{F}$ is a nonempty flock of a vector space, then the maximum number of linearly independent differences of elements of $\mathbf{F}$, if it exists, is called *the dimension of* $\mathbf{F}$ and is denoted by dim $\mathbf{F}$. The empty flock is said to have dimension -1. A flock of dimension d of a vector space $\mathbf{V}$ is called a *point* if $d = 0$, a *line* if $d = 1$, a *plane* if $d = 2$, and a *hyperplane* if $d = \dim \mathbf{V} - 1$. The zero vector $\mathbf{0}$ is also called the *origin*.

By exercise 8.19, the dimension of a nonempty flock $\mathbf{F}$ is equal to the dimension of the associated subspace $\mathbf{S}$ of all differences of elements of $\mathbf{F}$.

The last part of definition 9.3 is the key to the generalization of geometric ideas to higher-dimensional vector spaces. For example, if $\mathbf{u}$ and $\mathbf{v}$ are two different vectors of $\mathbf{V}$ then the set of all vectors of the form

$$\alpha\mathbf{u} + \beta\mathbf{v} \quad \text{with} \quad \alpha + \beta = 1 \quad \text{and} \quad \alpha, \beta \geq 0 \qquad (9.10)$$

will be called the *line segment from* $\mathbf{u}$ *to* $\mathbf{v}$.

Note: If definition 9.3 is applied to the vector space $\mathbf{R}^3$ of dimension 3, then the *points* are now identified with *position vectors*, and, similarly, the *lines* are identified with the *sets of their position vectors*. This identification is made for $\mathbf{R}^3$ and $\mathbf{R}^2$ by some authors, but it may lead to confusion, since *translation* and *point* are different concepts. *Therefore, we shall not apply definition* 9.3 *to* $\mathbf{R}^2$ *and* $\mathbf{R}^3$. In higher-dimensional cases, however, the distinction between translation and point is not customary, although it may be made.

Theorem 9.1 makes it possible to study the set of all zeros of a system of linear polynomials. At first we consider a system of *homogeneous* linear polynomials. By theorem 8.2, the set of its zeros is a vector space, and we are now interested in finding the dimension of this space. If the system is reduced to echelon form (8.6), we must have $d_1 = d_2 = \cdots = d_p = 0$, because no nonzero constants can come in by elimination and normalization. Here again p is equal to the number m of original polynomials minus the number of zero polynomials canceled during the reduction. Hence all zeros x^* must be of the form

$$
\begin{aligned}
x^* = \; & t_1 \; (-c_{1,p+1}, -c_{2,p+1}, \cdots, -c_{p,p+1}, 1, 0, \cdots, 0) \\
& + t_2 \; (-c_{1,p+2}, -c_{2,p+2}, \cdots, -c_{p,p+2}, 0, 1, \cdots, 0) \\
& + \cdots\cdots\cdots\cdots\cdots\cdots\cdots\cdots\cdots\cdots\cdots\cdots\cdots \qquad (9.11) \\
& + t_{n-p}(-c_{1,n} \quad, -c_{2,n} \quad, \cdots, -c_{p,n} \quad, 0, 0, \cdots, 1).
\end{aligned}
$$

Thus the vector space of all zeros of the homogeneous system is spanned by the n-tuples

$$
\begin{aligned}
& (-c_{1,p+1}, -c_{2,p+1}, \cdots, -c_{p,p+1}, 1, 0, \cdots, 0) \\
& (-c_{1,p+2}, -c_{2,p+2}, \cdots, -c_{p,p+2}, 0, 1, \cdots, 0) \\
& \qquad \vdots \qquad\quad \vdots \qquad\qquad \vdots \qquad \ddots \\
& (-c_{1,n} \quad, -c_{2,n} \quad, \cdots, -c_{p,n} \quad, 0, 0, \cdots, 1),
\end{aligned}
$$

which are linearly independent (see also exercise 8.13). Hence, the dimension of the vector space of zeros of a homogeneous system is equal to the number of t's in (8.8). In view of theorem 9.1, the question posed right at the beginning of this chapter is answered in the negative: The number of t's does not depend on the choice of procedure.

By corollary 8.2, the number of t's in (8.3) is equal to the number of t's in the corresponding set of zeros of the associated homogeneous system. Hence, the conclusion that this number is independent of the method of reduction to echelon form is also valid in the nonhomogeneous case.

To sum up we introduce

Definition 9.4:   Given a system of linear polynomials (or of linear equations); the dimension of the space of all zeros (or of all solutions) of the associated homogeneous system is called *the nullity of the* (original) *system.*

It is obvious from the previous chapter that there is a connection between the nullity, the number of variables, and the number of polynomials of a system. We know that the nullity is equal to the number of t's in (8.8), which, in turn, is equal to the number of variables minus the number of polynomials of the echelon system obtained by the reduction process. Now this last number equals the number of polynomials of the original system minus the number of (zero) polynomials canceled during the reduction procedure.

Consider the span $[f_1, f_2, \cdots, f_i, \cdots, f_m]$ of a system of polynomials (8.3). It is easy to see (exercises 5.14 and 5.15) that the system obtained from (8.3) by elimination or normalization has the same span. Hence, the echelon system obtained by the reduction process must still have the same span, except that some variables may possibly have to be transposed back to their original numbering. At any rate, the dimensions of the span of (8.3) and of the span of the reduced system in echelon form must be equal. As the echelon system (8.6) is linearly independent (exercise 8.13), it forms a basis of the span of the original system, by theorem 9.1. Thus the dimension of the span of the original system is equal to the number of original polynomials minus the number of zero polynomials canceled during the reduction procedure. Hence the sum of this dimension and the number of t's in (8.8) is equal to the number of variables. To formulate this result we introduce first the following definition.

Definition 9.5:   The maximum number of linearly independent linear polynomials of a system [or of linearly independent left-hand sides of equations written in the form (8.1)] is called the *rank of the system*.

Then we may summarize.

Theorem 9.2:   *If a system of linear polynomials in m variables of rank r has zeros and if the nullity of the system is n, then*

$$r + n = m.$$

Since a single *nonconstant* linear polynomial in m variables always has zeros, the flock of its zeros has dimension $m - 1$, by theorem 9.2; that is, it is a *hyperplane*, by definition 9.3. Similarly the flock vectors whose coordinates (relative to a basis of the vector space) satisfy a non-constant linear equation is a *hyperplane*. Thus the hyperplanes are connected with systems of a *single* linear polynomial or of a *single* linear equation.

EXERCISES

1. Determine the nullity of the following linear systems:

(a) $3x_1 + 4x_2 - 6x_3 + 5$ (c) $x_1 - x_2 + x_3 - 1$

        $2x_1 - 3x_2 + x_3 - 4$ $-x_1 + x_2 - x_3 + 1$

        $8x_1 - 2x_2 + 3x_3 - 6;$ $x_1 + x_2;$

(b) $2x_1 - 3x_2 + x_3 + x_4$ (d) $x_1 - 2x_2 + x_3$

$3x_1 - 2x_2 + 7x_3 - x_4$ $x_1 - 3x_2 + x_3$

$5x_1 - 5x_2 + 8x_3 + 2;$ $2x_1 - x_2 - 2x_3$

$x_3.$

Which of those systems do not have zeros?

2. Find all zeros of every system in the previous exercise.

3. Prove that the minimum number of elements generating a finite-dimensional vector space is equal to its dimension.

4. Prove corollary 9.1.

5. Prove: The dimension of the span of a finite (nonempty) set of vectors is finite.

6. Prove: Two finite-dimensional real vector spaces are isomorphic if and only if they have the same dimension.

7. Prove: If U and V are finite-dimensional vector spaces with dim U < dim V, then there exists a homomorphism of U into V and a homomorphism of V onto U.

8. Prove: A finite-dimensional vector space is not isomorphic with a proper subspace. Give a counterexample in the case of *infinite-dimensional* vector spaces.

9. Determine the dimension of the following spans:
   (a) $[(2,1,3), (1,2,2), (1,-1,1)]$;   (b) $[v, -v]$;
   (c) $[3x^2 - 4x + 5, x - 6, x^2 + 8]$;
   (d) $[\{p(x)|p(x) \ \varepsilon \ R[x], \ p(x) \text{ divisible by } x - 1\}]$.

10. A complex vector space C can be made into a real vector space C_R by restricting the external composition law to the real numbers. Prove: If C is finite-dimensional, then dim C_R = 2 dim C.

11. Prove that the rank of a system of linear polynomials is equal to the dimension of the span of these polynomials.

12. Prove that no system of $n + 1$ linearly independent linear polynomials in n variables has a zero.

13. Given a finite sequence of m linear homogeneous real polynomials in n variables $x = (x_1, x_2, \cdots, x_n) : (f_i(x))_{1 \le i \le m}$. Define a mapping f of R^n into R^m, by assigning to every $a = (a_1, a_2, \cdots, a_n) \ \varepsilon \ R^n$ the m-tuple $(f_1(a), f_2(a), \cdots, f_m(a))$. Prove: (a) The range of f is a subspace of R^m; (b) The dimension of this subspace is equal to the rank of the given system of polynomials.

14. Let $c^{(1)}, \cdots, c^{(k)}$ be k ($<n$) linearly independent elements of a vector space V of finite dimension n. Prove: It is possible to find a basis of V that contains all c's. In other words, every set of linearly in-

dependent elements of a finite-dimensional vector space can be extended to a basis of that vector space.

15. Prove: In a nonempty flock of a finite-dimensional vector space there exists an element $\mathbf{s}^{(0)}$ and a finite linearly independent set $\mathbf{S} = \{\mathbf{s}^{(i)}\}_{0 \le i \le k}$ such that every element of $\mathbf{S}$ has a *unique* representation

$$\mathbf{s}^{(0)} + \alpha_1 \mathbf{s}^{(1)} + \alpha_2 \mathbf{s}^{(2)} + \cdots + \alpha_k \mathbf{s}^{(k)}$$

(compare with exercise 8.19).

16. Prove: A linear mapping maps flocks on flocks.

17. Call two elements $a = (a_1, a_2, \cdots, a_n)$ and $b = (b_1, b_2, \cdots, b_n)$ of R^n perpendicular (see also Chapter 15) if $a_1 b_1 + a_2 b_2 + \cdots + a_n b_n = 0$. Call a real n-tuple perpendicular to a subset S of R^n if it is perpendicular to every element of that subset. Prove: The set of all real n-tuples perpendicular to a subspace S of dimension m ($\le n$) is a subspace $\hat{S}$ of dimension $n - m$.

Hint: Reinterpret this problem in the language of polynomials.

18. Definitions as in the previous exercise. Prove: If $\{b^{(1)}, b^{(2)}, \cdots, b^{(m)}\}$ and $\{c^{(1)}, c^{(2)}, \cdots, c^{(n-m)}\}$ are bases of S and $\hat{S}$, respectively, then $\{b^{(1)}, b^{(2)}, \cdots, b^{(m)}, c^{(1)}, c^{(2)}, \cdots, c^{(n-m)}\}$ is a basis of R^n.

19. Define "$\hat{\ }$" as in exercise 17. Prove: If $S \subset T$, then $\hat{S} \supset \hat{T}$.

10

On Positive Solutions of Systems of Linear Equations

In many applications of linear equations, especially to practical problems outside pure mathematics, only those solutions $y = (y_1, y_2, \cdots, y_n)$ are significant in which no coordinate is negative and at least one coordinate is not zero. In this chapter the set of these special solutions of a given system of linear equations will be investigated.

Definition 10.1: An n-tuple $y = (y_1, y_2, \cdots, y_n)$ of real numbers is called *nonnegative* if all its coordinates are nonnegative, and this is denoted by $y \geq 0$. A nonnegative n-tuple is called *positive* if it is not the zero n-tuple, and this is denoted by $y > 0$.

Thus, $(3,2,0,0,1) > 0$, $(0,0,0,0) \geq 0$, but not $(3,2,0,0,-1) > 0$.

From this definition one can deduce very easily the following lemma.

Lemma 10.1: *The sum of two positive n-tuples and the multiple of a positive n-tuple by a positive scalar are also positive.*

Suppose we are now interested in the positive solutions of the following system of nonhomogeneous linear equations:

$$
\begin{aligned}
a_{11}x_1 + a_{12}x_2 + \cdots + a_{1m}x_m &= b_1 \\
a_{21}x_1 + a_{22}x_2 + \cdots + a_{2m}x_m &= b_2 \\
&\cdots\cdots\cdots\cdots\cdots\cdots\cdots\cdots\cdots \\
a_{n1}x_1 + a_{n2}x_2 + \cdots + a_{nm}x_m &= b_n,
\end{aligned}
\tag{10.1}
$$

or (shorter)

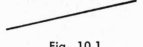

Fig. 10.1

$$\sum_{j=1}^{m} a_{ij}x_j = b_i \qquad \text{for} \quad i = 1, 2, \cdots, n.$$

There are no restrictions on n or m, but, in order to get several solutions, we may assume $n < m$ for simplicity.

If y and z are (not necessarily positive) solutions of (10.1), then the flock combination

$$z + \lambda(y - z) = \lambda y + (1 - \lambda)z \qquad (10.2)$$

is also a solution of (10.1), by theorem 8.3. If, in particular, both y and z are positive and if λ satisfies the condition

$$0 \leq \lambda \leq 1, \qquad (10.3)$$

then (10.2) is also a positive m-tuple. For, if $\lambda = 0$, then (10.2) reduces to z; if $\lambda = 1$, then (10.2) reduces to y; and, if $0 < \lambda < 1$, then one can see, by repeated application of lemma 10.1, that λy, $(1 - \lambda)z$, and therefore also their sum (10.2) are positive.

If $m \leq 3$, y and z may be interpreted as the coordinate vectors of points Y and Z of the point space $\mathfrak{R}^m$. If Y and Z are two distinct points, then the points corresponding to the m-tuples (10.2) for any choices of λ are the points on the straight line through Y and Z, by corollary 7.2. The restriction (10.3) reduces (10.2) to the points on the line segment *between* Y and X (exercise 7.3). Thus, if the coordinate vectors of two distinct points solve (10.1) and are positive, then the coordinate vectors of *any* point on the line segment between those two points solve (10.1) and are positive.

Now, in geometry a set of points is called *convex* if, for any two distinct points of the set, *any* point on the line segment joining those two points belongs to that set. In $\mathfrak{R}^1$ a line segment is convex (Fig. 10.1). In $\mathfrak{R}^2$ a (solid) circle and a (solid) polygon none of whose interior angles exceeds

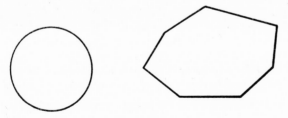

Fig. 10.2

Fig. 10.3

180 degrees are convex (Fig. 10.2), but no other polygon is convex (Fig. 10.3). In three dimensions a (solid) hemisphere, a (solid) sphere and a (solid) cube are convex (Fig. 10.4), but a (solid) doughnut (Fig. 10.5) is not. Following this geometric idea, we define convexity for an arbitrary *real* vector space.

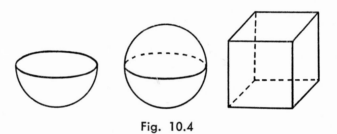

Fig. 10.4

Definition 10.2: A flock combination

$$\sum_{i=1}^{n} \lambda_i \mathbf{u}_i \quad \text{with} \quad \sum_{i=1}^{n} \lambda_i = 1 \quad \text{and} \quad \lambda_i \, \varepsilon \, R$$

of a set $\{\mathbf{u}_i\}_{1 \le i \le n}$ of elements of a *real* vector space **V** is called a *convex combination* if every coefficient is nonnegative, that is, if $\lambda_i \ge 0$ for $i = 1, \cdots , n$. A subset **S** of **V** is called *convex* if, for any two elements of **S**, every convex combination of these elements also belongs to **S**.

Convex combinations of position vectors and the points corresponding to them were discussed in exercises 7.7 and 7.8. The graphs of the sets of all convex combinations of a finite set of real couples or triples are

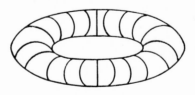

Fig. 10.5

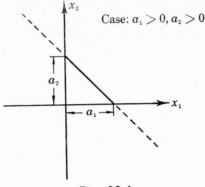

Case: $a_1 > 0, a_2 > 0$

Fig. 10.6

points, line segments, solid polygons, or solid polyhedra. The following general statement is also easy to prove.

Lemma 10.2:   *A convex combination of convex combinations of a subset* **S** *of a real vector space is itself a convex combination of* **S**.

Now the result obtained above can be expressed in the form:

Theorem 10.1:   *The set of all positive solutions of a system of linear equations is convex.*

EXAMPLES OF GRAPHS OF POSITIVE SOLUTIONS

1. The system consisting of one equation $x_1/a_1 + x_2/a_2 = 1$ (see exercise 6.14) has positive solutions if and only if a_1 or a_2 (or both) are positive. If $a_1, a_2 > 0$, then the graph of this positive solution set is the line

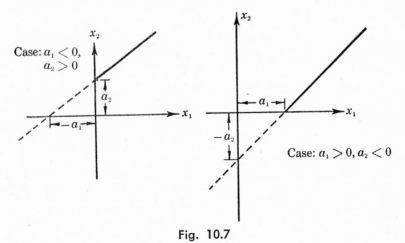

Case: $a_1 < 0,$ $a_2 > 0$

Case: $a_1 > 0, a_2 < 0$

Fig. 10.7

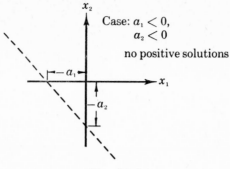

Fig. 10.8

segment between the two points where the given line intersects the coordinate axes (see Fig. 10.6). If $a_1 a_2 < 0$, then the graph of the positive solution set is a half-line (Fig. 10.7).

2. A solvable system consisting of two equations in two unknowns has either infinitely many solutions (namely, if the equations are multiples of each other, in which case the problem reduces to Example 1), or it has a unique solution (x_1^*, x_2^*). If this solution is positive (Fig. 10.9), then x_1^* and x_2^* are the coordinates of a point in the quadrant bounded by the coordinate semi-axes in the directions of the base translations. A single point is always convex.

3. The system consisting of the single equation $x_1/a_1 + x_2/a_2 + x_3/a_3 = 1$ has positive solutions if and only if at least one of the a_i is positive (see exercise 6.15). If $a_1, a_2, a_3 > 0$, then the graph of the positive solution set is the triangle whose vertices A, B, C have coordinate vectors $a_1 \mathbf{b}^{(1)}$, $a_2 \mathbf{b}^{(2)}$, $a_3 \mathbf{b}^{(3)}$ (Fig. 10.10).

4. A solvable system of two equations in 3 unknowns that are not multiples of each other has a solution set whose graph is a line (the inter-

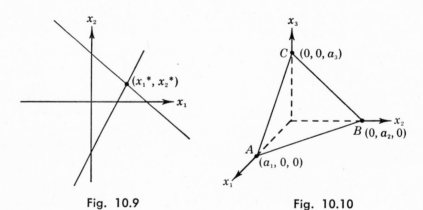

Fig. 10.9   Fig. 10.10

section of the two planes that are the graphs of each single equation). A part of this line may have positive coordinates (Fig. 10.11).

In the examples of point sets shown in Figs. 10.1 to 10.10 (except for Fig. 10.8), points can be found that do not lie on any line segment joining two *other* points of the set. For example, the two endpoints of the line segment (Figs. 10.1 and 10.6) have this property, and so have *all* points on the circumference of the circle, the vertices of the convex polygon (Fig. 10.2), and the vertices A, B, C in Fig. 10.10. In some cases there are only finitely many distinct points with this property; in other cases there are infinitely many. The algebraic equivalent of this property is defined as follows.

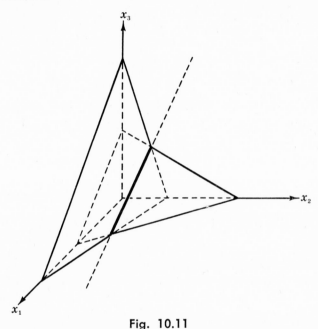

Fig. 10.11

Definition 10.3:   An element of a convex subset **S** of a real vector space is called *extremal* if it is not a convex combination of two *other* elements of **S**.

In other words, if an element **v** of a convex vector set **S** can be written in the form (10.2) with the restriction (10.3), then *either* **y** *or* **z** (*or both*) does *not* belong to **S**, *or else* **y** or **z** is equal to **v**. One can also express definition 10.3 in the following way: **v** is extremal *if there do not exist* distinct elements $\mathbf{y}^{(1)}$ and $\mathbf{y}^{(2)}$ *in* **S** such that, for suitable scalars μ_1 and μ_2

$$\mu_1 \mathbf{y}^{(1)} + \mu_2 \mathbf{y}^{(2)} = \mathbf{v} \quad \text{with} \quad \mu_1 + \mu_2 = 1, \quad \mu_1 > 0, \mu_2 > 0 \qquad (10.4)$$

is possible.

After these preparations the first main theorem of this chapter can be stated; its proof will keep us busy for a while.

Theorem 10.2: *Any system of linear equations has only finitely many extremal positive solutions.*

The examples showed, by inspection of all possible cases, that in the two-dimensional situation there can be at most two extremal positive solutions. By a similar investigation (see exercise 3) it can be proved that in the three-dimensional case there can be at most three extremal positive solutions.

The proof in the general case will be established if we exhibit *all* extremal positive solutions and show that there are only finitely many possibilities. At first we shall reinterpret equations (10.1) in the language of algebraic vector spaces. Let us denote the n-tuple of coefficients of x_j by $a^{(j)}$ ($j = 1$, $2, \cdots, m$). In order to remember how these n-tuples are formed from (10.1), we shall write them as vertical sequences (columns):

$$a^{(1)} = \begin{bmatrix} a_{11} \\ a_{21} \\ \vdots \\ a_{n1} \end{bmatrix}, \cdots, a^{(j)} = \begin{bmatrix} a_{1j} \\ a_{2j} \\ \vdots \\ a_{nj} \end{bmatrix}, \cdots, a^{(m)} = \begin{bmatrix} a_{1m} \\ a_{2m} \\ \vdots \\ a_{nm} \end{bmatrix}. \qquad (10.5)$$

Likewise let us abbreviate:

$$b = \begin{bmatrix} b_1 \\ b_2 \\ \vdots \\ b_n \end{bmatrix}. \qquad (10.6)$$

A solution of (10.1) can now be interpreted as an m-tuple $x = (x_1, x_2, \cdots, x_m)$ of real numbers that satisfies the single *vector* equation

$$x_1 a^{(1)} + x_2 a^{(2)} + \cdots + x_m a^{(m)} = b \quad \text{or (shorter)} \quad \sum_{j=1}^{m} x_j a^{(j)} = b. \quad (10.7)$$

If (10.1) is given, then we have m vertical sequences, defined by (10.5), on the left-hand side of (10.7). For any natural number m, any set of m objects has only *finitely many* subsets. Hence, in particular, the set

$$T = \{a^{(1)}, a^{(2)}, \cdots, a^{(m)}\} \qquad (10.8)$$

has only *finitely many linearly independent subsets*. Some, but not necessarily all, of these finitely many linearly independent subsets of (10.8) are connected with one and only one extremal positive solution of (10.7), as we shall describe in detail. Once we have shown this intimate connection between some linearly independent subsets of (10.8) and the totality of all extremal positive solutions, we shall also have verified, by implication, that theorem 10.2 is correct. For there can be only *finitely many* linearly independent subsets of T that can be connected with the extremal positive solutions. To be specific, we formulate and prove the following theorem.

Theorem 10.3: *A positive solution* $x^* = (x_1^*, x_2^*, \cdots, x_m^*)$ *of* (10.7) *is extremal if and only if the set of all those vertical sequences of* (10.8) *that occur on the left-hand side of* (10.7) *with nonzero coefficients is linearly independent.*

In other words, suppose it is possible to express the column vector b as a linear combination $x_1^* a^{(1)} + x_2^* a^{(2)} + \cdots + x_m^* a^{(m)}$ in such a way that, if all terms of the form $0 a^{(i)}$ in this sum are disregarded, the remaining $a^{(i)}$'s are linearly independent. If the m-tuple $x^* = (x_1^*, x_2^*, \cdots, x_m^*)$ is positive, then and only then, it is extremal. Before proving this theorem we will explain its meaning by an example.

EXAMPLE OF EXTREMAL SOLUTIONS

Consider the system

$$-x_1 + x_2 + x_3 = 1$$
$$4x_1 - x_2 + x_4 = 12 \tag{10.9}$$
$$-2x_1 - x_2 + x_5 = -2,$$

which may be written in the form

$$x_1 \begin{bmatrix} -1 \\ 4 \\ -2 \end{bmatrix} + x_2 \begin{bmatrix} 1 \\ -1 \\ -1 \end{bmatrix} + x_3 \begin{bmatrix} 1 \\ 0 \\ 0 \end{bmatrix} + x_4 \begin{bmatrix} 0 \\ 1 \\ 0 \end{bmatrix} + x_5 \begin{bmatrix} 0 \\ 0 \\ 1 \end{bmatrix} = \begin{bmatrix} 1 \\ 12 \\ -2 \end{bmatrix}. \tag{10.10}$$

In this case we have $m = 5$, and

$$T = \left\{ \begin{bmatrix} -1 \\ 4 \\ -2 \end{bmatrix}, \begin{bmatrix} 1 \\ -1 \\ -1 \end{bmatrix}, \begin{bmatrix} 1 \\ 0 \\ 0 \end{bmatrix}, \begin{bmatrix} 0 \\ 1 \\ 0 \end{bmatrix}, \begin{bmatrix} 0 \\ 0 \\ 1 \end{bmatrix} \right\}. \tag{10.11}$$

Every linearly independent subset of T of three real triples spans the set of all real triples. In this example (*but not in general*), every subset of T of *three* triples is linearly independent, and there are 10 subsets U_i having this property:

$$U_1 = \left\{ \begin{bmatrix} -1 \\ 4 \\ -2 \end{bmatrix}, \begin{bmatrix} 1 \\ -1 \\ -1 \end{bmatrix}, \begin{bmatrix} 1 \\ 0 \\ 0 \end{bmatrix} \right\}, \qquad U_2 = \left\{ \begin{bmatrix} -1 \\ 4 \\ -2 \end{bmatrix}, \begin{bmatrix} 1 \\ -1 \\ -1 \end{bmatrix}, \begin{bmatrix} 0 \\ 1 \\ 0 \end{bmatrix} \right\},$$

$$U_3 = \left\{ \begin{bmatrix} -1 \\ 4 \\ -2 \end{bmatrix}, \begin{bmatrix} 1 \\ -1 \\ -1 \end{bmatrix}, \begin{bmatrix} 0 \\ 0 \\ 1 \end{bmatrix} \right\}, \qquad U_4 = \left\{ \begin{bmatrix} -1 \\ 4 \\ -2 \end{bmatrix}, \begin{bmatrix} 1 \\ 0 \\ 0 \end{bmatrix}, \begin{bmatrix} 0 \\ 1 \\ 0 \end{bmatrix} \right\},$$

$$U_5 = \left\{ \begin{bmatrix} -1 \\ 4 \\ -2 \end{bmatrix}, \begin{bmatrix} 1 \\ 0 \\ 0 \end{bmatrix}, \begin{bmatrix} 0 \\ 0 \\ 1 \end{bmatrix} \right\}, \qquad U_6 = \left\{ \begin{bmatrix} -1 \\ 4 \\ -2 \end{bmatrix}, \begin{bmatrix} 0 \\ 1 \\ 0 \end{bmatrix}, \begin{bmatrix} 0 \\ 0 \\ 1 \end{bmatrix} \right\}, \qquad (10.12)$$

$$U_7 = \left\{ \begin{bmatrix} 1 \\ -1 \\ -1 \end{bmatrix}, \begin{bmatrix} 1 \\ 0 \\ 0 \end{bmatrix}, \begin{bmatrix} 0 \\ 1 \\ 0 \end{bmatrix} \right\}, \qquad U_8 = \left\{ \begin{bmatrix} 1 \\ -1 \\ -1 \end{bmatrix}, \begin{bmatrix} 1 \\ 0 \\ 0 \end{bmatrix}, \begin{bmatrix} 0 \\ 0 \\ 1 \end{bmatrix} \right\},$$

$$U_9 = \left\{ \begin{bmatrix} 1 \\ -1 \\ -1 \end{bmatrix}, \begin{bmatrix} 0 \\ 1 \\ 0 \end{bmatrix}, \begin{bmatrix} 0 \\ 0 \\ 1 \end{bmatrix} \right\}, \qquad U_{10} = \left\{ \begin{bmatrix} 1 \\ 0 \\ 0 \end{bmatrix}, \begin{bmatrix} 0 \\ 1 \\ 0 \end{bmatrix}, \begin{bmatrix} 0 \\ 0 \\ 1 \end{bmatrix} \right\}.$$

Since every set of (10.12) is linearly independent, the right-hand side of (10.10) can be expressed as a *unique* linear combination of each of these sets U_i $(i = 1, 2, \cdots, 10)$. To find the coefficients, one has to solve 10 systems of 3 equations in 3 unknowns. The solutions are, in order:

$$\left(\frac{7}{3}, -\frac{8}{3}, 6\right), \qquad \left(\frac{1}{3}, \frac{4}{3}, 12\right), \qquad \left(\frac{13}{3}, \frac{16}{3}, 12\right),$$

$$(1, 2, 8), \qquad (3, 4, 4), \qquad (-1, 16, -4), \qquad (10.13)$$

$$(2, -1, 14), \qquad (-12, 13, -14), \qquad (1, 13, -1),$$

$$(1, 12, -2).$$

Thus,

$$\frac{7}{3} \begin{bmatrix} -1 \\ 4 \\ -2 \end{bmatrix} - \frac{8}{3} \begin{bmatrix} 1 \\ -1 \\ -1 \end{bmatrix} + 6 \begin{bmatrix} 1 \\ 0 \\ 0 \end{bmatrix} = \begin{bmatrix} 1 \\ 12 \\ -2 \end{bmatrix},$$

$$\frac{1}{3} \begin{bmatrix} -1 \\ 4 \\ -2 \end{bmatrix} + \frac{4}{3} \begin{bmatrix} 1 \\ -1 \\ -1 \end{bmatrix} + 12 \begin{bmatrix} 0 \\ 1 \\ 0 \end{bmatrix} = \begin{bmatrix} 1 \\ 12 \\ -2 \end{bmatrix},$$

and so forth.

Every triple of (10.13) can be extended to a solution of (10.10) by the addition of two zeros in the appropriate places. In this way the following 10 solutions of (10.10) [or (10.9)] are obtained, in order:

$$\left(\frac{7}{3}, -\frac{8}{3}, 6, 0, 0\right), \quad \left(\frac{1}{3}, \frac{4}{3}, 0, 12, 0\right), \qquad \left(\frac{13}{3}, \frac{16}{3}, 0, 0, 12\right),$$

$$(1, 0, 2, 8, 0), \qquad (3, 0, 4, 0, 4), \qquad (-1, 0, 0, 16, -4), \quad (10.14)$$

$$(0, 2, -1, 14, 0), \qquad (0, -12, 13, 0, -14), \quad (0, 1, 0, 13, -1),$$

$$(0, 0, 1, 12, -2).$$

Every solution (10.14) has, by construction, the property that the set of all vertical sequences of (10.11) that occur on the left-hand side of (10.10) *with nonzero coefficients* is linearly independent. It is not hard to see (exercise 11) that no other solution of (10.10) has this property. Hence, by theorem 10.3, the extremal positive solutions of (10.10) are those four solutions of (10.14) that are positive, namely

$$\left(\frac{1}{3}, \frac{4}{3}, 0, 12, 0\right), \left(\frac{13}{3}, \frac{16}{3}, 0, 0, 12\right), (1, 0, 2, 8, 0), (3, 0, 4, 0, 4). \quad (10.15)$$

The condition in theorem 10.3 may be rephrased again: Suppose we have found a positive solution x^* of (10.7). Then some coordinates of x^* may be equal to zero, but at least one has to be different from zero. Now let us renumber the unknowns in (10.1) and thence in (10.7) (by transposing suffixes, as we did in Chapter 8) in such a way that, in the new sequence $x_1^*, x_2^*, \cdots, x_m^*$, all nonzero coefficients appear first and all zero coefficients afterward. Suppose we have $x_1^* \neq 0, \cdots, x_p^* \neq 0$, but $x_{p+1}^* = x_{p+2}^* = \cdots = x_m^* = 0$. Here p must be a natural number ≥ 1, because a positive vector x has at least *one* nonzero coordinate. Now theorem 10.3 claims that this x^* is *extremal* or not according as the set $\{a^{(1)}, a^{(2)}, \cdots, a^{(p)}\}$ is *linearly independent* or not. To sum up, we will have proved theorem 10.3 if we can prove the following lemma.

Lemma 10.3: *Let y be a solution of* (10.7) *whose first p coordinates are positive, and whose other coordinates are equal to zero:*

$$y = (y_1, y_2, \cdots, y_p, 0, 0, \cdots, 0) \quad \text{with} \quad y_1 > 0, y_2 > 0, \cdots, y_p > 0. \quad (10.16)$$

Then y is extremal if and only if the set $\{a^{(1)}, a^{(2)}, \cdots, a^{(p)}\}$ is linearly independent.

The proof consists of two parts. First, we show that the linear independence described implies that y is extremal; second, that the extremality implies that the subset of (10.8) in question is linearly independent.

PROOF, *First part:* Let the set $\{a^{(1)}, a^{(2)}, \cdots, a^{(p)}\}$ be linearly independent, and let (10.16) be a solution of (10.7). We shall give an indirect proof that (10.16) must be extremal. Suppose y is not extremal. Then there exist *positive* solutions of (10.7) u and v, both different from y, such that, for a suitable scalar λ, the equation

$$y = \lambda u + (1 - \lambda)v \quad \text{with} \quad 0 < \lambda < 1 \tag{10.17}$$

holds. This is a sum of two nonnegative column vectors. The $(p + 1)$st, $(p + 2)$nd, and all further coordinates of y are equal to zero; hence the sum of corresponding $(p + 1)$st, $(p + 2)$nd, etc., coordinates on the right-hand side must also be equal to zero. These coordinates on the right-hand sides are nonnegative numbers. A sum of two nonnegative numbers equals zero only if every summand equals zero. Consequently, the positive m-tuples u and v must have the property that their $(p + 1)$st, $(p + 2)$nd and all further coordinates are equal to zero. Thus, for example,

$$u_{p+1} = u_{p+2} = \cdots = u_m = 0. \tag{10.18}$$

Consequently,

$$\sum_{j=1}^{m} u_j a^{(j)} = b \tag{10.19}$$

implies that already

$$\sum_{j=1}^{p} u_j a^{(j)} = b \tag{10.20}$$

where the sum on the left-hand side breaks off after the term with $j = p$. But, since the set $\{a^{(1)}, a^{(2)}, \cdots, a^{(p)}\}$ is *linearly independent*, the representation of b as a linear combination of the elements of this set is *unique*, as we showed in the course of the proofs of theorem 5.2 and theorem 9.1. On the other hand we obviously have

$$\sum_{j=1}^{p} y_j a^{(j)} = b,$$

where the sum on the left-hand side also can be considered to break off after the term with $j = p$. Therefore, (10.20) implies

$$u_1 = y_1, \qquad u_2 = y_2, \qquad \cdots, \qquad u_p = y_p,$$

which, in conjunction with (10.18), means that $u = y$, *in contradiction* to our assumption that u and y are distinct. *Hence y is extremal.*

Second part: Now let the set $\{a^{(1)}, a^{(2)}, \cdots, a^{(p)}\}$ be linearly dependent. Then there exist real numbers $z_1, z_2, \cdots, z_p$, not all equal to zero, such that

$$\sum_{j=1}^{p} z_j a^{(j)} = 0. \tag{10.21}$$

Let us extend the p-tuple of coefficients of (10.21) to an m-tuple by making all further coordinates equal to zero:

$$z = (z_1, z_2, \cdots, z_p, 0, 0, \cdots, 0). \qquad (10.22)$$

Obviously, then, z satisfies the homogeneous equation

$$\sum_{j=1}^{m} z_j a^{(j)} = 0, \qquad (10.23)$$

and z is not the zero m-tuple. Note that z will not be positive, in general, but may have both positive and negative coordinates.

If (10.16) is a solution of the nonhomogeneous equation (10.7), then, as z is a solution of the corresponding homogeneous equation (10.23), for any scalar ϵ the two expressions

$$u = y + \epsilon z, \qquad v = y - \epsilon z \qquad (10.24)$$

must likewise be solutions of (10.7), by corollary 8.2. Here the elements u and v have nothing to do with the elements called u and v in the first part of this proof. If we choose ϵ arbitrarily we cannot expect u and v to be positive. But if we choose $\epsilon > 0$ sufficiently small, we can ensure that the addition of $\pm \epsilon z$ to the positive y still yields positive m-tuples u, v. We have only to make ϵ so small that the absolute value of every coordinate of ϵz is less than the corresponding coordinate of y. Then, in the worst case, we have to *subtract* these two coordinates, but we still end up with a positive difference. But

$$y = \tfrac{1}{2}u + \tfrac{1}{2}v. \qquad (10.25)$$

Thus, if u and v ($u \neq v$) are both positive, then y cannot be extremal. This completes the second part of the proof.

Additional remark: It is possible to specify ϵ explicitly so that u, $v > 0$. We consider the absolute values of the numbers $\dfrac{1}{2} \left| \dfrac{y_j}{z_j} \right|$ for all those suffixes j ($\leq p$) for which $z_j \neq 0$, and define our ϵ to be the *smallest* of these positive numbers. There is at least *one* coordinate of z different from zero; so we can find such an ϵ. In other words, we define

$$\epsilon = \text{minimum of all numbers } \frac{1}{2} \left| \frac{y_j}{z_j} \right| \text{ for which } z_j \neq 0. \qquad (10.26)$$

Then this ϵ will satisfy the conditions

$$\epsilon |z_j| \leq y_j \quad \text{for every} \quad j = 1, 2, \cdots, m, \qquad (10.27)$$

and also

$$\epsilon |z_j| < y_j \quad \textit{for at least one } j. \qquad (10.28)$$

PROOF: If $z_j \neq 0$, then $\epsilon \leq \dfrac{1}{2} \left| \dfrac{y_j}{z_j} \right|$; hence, certainly $\epsilon < \left| \dfrac{y_j}{z_j} \right| = y_j \left| \dfrac{1}{z_j} \right|$, which implies (10.28); and there exists a $j < p$ for which $z_j \neq 0$. If, for some other suffix $j < p$, we have $z_j = 0$, then (10.27) is trivially satisfied; for the coordinates of y are nonnegative.

From (10.27) and (10.28) it follows that, for both signs,

$$y \pm \epsilon z > 0. \tag{10.29}$$

This concludes the proof of lemma 10.3 and, therefore, of theorem 10.3.

The set of all positive solutions of a linear system will have one of the following two properties: Either *no* coordinate of any solution will exceed some fixed number N, or there will exist solutions for which (at least) one coordinate is arbitrarily large. Figures 10.6 and 10.10 show cases in which the coordinates of the positive solutions cannot become arbitrarily large. Figure 10.7 shows a case in which positive solutions exist with (both) coordinates as large as we please, because their corresponding points lie on an infinite half-line.

To describe the situation in the general n-dimensional case, we introduce

Definition 10.4:   A set S of n-tuples of real numbers is called *bounded* if there exists a nonnegative real number N such that the absolute value of no coordinate of any element of S exceeds N. A set of real n-tuples that is not bounded is called *unbounded*.

We have as an immediate consequence of this definition

Lemma 10.4:   *Let* $\{f_i = 0\}$ *be a nonhomogeneous linear system whose set of positive solutions is bounded. If* z^* *is a positive solution of* $\{f_i = 0\}$ *and if* a^* *is any solution of the corresponding homogeneous system, then the set of all positive solutions of* $\{f_i = 0\}$ *of the form* $z^* + ta^*$ *(for real t) is a line segment.*

We can now formulate the following remarkable theorem.

Theorem 10.4:   *If the set of all positive solutions of a nonhomogeneous system of linear equations is bounded, it consists of all convex combinations of the extremal positive solutions.*

PROOF: Every extremal positive solution is, trivially, a convex combination of all extremal positive solutions. Suppose there exists a positive solution s of a system that is not a convex combination of the extremal solutions. Then, as s is not extremal, there exist two distinct *positive* solutions u and v such that $s = \lambda u + (1 - \lambda)v$ with $0 < \lambda < 1$. Obviously, all n-tuples $u + (1 - \lambda)v = v + \lambda(u - v)$, for *any* λ, are solutions of the system; but, by lemma 10.4, we have only a line segment of *positive* solutions among all solutions of this form. Suppose that $\bar{u}$ and $\bar{v}$ are the endpoints of this line segment. Then u and v are convex combinations of $\bar{u}$ and $\bar{v}$; hence, by lemma 10.2, s also is a convex combination of $\bar{u}$ and $\bar{v}$. Now $\bar{u}$ and $\bar{v}$ cannot *both* be convex combinations of the extremal solutions, because, if they were, s would likewise be a convex combination of the extremal solutions, by lemma 10.2.

Hence we may assume that $\bar{u}$ is not a convex combination of the extremal positive solutions. Suppose that, in the n-tuple s, there are exactly p coordinates equal to zero. We shall denote this fact by writing $s = s^{(p)}$. Without loss of generality, let us assume that the *last* p coordinates of s vanish. Then it can be seen, as in the proof of lemma 10.3, that the last p coordinates of $\bar{u}$ (and of $\bar{v}$) must vanish, too.

We are now going to show that in $\bar{u}$ there are *at least* $p + 1$ coordinates equal to zero. Suppose that this were not true; that is, that all of the first $n - p$ coordinates of $\bar{u}$ were different from zero. Then, following the procedure in the proof of lemma 10.3, we could choose a positive real number ϵ so small that both

$$\bar{u} + \epsilon(\bar{v} - \bar{u}) \quad \text{and} \quad \bar{u} - \epsilon(\bar{v} - \bar{u})$$

are still positive. But this would mean that $\bar{u}$ is not an endpoint of the line segment of all positive solutions of the form $\bar{u} + \lambda(\bar{v} - \bar{u})$. Consequently, there must be exactly q coordinates of $\bar{u}$, with $q > p$, that vanish. We also note that $\bar{u}$ *cannot be an extremal solution*, because we assumed it was not a convex combination of extremal solutions.

Now we put $\bar{u} = s^{(q)}$ and repeat the procedure. Then we find a positive solution that is not extremal but contains at least $q + 1$ coordinates equal to zero.

After a finite number of iterations of this process, a positive *not extremal* solution $c^{(r)}$ is obtained having so few nonzero coordinates that the $a^{(i)}$'s with nonzero coefficients in $\sum_{i=1}^{m} c_i^{(r)} a^{(i)}$ are linearly independent. But then $c^{(r)}$ is extremal, by theorem 10.3. This gives the desired contradiction; hence there cannot exist a positive solution s that is not a convex combination of the extremal solutions.

Warning: The conclusion of theorem 10.4 fails if the set of all positive solutions is *unbounded*.

EXERCISES

1. Prove lemma 10.1. Prove also: The sum of two nonnegative n-tuples and a nonnegative scalar multiple of a nonnegative n-tuple are both nonnegative.

2. Discuss the cases of Example 3 of Graphs of Positive Solutions in which one or two a_i are negative.

3. How does the graph of all positive solutions of a system of one or two homogeneous linear equations look? What are the extremal points?

4. What possible types of graphs are there of the positive solutions of a system of two nonhomogeneous linear equations that are not multiples of each other?

5. Prove: The set of all convex combinations of a set of vectors is convex.

6. Find all extremal points of a solid hemisphere, of a solid sphere, and of a solid cube.

7. Find all extremal positive solutions of the following systems:

    (a) $x_1 - x_2 + x_3 = 2$ (c) $2x_1 + x_2 - 2x_3 = -1$

             $x_1 + 2x_2 - x_3 = 3;$ $x_1 - x_2 + 3x_3 = 1;$

    (b) $x_1 - x_3 = 1$ (d) $x_1 + x_3 = 1$

             $x_2 - x_3 = 1;$ $x_2 + x_3 = 1.$

Is the set of all positive solutions bounded in these cases?

8. Prove lemma 10.2.

9. Prove lemma 10.4.

10. Prove that (10.13) gives the coefficients of those linear combinations of (10.12), respectively, that are equal to $\begin{bmatrix} 1 \\ 12 \\ -2 \end{bmatrix}$.

11. Prove that only the solutions of the form (10.14) have the property required by theorem 10.3.

12. Interpret the proof of theorem 10.4 geometrically in the two- and three-dimensional cases.

13. Consider the *system of linear inequalities* obtained from (10.1) by replacing the equality signs "$=$" by "$\leq$". A *solution* of such a system is an m-tuple $x^* = (x_1^*, x_2^*, \cdots, x_m^*)$ such that the substitution $x = x^*$ in (10.1) yields the demanded inequalities. Prove: The set of all positive solutions of a system of linear inequalities is convex.

14. Prove that every *finite* set of real n-tuples is bounded.

15. Let $\{P_i\}_{1 \leq i \leq n}$ be a set of points of $\mathfrak{R}^2$. Let $\mathfrak{E}$ be the set of all points with position vectors

$$\sum_{i=1}^{n} \alpha_i \mathbf{p}_i, \qquad \sum_{i=1}^{n} \alpha_i = 1, \quad \text{all} \quad \alpha_i \geq 0.$$

Describe geometrically those points of $\mathfrak{E}$ for whose position vectors the above convex combination is unique.

16. Generalize the result of the previous exercise to the three-dimensional case for four points that are not coplanar.

11

On Linear Programming

In many problems in economics, business administration, military strategy, and other fields one is asked to find from the set *of all solutions* of a system of equations or inequalities *a solution* that is *optimal* in some sense. In many cases the underlying mathematical structure is so complicated that our contemporary mathematics is still not advanced and well tailored enough to contribute to a solution. But, during the last decades, the particularly easy case has been settled in which all the equations of the system are *linear* and in which the optimality condition can be expressed as a demand that a *linear* polynomial function should have a minimum or a maximum value. The methods developed to solve this limited problem can be used in electronic computing machines and have become familiar to the scientific community under the name of "Linear Programming". In this chapter we shall formulate some problems of this type and present a standard way to find an optimal solution of them under certain conditions, making use of the results of the last chapter.

We start with an example from ordinary life, the so-called *diet problem*: Assume a person can obtain n types of food $\mathcal{F}_1$, $\mathcal{F}_2$, $\cdots$, $\mathcal{F}_n$ (for example, bread, butter, cheese) in any desired quantities x_1, x_2, $\cdots$, x_n, measured in pounds. Let the price for one pound of $\mathcal{F}_j$ be p_j cents $(j = 1, \cdots, n)$. Suppose that there are m substances $\mathcal{S}_1$, $\mathcal{S}_2$, $\cdots$, $\mathcal{S}_m$ (for example, protein, starch, vitamin A) of which the person has to consume *at least* c_1, c_2, $\cdots$, c_m units per day. Let one pound of $\mathcal{F}_j$ contain a_{ij} units of the substance $\mathcal{S}_i$. How must the quantities $x = (x_1, x_2, \cdots, x_n)$ be chosen so that the person gets what he needs, but pays the *least* price for his food?

Since x_j pounds of the food $\mathcal{F}_j$ contain $a_{ij}x_j$ units of the substance $\mathcal{S}_i$, the consumption of all chosen quantities of all foodstuffs implies, in particular, a consumption of $\sum_{j=1}^{n} a_{ij}x_j$ units of the substance $\mathcal{S}_i$. Hence, the dietetic conditions are expressible by the m inequalities

$$\sum_{j=1}^{n} a_{ij}x_j \geq c_i \qquad \text{for} \quad i = 1, 2, \cdots, m. \tag{11.1}$$

Since x_j pounds of the food $\mathcal{F}_j$ cost p_jx_j cents, the total cost of all foodstuffs is equal to

$$p(x) = \sum_{j=1}^{n} p_jx_j \tag{11.2}$$

cents.

From the nature of the problem it is obvious that none of the real numbers x_j can be negative; hence, we must also have

$$x_j \geq 0 \qquad \text{for} \quad j = 1, 2, \cdots, n. \tag{11.3}$$

The person now has the problem of finding a solution of (11.1) and (11.3) that makes (11.2) *as small as possible*. Note that (11.3) allows the zero vector as a solution.

This and other examples lead to the following concepts.

Definition 11.1: A positive solution x^* of (11.1) is called *minimal with respect to* (11.2) if $p(x^*) \leq p(x)$ for all positive solutions x of (11.1), and *maximal* if $p(x^*) \geq p(x)$. A minimal or maximal solution is also called *optimal*.

Now the mathematical problem of linear programming can be stated: *Find a positive solution of a finite system of linear inequalities that is optimal with respect to a linear polynomial function.*

Note: If x^* is minimal with respect to $p(x)$, then it is maximal with respect to $-p(x)$, and vice versa. Hence it suffices in the following to deal with minimal solutions.

For many purposes it is convenient to express the inequality conditions (11.1) in the form of equations. It is very easy to make this transition. We introduce m additional variables $y_1, y_2, \cdots, y_m$, one for every inequality, and consider instead of (11.1) and (11.3) the system of corresponding *equations*

$$\sum_{j=1}^{n} a_{ij}x_j - y_i = c_i \qquad \text{for} \quad i = 1, 2, \cdots, m \tag{11.4}$$

with $x_j \geq 0$ for $j = 1, 2, \cdots, n$ and $y_i \geq 0$ for $i = 1, 2, \cdots, m$.

From every solution $(x_1^*, x_2^*, \cdots, x_n^*, y_1^*, y_2^*, \cdots, y_m^*)$ of (11.4) we can construct a solution of (11.1) satisfying (11.3) simply by cutting off the last m coordinates. And vice versa: From every solution x^* of (11.1) satisfying

(11.3) a solution of (11.4) can be found by enlarging the n-tuple x^* to an $(n + m)$-tuple (x^*, y^*) by adding m new coordinates defined by

$$y_i^* = \sum_{j=1}^{n} a_{ij} x_j^* - c_i \qquad \text{for} \quad i = 1, \cdots, m. \tag{11.5}$$

Hence, there is a natural one-to-one correspondence between the non-negative solutions x^* of (11.1) and the nonnegative solutions (x^*, y^*) of (11.4):

$$x^* \rightarrow (x^*, y^*). \tag{11.6}$$

The value y_i^* in (11.5) indicates how tightly or loosely the solution x^* satisfies the ith inequality of (11.1). Therefore, the dummy unknowns y_i are frequently called *slack variables*.

Since definition 10.3 was given for an arbitrary convex vector set and the set of positive solutions of (11.1) is convex (exercise 10.13), there may be n-tuples that are extremal solutions of (11.1). Suppose we enlarge such an extremal n-tuple x^* to an $(m + n)$-tuple (x^*, y^*) by adding new coordinates defined by (11.5). Then (x^*, y^*) is an *extremal* positive solution of (11.4), as can easily be seen (exercise 11.4). Hence, all possible extremal positive solutions of (11.1) are among the positive n-tuples obtained by

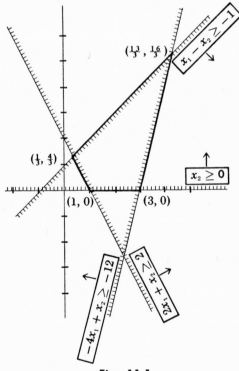

Fig. 11.1

cutting off the last m coordinates of the finitely many extremal positive solutions (x^*, y^*) of (11.4).

EXAMPLE OF A SYSTEM OF LINEAR INEQUALITIES AND ITS CORRESPONDING SYSTEM OF LINEAR EQUATIONS

Consider the system of linear inequalities

$$x_1 - x_2 \geq -1$$
$$-4x_1 + x_2 \geq -12 \tag{11.7}$$
$$2x_1 + x_2 \geq 2.$$

The graph of the positive solution set (Fig. 11.1) is the set of all points of the convex polygon bounded by the four vertices with coordinates

$$\left(\frac{1}{3}, \frac{4}{3}\right), \quad \left(\frac{13}{3}, \frac{16}{3}\right), \quad (3, 0), \quad (1, 0). \tag{11.8}$$

These are the only extremal positive solutions of (11.7).

The corresponding system of linear equations is

$$-x_1 + x_2 + x_3 = 1$$
$$4x_1 - x_2 + x_4 = 12 \tag{11.9}$$
$$-2x_1 - x_2 + x_5 = -2;$$

that is, the system (10.9) discussed in the previous section.

It can be seen at once that the one-to-one correspondence (11.6) assigns to every couple of (11.8) a quintuple of (10.15). This shows how the nonnegative solutions of a system of linear inequalities in two unknowns are found by computing the nonnegative solutions of the corresponding system of linear equations and cutting off the dummy unknowns.

Since the solutions of (11.1) with (11.3) and of the *equations* (11.4) correspond to each other so completely, we shall from now on pursue the problem of linear programming in the following simplified form:

To find a positive solution of the system

$$\sum_{j=1}^{k} a_{ij}x_j = c_i \qquad \text{for} \quad i = 1, 2, \cdots, m \tag{11.10}$$

that is optimal with respect to a linear polynomial (11.2).

The connection with (11.4) is given by the substitution $x_j = y_{j-n}$ for $j = n + 1, n + 2, \cdots, n + m = k$. The slack variables do not enter (11.2), but it is possible to continue the summation index j in (11.2) formally up to k by putting the newly entering coefficients equal to zero.

We shall not, at first, deal with the most general form of this problem, but only with the case in which the set of all positive solutions of (11.10) is *bounded*. This bounded case will occur in all but very few instances of the practical application of the theory. Also, in the unbounded case there may be no optimal solution, for then it may happen that (11.2) can become as large as desired or as small as desired, for suitable positive solutions of (11.10).

Theorem 11.1:   *If the set of all positive solutions of* (11.10) *is bounded, then there exists an extremal solution that is minimal and an extremal solution that is maximal.*

Note: This theorem does *not* state that in the bounded case every optimal solution must be extremal; this does not need to be true. It claims only that *of all maximal solutions* at least one must be extremal and *of all minimal solutions* at least one must be extremal.

PROOF: We confine ourselves to showing the existence of an extremal solution that is *minimal*. The existence of a maximal extremal solution can be shown in the same manner.

Let $\{x^{(1)}, x^{(2)}, \cdots, x^{(h)}\}$ be the set of all extremal solutions of (11.10), numbered in such a way that

$$p(x^{(1)}) \leq p(x^{(j)}) \qquad \text{for} \quad j = 2, 3, \cdots, h. \tag{11.11}$$

By theorem 10.4, any positive solution x^* of (11.10) has the form

$$x^* = \sum_{j=1}^{h} \lambda_j x^{(j)} \quad \text{with} \quad \sum_{j=1}^{h} \lambda_j = 1, \quad \text{all} \quad \lambda_j \geq 0.$$

As $p(x)$ is linear and homogeneous, we have

$$p(x^*) = p\left(\sum_{j=1}^{h} \lambda_j x^{(j)} \right) = \sum_{j=1}^{h} \lambda_j p(x^{(j)}). \tag{11.12}$$

But from (11.11) it follows that

$$\sum_{j=1}^{h} \lambda_j p(x^{(j)}) \geq \sum_{j=1}^{h} \lambda_j p(x^{(1)}) = p(x^{(1)}).$$

Consequently $p(x^{(1)}) \leq p(x^*)$ holds for any positive solution x^* of (11.10).

From the standpoint of pure mathematics, this theorem settles the problem of linear programming in the bounded case. The finitely many extremal solutions $x^{(j)}$ can be computed in finite time, and, by calculating $p(x^{(j)})$ for all $j = 1, 2, \cdots, h$, one can check which of these solutions is optimal. If the number of unknowns in the linear inequalities is 2, then the linear programming problem can be solved graphically. Since, in two dimensions, the graph of $p(x_1, x_2) = \alpha(\alpha \ \varepsilon \ R)$ is a line, all solutions of the system for which $p(x)$ has the same value must lie on a line. Since the graphs of $p(x) = \alpha$ and $p(x) = 0$ are parallel lines, by exercise 6.16, one has to construct the lines through all extremal points parallel to the graph of $p(x) = 0$ and check which of these lines gives the smallest value of α (in the minimal problem).

EXAMPLES OF GRAPHIC SOLUTIONS OF LINEAR PROGRAMMING

1. Which positive solution of the system (11.7) is *minimal* with respect to the polynomial $p(x_1,x_2) = x_1 + x_2$? The lines defined by $x_1 + x_2 = \alpha > 0$ increase in distance from the origin with increasing α. Hence, a minimal positive solution must be given by an extremal positive solution lying on the line, parallel to the graph of $x_1 + x_2 = 0$, that is least distant from the origin (Fig. 11.2). In our case $(1,0)$ is minimal; it lies on the graph of $x_1 + x_2 = 1$.

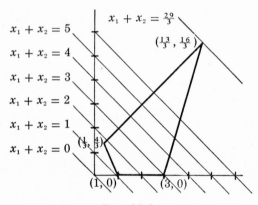

Fig. 11.2

2. Similarly, it can be shown that $(\frac{13}{3},\frac{16}{3})$ is a maximal positive solution of (11.7) with respect to $p(x_1,x_2) = x_1 + x_2$ (Fig. 11.2).

3. Both $(\frac{1}{3},\frac{4}{3})$ and $(\frac{13}{3},\frac{16}{3})$ are minimal positive solutions of (11.7) with respect to $p(x_1,x_2) = x_1 - x_2$. In fact, all positive solutions whose graphs lie on the line through $(\frac{1}{3},\frac{4}{3})$ and $(\frac{13}{3},\frac{16}{3})$ are minimal in this case. This shows that, in addition to extremal solutions, other solutions can also be optimal (Fig. 11.3).

4. $(3,0)$ is a maximal positive solution of (11.7) with respect to $p(x_1,x_2) = x_1 - x_2$ (Fig. 11.3).

However, in practice, the number both of unknowns and of equations may be very large (for example, $n = 1000$, $m = 2000$); so the time and effort to check the values of $p(x)$ for every extremal x^* may be prohibitive, even for modern electronic computing machines.

A much faster procedure for obtaining an optimal solution has been developed by the American mathematician *G. B. Dantzig* (1914–) known as the *simplex method*. It is an iterative process by which one steps from some arbitrary extremal solution to "more and more optimal" extremal solutions. It even shows whether, in the unbounded case, an optimal solution exists, which then turns out to be extremal, too. We shall outline this method only under the assumption that every extremal solution caught during the procedure has *exactly* r nonzero coordinates, where r is the maximum number of linearly independent vertical sequences $a^{(j)}$ in (11.13). This assumption, that no occurring extremal solution has less than r nonzero coordinates, is not always satisfied. The case in which an extremal solution with too few nonzero coordinates is caught is called

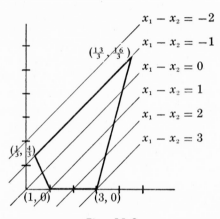

Fig. 11.3

degeneracy: the simplex method has then to be modified. By a slight alteration in the right-hand sides of (11.10) it is always possible to avoid degeneracy; but we will not consider this.

As in the previous chapter, we write equations (11.10) as *one* vector equation

$$\sum_{j=1}^{k} x_j a^{(j)} = c \tag{11.13}$$

with the abbreviations

$$a^{(j)} = \begin{bmatrix} a_{1j} \\ a_{2j} \\ \cdot \\ \cdot \\ \cdot \\ a_{mj} \end{bmatrix} \quad \text{for} \quad j = 1, 2, \cdots, k, \quad c = \begin{bmatrix} c_1 \\ c_2 \\ \cdot \\ \cdot \\ \cdot \\ c_m \end{bmatrix}.$$

Suppose that the maximum number of linearly independent $a^{(j)}$ ($j = 1, 2, \cdots, k$) is r and that the first r of them, $a^{(1)}, a^{(2)}, \cdots, a^{(r)}$, are linearly independent. Then all $a^{(j)}$ (for $j = 1, 2, \cdots, k$) can be expressed as unique linear combinations of the first r $a^{(j)}$'s:

$$a^{(j)} = \sum_{i=1}^{r} h_{ji} a^{(i)} \qquad \text{for} \quad j = 1, \cdots, k. \tag{11.14}$$

This equation (11.14) means that the k-tuple

$$h^{(j)} = (-h_{j1}, -h_{j2}, \cdots, -h_{jr}, 0, \cdots, 0, 1, 0, \cdots, 0)$$

$$\text{for} \quad j = r + 1, \cdots, k, \tag{11.15}$$

which has 1 as the jth coordinate, is a solution of the homogeneous equation associated with (11.13)

$$\sum_{j=1}^{k} x_j a^{(j)} = 0. \tag{11.16}$$

If (11.13) has any solutions at all, it must have a solution x^* of the form

$$x^* = (x_1^*, x_2^*, \cdots, x_r^*, 0, \cdots, 0), \tag{11.17}$$

where all but the first r coordinates vanish. Suppose furthermore

$$x_1^* > 0, \qquad x_2^* > 0, \qquad \cdots, \qquad x_r^* > 0. \tag{11.18}$$

Then (11.17) is extremal, by lemma 10.3.

By corollary 8.2, with x^*,

$$x^{**} = x^* + \lambda h^{(j)} \qquad \text{for any} \quad j = r + 1, \cdots, k \tag{11.19}$$

is also a solution of (11.13). This solution (11.19) is positive if and only if λ is nonnegative and satisfies the conditions

$$\lambda \leq \frac{x_i^*}{h_{ji}} \qquad \text{for those } i \text{ for which} \quad h_{ji} > 0. \tag{11.20}$$

The value of polynomial (11.2) for $x = x^{**}$ is given by

$$p(x^{**}) = p(x^* + \lambda h^{(j)}) = p(x^*) + \lambda\left(p_j - \sum_{i=1}^{r} p_i h_{ji}\right) \tag{11.21}$$

as can be seen by straightforward substitution and rearranging of terms. With the further abbreviation

$$d_j = p_j - \sum_{i=1}^{r} p_i h_{ji} \qquad \text{for} \quad j = r + 1, \cdots, k \tag{11.22}$$

we can simplify the previous equation to

$$p(x^{**}) = p(x^*) + \lambda d_j. \tag{11.23}$$

This shows that $p(x^{**})$ is less than $p(x^*)$; that is, that x^{**} is *"more minimal"* than x^*, if d_j is *negative*.

If, *for some* $j (> r), d_j < 0$ and $h_{ji} \leq 0$ *for all* $i = 1, \cdots, r$ then condition (11.20) is satisfied for *any* positive λ, regardless of how large. But then λd_j can be made *as small as desired*, namely, by choosing λ sufficiently large. Consequently, in this case (in which the set of positive solutions is obviously unbounded) there cannot exist a minimal solution of the problem.

But if, *for some* $j (> r), d_j < 0$ and $h_{ji} > 0$ *for some* i then (11.20) is a genuine condition. To make (11.23) as small as possible under the given conditions we have to choose λ as large as possible; hence we take

$$\lambda = \text{minimum} \ \frac{x_i^*}{h_{ji}} \qquad \text{for those } i \text{ for which} \quad h_{ji} > 0. \qquad (11.24)$$

Suppose we have $\lambda = x_q^*/h_{jq}$, where $1 \leq q \leq r$. Then the qth coordinate of the solution x^{**} defined by (11.19) vanishes. Hence, in this case, x^{**} possesses *at most* r nonzero coefficients and must again be extremal, by exercise 10. If this x^{**} has *exactly* r nonzero coefficients; that is, if

$$\frac{x_q^*}{h_{jq}} \neq \frac{x_i^*}{h_{ji}} \qquad \text{for all other } i \ (\neq q) \text{ for which } h_{ji} > 0, \qquad (11.25)$$

then the procedure can be repeated with x^* replaced by x^{**}. If (11.25) is not satisfied, then additional rules must be introduced for which we refer the reader to the mathematical literature on linear programming.

So far we have assumed that some d_j is negative. If we have

$$d_j \geq 0 \qquad \text{for } all \quad j = r + 1, \cdots, k, \qquad (11.26)$$

then it can be shown that x^* is minimal. For let y^* be any other positive solution of (11.13). Then we have $\sum_{j=1}^{k} y_j^* a^{(j)} = c$, or, in view of (11.14)

$$c = \sum_{j=1}^{k} y_j^* \sum_{i=1}^{r} h_{ji} a^{(i)} = \sum_{i=1}^{r} \left(\sum_{j=1}^{k} y_j^* h_{ji} \right) a^{(i)}.$$

Since the $a^{(i)}$ are linearly independent and we also have $\sum_{i=1}^{r} x_i^* a^{(i)} = c$, it follows that

$$x_i^* = \sum_{j=1}^{k} y_j^* h_{ji}.$$

Consequently, we may write $p(x^*)$ in the form

$$p(x^*) = \sum_{i=1}^{r} p_i \left(\sum_{j=1}^{k} y_j^* h_{ji} \right) = \sum_{j=1}^{k} y_j^* \sum_{i=1}^{r} p_i h_{ji}. \qquad (11.27)$$

But (11.22) and (11.26) together mean

$$p_j \geq \sum_{i=1}^{r} p_i h_{ji} \qquad \text{for} \quad j = 1, \cdots, k$$

where we have trivial equalities for $j = 1, \cdots, r$. Hence, by substituting p_i for $\sum_{i=1}^{r} p_i h_{ji}$ in (11.27), we do not decrease (11.27). In other words, (11.26) implies

$$p(x^*) \leq \sum_{j=1}^{k} y_j^* p_j.$$

Since the right-hand side of this inequality is equal to $p(y^*)$, our assertion that x^* is minimal is proved.

We may sum up the preceding results as follows.

Theorem 11.2: *Let (11.17) with (11.18) be an extremal solution x^* of (11.13), and assume that all $a^{(i)}$ can be expressed as unique linear combinations of the first r $a^{(i)}$'s, by (11.14). Consider, for $j = r + 1, \cdots, k$, all expressions d_j defined by (11.22). Then three and only three cases are possible:*

1. *For some j, d_j is negative, but no h_{ji} is positive. Then there does not exist a minimal solution.*
2. *For some j, d_j is negative, but at least one h_{ji} is positive. Then x^{**}, defined by (11.19) in conjunction with (11.24), is another extremal solution, and $p(x^{**}) < p(x^*)$.*
3. *No d_j is negative. Then x^* is minimal.*

Accordingly, if a positive solution x^* with exactly r nonzero coefficients is found, the procedure indicated in the proof of the theorem shows that either (1) there cannot exist a minimal solution or (2) the extremal solution leads to *another* extremal solution x^{**} or (3) x^* is minimal. In case 2 the procedure can be repeated if x^{**} also has exactly r nonzero coefficients. Assuming that no newly found extremal solution has fewer than r nonzero coordinates, this procedure must terminate with case 1 or 3 after a finite number of steps.

Note: No extremal solution can appear repeatedly because of the strict inequality $p(x^{**}) < p(x^*)$ in case 2.

EXAMPLE OF SIMPLEX METHOD

Suppose we consider the system

$$x_1 \quad - \quad x_4 + 2x_5 + \quad x_6 - x_7 = 2$$
$$x_2 + 2x_4 - \quad x_5 + \quad x_6 - x_7 = 4$$
$$x_3 + 3x_4 + \quad x_5 - 2x_6 + x_7 = 5$$

with $k = 7$, $m = 3$, and $r = 3$. This system obviously has the positive extremal solution $x^* = (2,4,5,0,0,0,0)$.
Then

$$a^{(1)} = \begin{bmatrix} 1 \\ 0 \\ 0 \end{bmatrix}, \; a^{2)} = \begin{bmatrix} 0 \\ 1 \\ 0 \end{bmatrix}, \; a^{(3)} = \begin{bmatrix} 0 \\ 0 \\ 1 \end{bmatrix}, \; a^{(4)} = \begin{bmatrix} -1 \\ 2 \\ 3 \end{bmatrix},$$

$$a^{(5)} = \begin{bmatrix} 2 \\ -1 \\ 1 \end{bmatrix}, \; a^{(6)} = \begin{bmatrix} 1 \\ 1 \\ -2 \end{bmatrix}, \; a^{(7)} = \begin{bmatrix} -1 \\ -1 \\ +1 \end{bmatrix}; c = \begin{bmatrix} 2 \\ 4 \\ 5 \end{bmatrix}.$$

We have

$$
\begin{aligned}
a^{(1)} &= \; 1a^{(1)} + 0a^{(2)} + 0a^{(3)} \\
a^{(2)} &= \; 0a^{(1)} + 1a^{(2)} + 0a^{(3)} \\
a^{(3)} &= \; 0a^{(1)} + 0a^{(2)} + 1a^{(3)} \\
a^{(4)} &= -1a^{(1)} + 2a^{(2)} + 3a^{(3)}, \quad \text{hence} \quad (h_{ji}) = \\
a^{(5)} &= \; 2a^{(1)} - 1a^{(2)} + 1a^{(3)} \\
a^{(6)} &= \; 1a^{(1)} + 1a^{(2)} - 2a^{(3)} \\
a^{(7)} &= -1a^{(1)} - 1a^{(2)} + 1a^{(3)}
\end{aligned}
\qquad
\begin{bmatrix}
1 & 0 & 0 \\
0 & 1 & 0 \\
0 & 0 & 1 \\
-1 & 2 & 3 \\
2 & -1 & +1 \\
1 & 1 & -2 \\
-1 & -1 & 1
\end{bmatrix},
$$

and, therefore,

$$
\begin{aligned}
h^{(4)} &= (+1,-2,-3,1,0,0,0) \\
h^{(5)} &= (-2,+1,-1,0,1,0,0) \\
h^{(6)} &= (-1,-1,+2,0,0,1,0) \\
h^{(7)} &= (\;1,\;\;1,-1,0,0,0,1).
\end{aligned}
$$

Suppose furthermore that $p(x) = x_4 - 2x_5 + 3x_6 - 4x_7$; that is, $p_1 = p_2 = p_3 = 0$, $p_4 = 1$, $p_5 = -2$, $p_6 = 3$, $p_7 = -4$. Then, by (11.22),

$$d_4 = 1, \qquad d_5 = -2, \qquad d_6 = 3, \qquad d_7 = -4.$$

Hence, for $j = 5$, $d_j < 0$. Checking h_{51}, h_{52}, h_{53}, we find that $h_{51} > 0$, $h_{52} < 0$, $h_{53} > 0$. Therefore, we have case 2 of theorem 11.2, and λ has to be determined such that

$$\lambda = \text{minimum} \left(\frac{x_1^*}{h_{51}}, \frac{x_3^*}{h_{53}} \right) = \text{minimum} \left(\frac{2}{2}, \frac{5}{1} \right) = 1.$$

Consequently

$$
\begin{aligned}
x^{**} = x^* + \lambda h^{(5)} &= (2,4,5,0,0,0,0) + (-2,1,-1,0,1,0\;0) \\
&= (0,5,4,0,1,0,0)
\end{aligned}
$$

is another extremal solution, which is "more minimal".

EXERCISES

1. Prove: If $p(x) = p(y)$, then $p(z) = p(y)$ for every convex combination z of x and y.

2. Construct and prove a theorem analogous to theorem 11.2 for the maximal problem.

3. Sketch the graph of all positive solutions of the system

$$4x_1 + \quad x_2 \geq 4$$
$$x_1 + \quad x_2 \geq 2$$
$$-x_1 + \quad x_2 \geq -1 \qquad (11.28)$$
$$-8x_1 - 15x_2 \geq -120$$
$$3x_1 - \quad x_2 \geq -3,$$

and determine all extremal positive solutions.

4. Transform the system (11.28) into a system of linear equations by introduction of slack variables, find all extremal positive solutions of the new system, and relate them with the extremal solutions of the previous problem.

5. Find a positive solution of (11.28) that is (a) minimal with respect to $2x_1 - x_2$; (b) maximal with respect to $2x_1 - x_2$; (c) minimal with respect to $x_1 + x_2$; (d) maximal with respect to $x_1 - x_2$; and (e) minimal with respect to x_2. Determine your answers graphically.

6. Find a positive solution of $2x_1 + 6x_2 \leq 3$ that is (a) minimal with respect to $x_1 - x_2$; (b) maximal with respect to $x_1 + x_2$; (c) minimal with respect to x_1.

7. Transform the following problem into the form of linear programming: Find a solution (*not necessarily positive*) of the inequality $x_1 + 3x_1 \leq 4$ that satisfies $-2 \leq x_1 \leq 2$ and $-3 \leq x_2 \leq +3$ and is minimal with respect to $x_1 + x_2$.

8. Check Examples 2, 3, and 4 of Graphic Solutions of Linear Programming.

9. Prove (11.12) and (11.21).

10. Prove: (11.19), with (11.24), is extremal if $d_i < 0$.

11. Prove by an example: If the set of all positive solutions of (11.10) is not bounded, there may exist optimal solutions.

12. How would you handle a linear programming problem that involves a system consisting of both equations and inequalities?

13. Prove that (11.17) is extremal even if (11.18) does not hold.

12

The Calculus of Matrices

In this section we shall introduce two partial internal composition laws, written as multiplication and addition, respectively, and an external composition law, written as a scalar multiplication, for sets of double sequences or *matrices*. The notions and notations introduced are very useful in almost all parts of mathematics and in many applications to physics, chemistry, business administration, economics, military strategy, and many other fields. For the purpose of this elementary text it is more convenient to consider matrices as ordered arrays of numbers than as sets of images of mappings (as in Chapter 2).

Definition 12.1: A (nonempty) rectangular array of elements of a set S, in which the order of listing of the elements matters, of the form

$$A = \begin{bmatrix} a_{11} & a_{12} & \cdots & a_{1j} & \cdots & a_{1n} \\ a_{21} & a_{22} & \cdots & a_{2j} & \cdots & a_{2n} \\ \vdots & \vdots & & \vdots & & \vdots \\ a_{i1} & a_{i2} & \cdots & a_{ij} & \cdots & a_{in} \\ \vdots & \vdots & & \vdots & & \vdots \\ a_{m1} & a_{m2} & \cdots & a_{mj} & \cdots & a_{mn} \end{bmatrix} \tag{12.1}$$

may be called a *matrix* (or a *finite double sequence*) of m *rows and* n *columns* or an $(m \times n)$-*matrix over* S. If $S = R$ or $= C$, the matrix is called *real* or *complex*, respectively. To indicate that a matrix is considered as an entity, the array is usually enclosed by parentheses. (12.1) is frequently abbreviated (a_{ij}) (where, unless otherwise indicated, the elements a_{ij} are designated by the lower-case letter corresponding to the capital letter designating the matrix). If $m = n$, then A is called a *square matrix of order n*. A $(1 \times n)$-matrix is called a *row (matrix)* (or *horizontal sequence*), an $(m \times 1)$-matrix is called a *column (matrix)* (or *vertical sequence*). A (1×1)-matrix (s) is usually identified with the element s. The n columns

$$a \overset{(j)}{\downarrow} = \begin{bmatrix} a_{1j} \\ a_{2j} \\ \vdots \\ a_{mj} \end{bmatrix} \qquad \text{for} \quad j = 1, 2, \cdots, n \qquad (12.2)$$

are called *the columns of A*, and the m rows

$$a \overset{(i)}{\rightarrow} = (a_{i1}, a_{i2}, \cdots, a_{in}) \qquad \text{for} \quad i = 1, 2, \cdots, m \qquad (12.3)$$

are called *the rows of A*. The elements of a horizontal sequence are often separated by commas [as in (12.3)] if there is any danger of misinterpreting the sequence as a multiple product.

Since we make the convention that (apart from the notation of algebraic equations) equality means identity, the relation $A = B$ or $(a_{ij}) = (b_{ij})$ for two matrices $A = (a_{ij})$, $B = (b_{ij})$ must mean that a_{ij} and b_{ij} are abbreviations for the same element of S for every $i = 1, \cdots, m$; $j = 1, \cdots, n$. In other words: *Two matrices are equal if and only if they have the same number of rows and the same number of columns and if corresponding elements "in the same places" are equal.* Thus, an equality of two $(m \times n)$-matrices over S is the same as m times n equalities of elements of S.

Definition 12.2: Any matrix obtained from a given matrix A by omission of some rows or some columns or some of both and by natural rearrangements to fill the gaps is called a *submatrix of A*. If the i_1st, i_2nd, $\cdots$, rows and the j_1st, j_2nd, $\cdots$, columns are canceled, then the submatrix is sometimes denoted by

$$A^{i_1, i_2, \cdots; j_1, j_2, \cdots}. \qquad (12.4)$$

If no rows or no columns are canceled, this is indicated by putting $\emptyset$ before or after the semicolon. A matrix may be cut up into submatrices by horizontal or vertical partitions and may be interpreted and written as the matrix of all these submatrices. In particular, A may be considered and written as the horizontal sequence

$$(a \overset{(1)}{\downarrow}, a \overset{(2)}{\downarrow}, \cdots, a \overset{(n)}{\downarrow}) \qquad (12.5)$$

of its columns or as the vertical sequence

$$\begin{pmatrix} a \stackrel{(1)}{\longrightarrow} \\ a \stackrel{(2)}{\longrightarrow} \\ \vdots \\ a \stackrel{(m)}{\longrightarrow} \end{pmatrix} \tag{12.6}$$

of its rows.

EXAMPLES OF SUBMATRICES

Take

$$A = \begin{bmatrix} 1 & 2 & 3 & 4 & 5 \\ 2 & 1 & -1 & 0 & 1 \\ 3 & 0 & -2 & 1 & 2 \\ 4 & 6 & 8 & 9 & 7 \end{bmatrix}.$$

1.
$$A^{1,3;2} = \begin{bmatrix} 2 & -1 & 0 & 1 \\ 4 & 8 & 9 & 7 \end{bmatrix}.$$

2.
$$A^{2;1,3,4} = \begin{bmatrix} 2 & 5 \\ 0 & 2 \\ 6 & 7 \end{bmatrix}.$$

3.
$$B = \begin{bmatrix} 1 & 2 & 3 \\ 2 & 1 & -1 \\ 3 & 0 & -2 \end{bmatrix} \quad \text{is the submatrix } A^{4;4,5}.$$

4. $C = (4 \quad 6 \quad 8)$ is the submatrix $A^{1,2,3;4,5}$.

5.
$$D = \begin{bmatrix} 4 \\ 0 \\ 1 \end{bmatrix} \quad \text{is the submatrix } A^{4;1,2,3,5}.$$

6.
$$E = \begin{bmatrix} 5 \\ 1 \\ 2 \end{bmatrix} \quad \text{is the submatrix } A^{4;1,2,3,4}.$$

7. A may be written in the form

$$A = \begin{bmatrix} B & D & E \\ C & 9 & 7 \end{bmatrix}.$$

Matrices are frequently applied to express the coefficients of systems of linear polynomials or linear equations in an abbreviated manner. More generally, matrices may be employed to write down a column of horizontal sequences (12.6) of coefficients of linear combinations

$$a_{11}x_1 + a_{12}x_2 + \cdots + a_{1n}x_n = \sum_{j=1}^{n} a_{1j}x_j$$

$$a_{21}x_1 + a_{22}x_2 + \cdots + a_{2n}x_n = \sum_{j=1}^{n} a_{2j}x_j$$

$$\cdots\cdots\cdots\cdots\cdots\cdots\cdots\cdots\cdots\cdots\cdots\cdots$$

$$a_{m1}x_1 + a_{m2}x_2 + \cdots + a_{mn}x_n = \sum_{j=1}^{n} a_{mj}x_j$$

where the sequence $(x_1,x_2,\cdots,x_n)$ denotes n arbitrary elements of any vector space†. *Note* that this time the x_i are not necessarily (real or complex) numbers, but *vectors*.

Definition 12.3: If $A = (a_{ij})$ is an $(m \times n)$-matrix of real (or complex) numbers and if

$$x = \begin{bmatrix} x_1 \\ x_2 \\ \vdots \\ x_n \end{bmatrix}$$

is a vertical sequence of n elements of a real (or complex) vector space V, then Ax is used as an abbreviation for the column of linear combinations

$$Ax = \begin{bmatrix} a_{11}\,a_{12}\cdots a_{1n} \\ a_{21}\,a_{22}\cdots a_{2n} \\ \vdots \quad \vdots \quad \quad \vdots \\ a_{m1}a_{m2}\cdots a_{mn} \end{bmatrix} \begin{bmatrix} x_1 \\ x_2 \\ \vdots \\ x_n \end{bmatrix} =$$

$$= \begin{bmatrix} a_{11}x_1 + a_{12}x_2 + \cdots + a_{1n}x_n \\ a_{21}x_1 + a_{22}x_2 + \cdots + a_{2n}x_n \\ \cdots\cdots\cdots\cdots\cdots\cdots\cdots\cdots \\ a_{m1}x_1 + a_{m2}x_2 + \cdots + a_{mn}x_n \end{bmatrix} = \begin{bmatrix} \sum_{j=1}^{n} a_{1j}x_j \\ \sum_{j=1}^{n} a_{2j}x_j \\ \vdots \\ \sum_{j=1}^{n} a_{mj}x_j \end{bmatrix} \quad (12.7)$$

The mapping

---

† However, if we apply matrices in this fashion we shall mainly deal with sequences of elements of R, C, $R[x]$ and $C[x]$ (in one or several variables). Since the elements of these vector spaces are denoted by *italic* letters we deviate here from our earlier convention and don't indicate unspecified vector spaces and their elements by boldfaced characters. A boldfaced notation for sequences of *vectors* would also conflict with our conventions of Chapter 6.

$$\mathbf{A}: x \to Ax \tag{12.8}$$

is called (pre)multiplication of a column (of vectors) by a matrix, and the image Ax is called the product of the column x by the matrix A.

Note: In order that this external product Ax with operator A be defined, the number of vectors in the sequence x must be equal to the number of columns of the matrix A.

EXAMPLES OF PRODUCTS OF VECTOR SEQUENCES BY REAL MATRICES

1. $\begin{bmatrix} 4 & 2 & 1 \\ 2 & 1 & -1 \\ 3 & 4 & 5 \\ 6 & 6 & 1 \end{bmatrix} \begin{bmatrix} \mathbf{b}^{(1)} \\ \mathbf{b}^{(2)} \\ \mathbf{b}^{(3)} \end{bmatrix} = \begin{bmatrix} 4\mathbf{b}^{(1)} + 2\mathbf{b}^{(2)} + \mathbf{b}^{(3)} \\ 2\mathbf{b}^{(1)} + \mathbf{b}^{(2)} - \mathbf{b}^{(3)} \\ 3\mathbf{b}^{(1)} + 4\mathbf{b}^{(2)} + 5\mathbf{b}^{(3)} \\ 6\mathbf{b}^{(1)} + 6\mathbf{b}^{(2)} + \mathbf{b}^{(3)} \end{bmatrix}$, $\mathbf{b}^{(i)} \; \varepsilon \; \mathbf{R}^3, \; i = 1, 2, 3.$

2. $\begin{bmatrix} 1 & 1 \\ 1 & -1 \\ 1 & 0 \end{bmatrix} \begin{bmatrix} x_1 + x_2 \\ x_1 - x_2 \end{bmatrix} = \begin{bmatrix} (x_1 + x_2) + (x_1 - x_2) \\ (x_1 + x_2) - (x_1 - x_2) \\ x_1 + x_2 \end{bmatrix} = \begin{bmatrix} 2x_1 \\ 2x_2 \\ x_1 + x_2 \end{bmatrix}$,

$$x_1, x_2 \; \varepsilon \; R[x_1, x_2]_L.$$

3. $\begin{bmatrix} 2 & 1 & -1 \\ 1 & -2 & 3 \\ 2 & -1 & -1 \end{bmatrix} \begin{bmatrix} \partial/\partial x_1 \\ \partial/\partial x_2 \\ \partial/\partial x_3 \end{bmatrix} = \begin{bmatrix} 2\partial/\partial x_1 + \partial/\partial x_2 - \partial/\partial x_3 \\ \partial/\partial x_1 - 2\partial/\partial x_2 + 3\partial/\partial x_3 \\ 2\partial/\partial x_1 - \partial/\partial x_2 - \partial/\partial x_3 \end{bmatrix} \cdot$

4. $\begin{bmatrix} 3 & 2 \\ -4 & 2 \end{bmatrix} \begin{bmatrix} (a_1, a_2) \\ (b_1, b_2) \end{bmatrix} = \begin{bmatrix} 3(a_1, a_2) + 2(b_1, b_2) \\ -4(a_1, a_2) + 2(b_1, b_2) \end{bmatrix}$

$$= \begin{bmatrix} (3a_1 + 2b_1, \quad 3a_2 + 2b_2) \\ (-4a_1 + 2b_1, -4a_2 + 2b_2) \end{bmatrix}, \qquad \begin{matrix} (a_1, a_2) \; \varepsilon \; R^2, \\ (b_1, b_2) \; \varepsilon \; R^2. \end{matrix}$$

The external product (12.7) is a column of m vectors; hence the mapping $\mathbf{A}$ defined by (12.8) assigns to every column of n vectors of a vector space a column of m vectors of that vector space. Suppose now that B is a real (or complex) $(p \times m)$-matrix

$$B = \begin{bmatrix} b_{11} b_{12} \cdots b_{1i} \cdots b_{1m} \\ b_{21} b_{22} \cdots b_{2i} \cdots b_{2m} \\ \vdots \quad \vdots \qquad \vdots \qquad \vdots \\ b_{k1} b_{k2} \cdots b_{ki} \cdots b_{km} \\ \vdots \quad \vdots \qquad \vdots \qquad \vdots \\ b_{p1} b_{p2} \cdots b_{pi} \cdots b_{pm} \end{bmatrix} \tag{12.9}$$

and **B** is the mapping

$$\mathbf{B} : y \to By$$

induced by B and assigning to every column y of m vectors a column of p vectors of the same vector space. Then the composite mapping $\mathbf{B} \circ \mathbf{A}$ is defined. With the abbreviation

$$y \;=\; Ax \tag{12.10}$$

for (12.7), the $(\mathbf{B} \circ \mathbf{A})$-image of x is equal to‡

$$
B(Ax) \;=\; By \;=\;
\begin{bmatrix}
b_{11}y_1 + b_{12}y_2 + \cdots + b_{1m}y_m \\
b_{21}y_1 + b_{22}y_2 + \cdots + b_{2m}y_m \\
\cdots\cdots\cdots\cdots\cdots\cdots\cdots \\
\cdots\cdots\cdots\cdots\cdots\cdots\cdots \\
b_{p1}y_1 + b_{p2}y_2 + \cdots + b_{pm}y_m
\end{bmatrix}
\;=\;
\begin{bmatrix}
\sum_{i=1}^{m} b_{1i}y_i \\
\sum_{i=1}^{m} b_{2i}y_i \\
\vdots \\
\sum_{i=1}^{m} b_{pi}y_i
\end{bmatrix}
\;=\;
$$

$$
\;=\;
\begin{bmatrix}
b_{11}(a_{11}x_1 + \cdots + a_{1n}x_n) + \cdots + b_{1m}(a_{m1}x_1 + \cdots + a_{mn}x_n) \\
b_{21}(a_{11}x_1 + \cdots + a_{1n}x_n) + \cdots + b_{2m}(a_{m1}x_1 + \cdots + a_{mn}x_n) \\
\cdots\cdots\cdots\cdots\cdots\cdots\cdots\cdots\cdots\cdots\cdots\cdots\cdots\cdots\cdots \\
\cdots\cdots\cdots\cdots\cdots\cdots\cdots\cdots\cdots\cdots\cdots\cdots\cdots\cdots\cdots \\
b_{p1}(a_{11}x_1 + \cdots + a_{1n}x_n) + \cdots + b_{pm}(a_{m1}x_1 + \cdots + a_{mn}x_n)
\end{bmatrix}
\;=\;
$$

$$
\;=\;
\begin{bmatrix}
\sum_{i=1}^{m} b_{1i}\left(\sum_{j=1}^{n} a_{ij}x_j \right) \\
\sum_{i=1}^{m} b_{2i}\left(\sum_{j=1}^{n} a_{ij}x_j \right) \\
\vdots \\
\sum_{i=1}^{m} b_{pi}\left(\sum_{j=1}^{n} a_{ij}x_j \right)
\end{bmatrix} .
$$

By employing the rules for vector spaces, every sum can be rearranged to the following form:

‡ It can be assumed that the computation proceeds from one unabbreviated form to another. The shorter summation convention is used *simultaneously* for instructive purposes.

$$B(Ax) = \begin{bmatrix} (b_{11}a_{11} + \cdots + b_{1m}a_{m1})x_1 + \cdots + (b_{11}a_{1n} + \cdots + b_{1m}a_{mn})x_n \\ (b_{21}a_{11} + \cdots + b_{2m}a_{m1})x_1 + \cdots + (b_{21}a_{1n} + \cdots + b_{2m}a_{mn})x_n \\ \vdots \\ (b_{p1}a_{11} + \cdots + b_{pm}a_{m1})x_1 + \cdots + (b_{p1}a_{1n} + \cdots + b_{pm}a_{mn})x_n \end{bmatrix}$$

$$= \begin{bmatrix} \sum_{j=1}^{n}\left(\sum_{i=1}^{m} b_{1i}a_{ij}\right)x_j \\ \sum_{j=1}^{n}\left(\sum_{i=1}^{m} b_{2i}a_{ij}\right)x_j \\ \cdots \\ \sum_{j=1}^{n}\left(\sum_{i=1}^{m} b_{pi}a_{ij}\right)x_j \end{bmatrix} = \qquad (12.11)$$

$$= \begin{bmatrix} \left(\sum b_{1i}a_{i1}\right)x_1 + \left(\sum b_{1i}a_{i2}\right)x_2 + \cdots + \left(\sum b_{1i}a_{in}\right)x_n \\ \left(\sum b_{2i}a_{i1}\right)x_1 + \left(\sum b_{2i}a_{i2}\right)x_2 + \cdots + \left(\sum b_{2i}a_{in}\right)x_n \\ \vdots \\ \left(\sum b_{ki}a_{i1}\right)x_1 + \left(\sum b_{ki}a_{i2}\right)x_2 + \cdots + \left(\sum b_{ki}a_{in}\right)x_n \\ \vdots \\ \left(\sum b_{pi}a_{i1}\right)x_1 + \left(\sum b_{pi}a_{i2}\right)x_2 + \cdots + \left(\sum b_{pi}a_{in}\right)x_n \end{bmatrix}$$

where the summations are to be extended from $i = 1$ to $i = m$. Hence (12.11) can be written in the form

$$B(Ax) = Cx \qquad (12.12)$$

where

$$C = \begin{bmatrix} \sum b_{1i}a_{i1}, & \sum b_{1i}a_{i2}, \cdots, & \sum b_{1i}a_{ij}, \cdots, & \sum b_{1i}a_{in} \\ \sum b_{2i}a_{i1}, & \sum b_{2i}a_{i2}, \cdots, & \sum b_{2i}a_{ij}, \cdots, & \sum b_{2i}a_{in} \\ \vdots & \vdots & \vdots & \vdots \\ \sum b_{ki}a_{i1}, & \sum b_{ki}a_{i2}, \cdots, & \sum b_{ki}a_{ij}, \cdots, & \sum b_{ki}a_{in} \\ \vdots & \vdots & \vdots & \vdots \\ \sum b_{pi}a_{i1}, & \sum b_{pi}a_{i2}, \cdots, & \sum b_{pi}a_{ij}, \cdots, & \sum b_{pi}a_{in} \end{bmatrix} \begin{matrix} \\ \\ \\ \leftarrow k\text{th row} \quad (12.13) \\ \\ \\ \end{matrix}$$

$$\uparrow j\text{th column}$$

with summations from $i = 1$ to $i = m$.

Equation (12.12) shows that the operator product BA (see definition 4.5) and the matrix operator C give the same image. It is, therefore, convenient to define $C = BA$; that is, to introduce a (partially defined) multiplication of matrices that *coincides with the operator multiplication*. But first we shall introduce another concept, which will make it easier to discuss how BA is to be computed if B and A are given.

Definition 12.4: Let $s = (s_1, s_2, \cdots, s_m)$ be a sequence of m scalars (rows or columns), and $v = (v_1, v_2, \cdots, v_m)$ be a sequence of m vectors (rows or columns). Then the linear combination $\sum_{i=1}^{m} s_i v_i$ is called *the inner product* of s and v and is denoted by $s \cdot v$. In particular, this is employed in the case where $s_i \ \varepsilon \ R$ and $v_i \ \varepsilon \ R = R^1$. If $s = (s_1, s_2, \cdots, s_m) \ \varepsilon \ R^m$ the inner product $s \cdot s = \sum_{i=1}^{m} s_i^2$ is also called the *inner square* of s and is denoted by s^2. If $s^2 = 1$, then s is called a *unit sequence* (or *unit m-tuple*, or *unit vector*).

Now the construction of (12.13) from A and B leads to

Definition 12.5: Let B be a real (or complex) matrix of p rows and m columns, and let A be a real (or complex) matrix of m rows and n columns. Then the matrix C of p rows and n columns whose element in the kth row and jth column (for any $k = 1, 2, \cdots, p$ and any $j = 1, 2, \cdots, n$) is equal to the inner product

$$\sum_{i=1}^{m} b_{ki} a_{ij}$$

of the kth row of B and the jth column of A is called *the product of B and A* and denoted by BA.

EXAMPLE OF A MATRIX PRODUCT

$$\begin{pmatrix} 2 & 1 & 3 \\ 1 & 2 & -1 \\ 4 & 5 & 6 \end{pmatrix} \begin{pmatrix} 1 & -1 & 0 \\ 0 & 1 & 2 \\ 3 & 3 & 1 \end{pmatrix} =$$

$$= \begin{pmatrix} 2 \cdot 1 + 1 \cdot 0 + 3 \cdot 3, \; 2 \cdot (-1) + 1 \cdot 1 + 3 \cdot 3, \; 2 \cdot 0 + 1 \cdot 2 + 3 \cdot 1 \\ 1 \cdot 1 + 2 \cdot 0 - 1 \cdot 3, \; 1 \cdot (-1) + 2 \cdot 1 - 1 \cdot 3, \; 1 \cdot 0 + 2 \cdot 2 - 1 \cdot 1 \\ 4 \cdot 1 + 5 \cdot 0 + 6 \cdot 3, \; 4 \cdot (-1) + 5 \cdot 1 + 6 \cdot 3, \; 4 \cdot 0 + 5 \cdot 2 + 6 \cdot 1 \end{pmatrix} \cdot$$

This definition can be generalized to matrices whose elements belong to more general sets than R or C, provided such a set S has an associative, commutative addition and an associative (not necessarily commutative) multiplication and that the two composition laws are connected by the distributive laws $r(s + t) = rs + rt$ and $(s + t)r = sr + tr$ for all $r, s, t \; \varepsilon \; S$. Matrix multiplication is also possible for some infinite matrices (see exercise 26).

Note: 1.   For a product FG of two matrices F and G to be defined, the number of *columns* of the *left* factor F must be equal to the number of *rows* of the *right* factor G. The two products FG and GF are simultaneously defined only if both are square matrices of the same number of rows (and columns). It is easy to see that, even if both FG and GF are defined, these two products are generally not equal, except under very special circumstances.

2. A comparison of (12.12) and (12.13) shows that definition 12.5 implies

$$B(Ax) = (BA)x \qquad\qquad (12.14)$$

provided that both sides are defined.

3. If definition (12.3) is restricted to the real vector space $V = R$ of all real numbers (or to the complex vector space $V = C$ of all complex numbers), then a comparison of (12.7) and (12.13) shows that (12.7) becomes a special case of (12.13). This is the reason why, in definition 12.3, the originally strange assumption is made that x is a column *and not a row*.

Lemma 12.1:   *The multiplication of matrices is, if defined, associative but not in general commutative.*

PROOF: *Associativity*: Let F, G, and H be matrices and let x be a column matrix of *linearly independent* vectors x_i (for example, *independent variables*) such that FG, $(FG)H$, and Hx are defined. Then both $((FG)H)x$ and $((FGH))x$ are defined, too, and both are seen to be equal to $F(G(Hx))$ by repeated application of (12.14). $F(G(Hx))$ is a column of linear combinations of the x_i. Since no vector can be expressed as a linear combination of a given *linearly independent* vector set in two different ways (see the proof of theorem 5.2), the coefficients of $((FG)H)x = (F(GH)x) = F(G(Hx))$ are *uniquely* defined, that is, $(FG)H = F(GH)$.

Alternatively the equality $F(GH) = (FG)H$ can be proved by showing that in both triple products the element in the ith row and jth column is equal to

$$\sum_{q=1}^{n} \sum_{p=1}^{m} f_{ip} g_{pq} h_{qk} = \sum_{p=1}^{m} \sum_{q=1}^{n} f_{ip} g_{pq} h_{qk}.$$

Lack of commutativity: The following example suffices:

$$\begin{bmatrix} 1 & 0 \\ 0 & 0 \end{bmatrix} \begin{bmatrix} 0 & 1 \\ 0 & 0 \end{bmatrix} = \begin{bmatrix} 0 & 1 \\ 0 & 0 \end{bmatrix}, \quad \text{but} \quad \begin{bmatrix} 0 & 1 \\ 0 & 0 \end{bmatrix} \begin{bmatrix} 1 & 0 \\ 0 & 0 \end{bmatrix} = \begin{bmatrix} 0 & 0 \\ 0 & 0 \end{bmatrix}.$$

Just as multiplication of matrices is defined as operator multiplication, so also addition of matrices will be defined as operator addition.

Suppose we have two matrices K and L, both of m rows and n columns, and a column matrix z of n rows whose elements z_i are elements of a vector space V:

$$K = \begin{bmatrix} k_{11} & k_{12} \cdots k_{1n} \\ k_{21} & k_{22} \cdots k_{2n} \\ \vdots & \vdots \\ k_{m1} & k_{m2} \cdots k_{mn} \end{bmatrix}, \quad L = \begin{bmatrix} l_{11} & l_{12} \cdots l_{1n} \\ l_{21} & l_{22} \cdots l_{2n} \\ \vdots & \vdots \\ l_{m1} & l_{m2} \cdots l_{mn} \end{bmatrix}. \tag{12.15}$$

Then Kz and Lz are both defined; *both* are m-tuples of linear combinations of the z's:

$$Kz = \begin{bmatrix} \sum k_{1i} z_i \\ \sum k_{2i} z_i \\ \vdots \\ \sum k_{mi} z_i \end{bmatrix}, \quad Lz = \begin{bmatrix} \sum l_{1i} z_i \\ \sum l_{2i} z_i \\ \vdots \\ \sum l_{mi} z_i \end{bmatrix}. \tag{12.16}$$

The two expressions of (12.16) can be added in the usual fashion of addition of two m-tuples. Their sum is obviously again an m-tuple *of linear combinations of the z's*; hence it must take the form

$$Dz = \begin{bmatrix} \sum d_{1i}z_i \\ \sum d_{2i}z_i \\ \vdots \\ \sum d_{mi}z_i \end{bmatrix} \quad \text{with} \quad D = \begin{bmatrix} d_{11} & d_{12} \cdots & d_{1n} \\ d_{21} & d_{22} \cdots & d_{2n} \\ \vdots & \vdots & \vdots \\ d_{m1} & d_{m2} \cdots & d_{mn} \end{bmatrix}. \tag{12.17}$$

But, by computing the sum of the two expressions of (12.16), we obtain the image of z *under the operator sum of K and L*:

$$Kz + Lz = \begin{bmatrix} \sum k_{1i}z_i + \sum l_{1i}z_i \\ \sum k_{2i}z_i + \sum l_{2i}z_i \\ \cdots\cdots\cdots\cdots\cdots \\ \cdots\cdots\cdots\cdots\cdots \\ \sum k_{mi}z_i + \sum l_{mi}z_i \end{bmatrix} = \begin{bmatrix} \sum (k_{1i} + l_{1i})z_i \\ \sum (k_{2i} + l_{2i})z_i \\ \cdots\cdots\cdots \\ \cdots\cdots\cdots \\ \sum (k_{mi} + l_{mi})z_i \end{bmatrix}. \tag{12.18}$$

A comparison of (12.17) and (12.18) shows that the matrix of coefficients of the column vector $Kz + Lz = Dz$ has the form

$$D = \begin{bmatrix} k_{11} + l_{11}, & k_{12} + l_{12}, & \cdots, & k_{1n} + l_{1n} \\ k_{21} + l_{21}, & k_{22} + l_{22}, & \cdots, & k_{2n} + l_{2n} \\ \cdots\cdots & \cdots\cdots & \cdots & \cdots\cdots \\ \cdots\cdots & \cdots\cdots & \cdots & \cdots\cdots \\ k_{m1} + l_{m1}, & k_{m2} + l_{m2}, & \cdots, & k_{mn} + l_{mn} \end{bmatrix}. \tag{12.19}$$

The matrix (12.19) is obtained from the matrices (12.15) "by the adding of corresponding elements." This is an extension of the process of adding two n-tuples by adding corresponding coordinates. It is advantageous to call (12.19) "the sum of matrices K and L of (12.15)" and to denote D by "$K + L$." From this convention and the equation $Kz + Lz = Dz$ that defines D we can then conclude

$$Kz + Lz = (K + L)z, \tag{12.20}$$

which is *a sort of* distributive law.

To sum up, it is useful to introduce

Definition 12.6: Let K and L be two matrices that both have m rows and n columns. Then the matrix D of m rows and n columns whose element in the ith row and jth column (for any $i = 1, 2, \cdots, m$ and any $j = 1, 2, \cdots, n$) is equal to

$$k_{ij} + l_{ij},$$

which is the sum of the elements of K and L in the ith row and jth column, is called *the sum of K and L* and is denoted by $K + L$.

Note: The circumstances under which the sum $K + L$ of two matrices K and L is defined are quite different from those under which their two possible products KL and LK are defined. The sum and the products of two matrices are defined simultaneously only if both are square matrices.

An immediate consequence of definition 12.6 is the following.

Lemma 12.2: *The set of all matrices of m rows and n columns is a commutative group relative to addition.*

Note: This lemma implies that, for any given matrix A, a matrix "$-A$" is defined uniquely, so that $A + (-A) = (-A) + A$ is equal to the neutral element of this group. Obviously this neutral element is the matrix of m rows and n columns all of whose elements are equal to zero. We shall call this neutral element *the zero matrix* (of m rows and n columns) and denote it by 0.

Lemma 12.3: *Let A, B, and C be matrices such that $(A + B)C$ is defined. Then AC, BC, and $AC + BC$ are also defined, and the distributive law*

$$(A + B)C = AC + BC \tag{12.21}$$

holds. Similarly, let F, G, and H be matrices such that $F(G + H)$ is defined. Then FG, FH, and $FG + FH$ are also defined, and the distributive law

$$F(G + H) = FG + FH \tag{12.22}$$

holds.

Proof: *First part*: Let C have n columns, and let u be an n-tuple of linearly independent vectors u_i, written as a column. Then Cu is an m-tuple of linear combinations of the u's, written as a column. From (12.20), that is, from the definition of addition of matrices, it follows that

$$A(Cu) + B(Cu) = (A + B)(Cu) \tag{12.23}$$

holds, where all expressions in (12.23) are easily seen to be defined. Applying (12.14), the definition of multiplication of matrices, three times, we conclude from (12.23) that

$$(AC)u + (BC)u = ((A + B)C)u \tag{12.24}$$

holds, where again all expressions in (12.24) are easily seen to be defined. But from (12.20) we have

$$(AC)u + (BC)u = (AC + BC)u,$$

and this, in conjunction with (12.24), proves (12.21) because of the linear independence of the u_i's.

Second part: Let G and H and hence $G + H$ have n columns, and let v be an n-tuple of linearly independent vectors v_i, written as a column.

Applying first (12.14) and then (12.20), we see that

$$(F(G + H))v = F((G + H)v) = F(Gv + Hv) \tag{12.25}$$

holds. Again it can be checked that all expressions in (12.25) are defined. Suppose that Gv and Hv are columns of m elements, and abbreviate them by the m-tuples y and z, respectively. We see next that (12.25) is equal to $F(Gv) + F(Hv)$. This is a special case of the more general result:

$$F(y + z) = Fy + Fz, \tag{12.26}$$

which can be proved without difficulty from definition 12.3. By applying (12.14) and thereafter (12.20), we obtain

$$F(Gv) + F(Hv) = (FG)v + (FH)v = (FG + FH)v. \tag{12.27}$$

A comparison of (12.25) and (12.27), which are equal because of (12.26), shows that (12.22) holds since the v_i's are linearly independent.

Alternatively (12.21) as well as (12.22) can be proved by showing that both the left-hand and right-hand sides have the same element in the ith row and jth column.

Now we shall introduce a multiplication of a real (or complex) matrix A by a real (or complex) number α, written either as a left or as a right operator. Suppose A has n columns and x is a column vector of n elements x_i. Then Ax is a column vector, too, and $\alpha(Ax)$ is defined *as a scalar multiple of* Ax. The column vector $\alpha(Ax)$ must have the form Bx, where B is a matrix having the same number of rows and columns as A. Multiplication of every linear combination in the x's by the number α has the effect of multiplying every coefficient by α. In other words, the matrix B is obtained from the matrix A by multiplication of *every* element of A by α. If we *define* $B = \alpha A$, then we have the rule

$$\alpha(Ax) = (\alpha A)x \tag{12.28}$$

which again is *a sort of* associative law. Similarly one can see that the rule

$$A(\alpha x) = (A\alpha)x \tag{12.29}$$

holds if one defines $A\alpha$ as the matrix obtained from A by multiplying every element of A by α; that is, if one defines $A\alpha = \alpha A$.

Thus, in order for (12.28) and (12.29) to hold, we now define formally the concept of scalar multiplication.

Definition 12.7: If A is any matrix and α is any real (or complex) number, then the matrix obtained from A by multiplying every element by α is called *the multiple of A by the scalar α* and denoted by αA or by $A\alpha$. The mapping $A \rightarrow \alpha A = A\alpha$ is called *scalar multiplication*.

Now it is not difficult to prove

Lemma 12.4:   *The set of all matrices of m rows and n columns is a vector space (relative to the addition of definition 12.6 and to the scalar multiplication of definition 12.7).*

Note: Strictly speaking, lemma 12.4 discusses two vector spaces: one where the external composition law is written as *left* scalar multiplication, and another where *right* scalar multiplication is used. But since both compositions give the same result, this fine distinction is usually disregarded. In particular, from now on we allow left- and right-multiplication of sequences by scalars whose composites are connected by the formula

$$\alpha x = x\alpha. \tag{12.30}$$

EXERCISES

1. Compute the products

$$\begin{bmatrix} a_{11}a_{12} \\ a_{21}a_{22} \end{bmatrix} \begin{bmatrix} b_{11}b_{12} \\ b_{21}b_{22} \end{bmatrix} \quad \text{and} \quad \begin{bmatrix} a_{11}a_{12}a_{13} \\ a_{21}a_{22}a_{23} \\ a_{31}a_{32}a_{33} \end{bmatrix} \begin{bmatrix} b_{11}b_{12}b_{13} \\ b_{21}b_{22}b_{23} \\ b_{31}b_{32}b_{33} \end{bmatrix}.$$

2. Compute the following products, and comment on the results:

$$\begin{bmatrix} 1 & 0 & 0 \\ 0 & 1 & 0 \\ 0 & 0 & 1 \end{bmatrix} \begin{bmatrix} a_{11}a_{12}a_{13} \\ a_{21}a_{22}a_{23} \\ a_{31}a_{32}a_{33} \end{bmatrix}, \quad \begin{bmatrix} a_{11}a_{12}a_{13} \\ a_{21}a_{22}a_{23} \\ a_{31}a_{32}a_{33} \end{bmatrix} \begin{bmatrix} 1 & 0 & 0 \\ 0 & 1 & 0 \\ 0 & 0 & 1 \end{bmatrix},$$

$$\begin{bmatrix} 1 & 0 & 0 & 0 \\ 0 & 1 & 0 & 0 \\ 0 & 0 & 0 & 1 \\ 0 & 0 & 1 & 0 \end{bmatrix} \begin{bmatrix} a_{11}a_{12}a_{13}a_{14} \\ a_{21}a_{22}a_{23}a_{24} \\ a_{31}a_{32}a_{33}a_{34} \\ a_{41}a_{42}a_{43}a_{44} \end{bmatrix}, \quad \begin{bmatrix} a_{11}a_{12}a_{13}a_{14} \\ a_{21}a_{22}a_{23}a_{24} \\ a_{31}a_{32}a_{33}a_{34} \\ a_{41}a_{42}a_{43}a_{44} \end{bmatrix} \begin{bmatrix} 1 & 0 & 0 & 0 \\ 0 & 1 & 0 & 0 \\ 0 & 0 & 0 & 1 \\ 0 & 0 & 1 & 0 \end{bmatrix}.$$

3. Compute the following products:

$$\begin{bmatrix} a & 0 & 0 \\ 0 & b & 0 \\ 0 & 0 & c \end{bmatrix} \begin{bmatrix} d_{11}d_{12}d_{13} \\ d_{21}d_{22}d_{23} \\ d_{31}d_{32}d_{33} \end{bmatrix} \quad \text{and} \quad \begin{bmatrix} d_{11}d_{12}d_{13} \\ d_{21}d_{22}d_{23} \\ d_{31}d_{32}d_{33} \end{bmatrix} \begin{bmatrix} a & 0 & 0 \\ 0 & b & 0 \\ 0 & 0 & c \end{bmatrix},$$

and comment on the results.

4. Let t be a real number, and define a matrix D by: $D = \begin{bmatrix} t & 0 & 0 \\ 0 & t & 0 \\ 0 & 0 & t \end{bmatrix}.$

Let S be the set of all matrices of three rows and three columns, and let A be an arbitrary element of S. Show that the mappings $A \to tA$ and $A \to DA$ are equal.

Note: This example shows how two distinct operators may induce the same mapping.

5. Compute the following products:

$$\begin{bmatrix} 1 & 0 & 0 & 0 \\ t & 1 & 0 & 0 \\ 0 & 0 & 1 & 0 \\ 0 & 0 & 0 & 1 \end{bmatrix} \begin{bmatrix} a_{11}a_{12}a_{13}a_{14} \\ a_{21}a_{22}a_{23}a_{24} \\ a_{31}a_{32}a_{33}a_{34} \\ a_{41}a_{42}a_{43}a_{44} \end{bmatrix} \quad \text{and} \quad \begin{bmatrix} a_{11}a_{12}a_{13}a_{14} \\ a_{21}a_{22}a_{23}a_{24} \\ a_{31}a_{32}a_{33}a_{34} \\ a_{41}a_{42}a_{43}a_{44} \end{bmatrix} \begin{bmatrix} 1 & 0 & 0 & 0 \\ t & 1 & 0 & 0 \\ 0 & 0 & 1 & 0 \\ 0 & 0 & 0 & 1 \end{bmatrix}$$

and comment on the results.

6. Compute the following products:

$$\begin{bmatrix} 1 & 0 & 0 & 0 \\ t_{21} & 1 & 0 & 0 \\ t_{31} & t_{32} & 1 & 0 \\ t_{41} & t_{42} & t_{43} & 1 \end{bmatrix} \begin{bmatrix} 1 & 0 & 0 & 0 \\ s_{21} & 1 & 0 & 0 \\ s_{31} & s_{32} & 1 & 0 \\ s_{41} & s_{42} & s_{43} & 1 \end{bmatrix} \quad \text{and} \quad \begin{bmatrix} 1 & r_{12} & r_{13} & r_{14} \\ 0 & 1 & r_{23} & r_{24} \\ 0 & 0 & 1 & r_{34} \\ 0 & 0 & 0 & 1 \end{bmatrix} \begin{bmatrix} 1 & q_{12} & q_{13} & q_{14} \\ 0 & 1 & q_{23} & q_{24} \\ 0 & 0 & 1 & q_{34} \\ 0 & 0 & 0 & 1 \end{bmatrix}$$

and comment on the results.

7. Let a_{11}, a_{12}, a_{21}, and a_{22} be four real numbers such that $a_{11}a_{22} - a_{12}a_{21} \neq 0$. Define numbers c_{11}, c_{12}, c_{21}, c_{22}:

$$c_{11} = \frac{a_{22}}{a_{11}a_{22} - a_{12}a_{21}}, \qquad c_{12} = \frac{-a_{12}}{a_{11}a_{22} - a_{12}a_{21}},$$

$$c_{21} = \frac{-a_{21}}{a_{11}a_{22} - a_{12}a_{21}}, \qquad c_{22} = \frac{a_{11}}{a_{11}a_{22} - a_{12}a_{21}}.$$

Compute the two products

$$\begin{bmatrix} a_{11}a_{12} \\ a_{21}a_{22} \end{bmatrix} \begin{bmatrix} c_{11}c_{12} \\ c_{21}c_{22} \end{bmatrix} \quad \text{and} \quad \begin{bmatrix} c_{11}c_{12} \\ c_{21}c_{22} \end{bmatrix} \begin{bmatrix} a_{11}a_{12} \\ a_{21}a_{22} \end{bmatrix}$$

and express the results in the a_{ij}'s only.

8. Compute the two products

$$\begin{bmatrix} a_{11} & a_{12} & a_{13} & a_{14} \\ a_{21} & a_{22} & a_{23} & a_{24} \end{bmatrix} \begin{bmatrix} b_{11} & b_{12} & b_{13} \\ b_{21} & b_{22} & b_{23} \\ b_{31} & b_{32} & b_{33} \\ b_{41} & b_{42} & b_{43} \end{bmatrix}$$

and (*attention*: watch the distribution of suffixes)

$$\begin{bmatrix} b_{11} & b_{21} & b_{31} & b_{41} \\ b_{12} & b_{22} & b_{32} & b_{42} \\ b_{13} & b_{23} & b_{33} & b_{43} \end{bmatrix} \begin{bmatrix} a_{11} & a_{21} \\ a_{12} & a_{22} \\ a_{13} & a_{23} \\ a_{14} & a_{24} \end{bmatrix}.$$

9. Comment on the two products of exercise 8.

10. Compute

$$\begin{bmatrix} 0 & 1 & 0 \\ 1 & 0 & 0 \\ 0 & 0 & 1 \end{bmatrix} \begin{bmatrix} 1 & 0 & 0 \\ 0 & 0 & 1 \\ 0 & 1 & 0 \end{bmatrix} \quad \text{and} \quad \begin{bmatrix} 1 & 0 & 0 & 0 \\ 0 & 0 & 1 & 0 \\ 0 & 1 & 0 & 0 \\ 0 & 0 & 0 & 1 \end{bmatrix} \begin{bmatrix} 0 & 1 & 0 & 0 \\ 1 & 0 & 0 & 0 \\ 0 & 0 & 1 & 0 \\ 0 & 0 & 0 & 1 \end{bmatrix} \begin{bmatrix} 0 & 0 & 1 & 0 \\ 0 & 1 & 0 & 0 \\ 1 & 0 & 0 & 0 \\ 0 & 0 & 0 & 1 \end{bmatrix}.$$

11. Compute

$$\begin{bmatrix} 1 & 0 & 0 & 0 \\ \alpha & 1 & 0 & 0 \\ 0 & 0 & 1 & 0 \\ 0 & 0 & 0 & 1 \end{bmatrix} \begin{bmatrix} 1 & 0 & 0 & 0 \\ 0 & 1 & 0 & 0 \\ 0 & \beta & 1 & 0 \\ 0 & 0 & 0 & 1 \end{bmatrix} \begin{bmatrix} 1 & 0 & 0 & 0 \\ 0 & 1 & 0 & 0 \\ 0 & 0 & 1 & 0 \\ 0 & 0 & \gamma & 1 \end{bmatrix}$$

and

$$\begin{bmatrix} 1 & 0 & 0 & \alpha \\ 0 & 1 & 0 & 0 \\ 0 & 0 & 1 & 0 \\ 0 & 0 & 0 & 1 \end{bmatrix} \begin{bmatrix} 1 & 0 & 0 & 0 \\ 0 & 1 & 0 & \beta \\ 0 & 0 & 1 & 0 \\ 0 & 0 & 0 & 1 \end{bmatrix} \begin{bmatrix} 1 & 0 & 0 & 0 \\ 0 & 1 & 0 & 0 \\ 0 & 0 & 1 & \gamma \\ 0 & 0 & 0 & 1 \end{bmatrix}.$$

12. Let A be any $(n \times m)$-matrix with $n, m \geq 2$, and define $B = A^{\alpha;\beta}$. Prove:

$$b_{\gamma\delta} = \begin{cases} a_{\gamma,\delta} & \text{if } \gamma < \alpha \text{ and } \delta < \beta \\ a_{\gamma,\delta+1} & \text{if } \gamma < \alpha \text{ and } \delta \geq \beta \\ a_{\gamma+1,\delta} & \text{if } \gamma \geq \alpha \text{ and } \delta < \beta \\ a_{\gamma+1,\delta+1} & \text{if } \gamma \geq \alpha \text{ and } \delta \geq \beta. \end{cases} \tag{12.31}$$

13. Let A be any $(n \times m)$-matrix with $n, m \geq 2$. Prove the iteration rule for submatrices of A:

$$(A^{\alpha\,;\beta})^{\gamma\,;\delta} = \begin{cases} A^{\alpha,\,\gamma\,;\beta,\,\delta} & \text{if } \gamma < \alpha \text{ and } \delta < \beta \\[4pt] A^{\alpha,\,\gamma\,;\beta,\,\delta+1} & \text{if } \gamma < \alpha \text{ and } \delta \geq \beta \\[4pt] A^{\alpha,\,\gamma+1\,;\beta,\,\delta} & \text{if } \gamma \geq \alpha \text{ and } \delta < \beta. \\[4pt] A^{\alpha,\,\gamma+1\,;\beta,\,\delta+1} & \text{if } \gamma \geq \alpha \text{ and } \delta \geq \beta. \end{cases} \qquad (12.32)$$

14. Determine the number of possible submatrices of an $(m \times n)$-matrix.

15. Let F be a matrix of m rows and n columns, G a matrix of n rows and p columns and H a matrix of p rows and q columns. Prove the associativity of the matrix multiplication by showing that both matrices $F(GH)$ and $(FG)H$ have the element

$$\sum_{\alpha=1}^{n} \sum_{\beta=1}^{p} f_{i\alpha} g_{\alpha\beta} h_{\beta j}$$

in the ith row and jth column (for $i = 1, 2, \cdots, m$ and $j = 1, 2, \cdots, q$).

16. Prove lemma 12.2.

17. Prove lemma 12.3. by computation directly from definitions 12.5 and 12.6.

18. Prove lemma 12.4, and find the dimension and a basis of the vector space of all matrices of m rows and n columns.

19. Let V^n be an n-dimensional vector space with two bases $\mathbf{B} = (\mathbf{b}^{(i)})_{1 \leq i \leq n}$, and $\mathbf{C} = (\mathbf{c}^{(i)})_{1 \leq i \leq n}$. Suppose

$$\mathbf{b}^{(i)} = b_{1i}\mathbf{c}^{(1)} + b_{2i}\mathbf{c}^{(2)} + \cdots + b_{ni}\mathbf{c}^{(n)} = \sum_{j=1}^{n} b_{ji}\mathbf{c}^{(j)}, \quad i = 1, 2, \cdots, n.$$

Prove: If sequences of coefficients, written as columns,

$$p^{\mathbf{B}} = \begin{pmatrix} p^{\mathbf{B}}_1 \\ p^{\mathbf{B}}_2 \\ \vdots \\ p^{\mathbf{B}}_n \end{pmatrix}, \qquad p^{\mathbf{C}} = \begin{pmatrix} p^{\mathbf{C}}_1 \\ p^{\mathbf{C}}_2 \\ \vdots \\ p^{\mathbf{C}}_n \end{pmatrix}, \qquad b^{(i)}_{\mathbf{C}} = \begin{pmatrix} b^{\mathbf{C}}_{1i} \\ b^{\mathbf{C}}_{2i} \\ \vdots \\ b^{\mathbf{C}}_{ni} \end{pmatrix} \quad \text{for } i = 1, \cdots, n$$

are defined by

$$\mathbf{p}^{\mathbf{B}} = p^{\mathbf{B}}_1 \mathbf{b}^{(1)} + p^{\mathbf{B}}_2 \mathbf{b}^{(2)} + \cdots + p^{\mathbf{B}}_n \mathbf{b}^{(n)} = \sum_{i=1}^{n} p^{\mathbf{B}}_i \mathbf{b}^{(i)}$$

$$\mathbf{p}^{\mathbf{C}} = p^{\mathbf{C}}_1 \mathbf{c}^{(1)} + p^{\mathbf{C}}_2 \mathbf{c}^{(2)} + \cdots + p^{\mathbf{C}}_n \mathbf{c}^{(n)} = \sum_{i=1}^{n} p^{\mathbf{C}}_i \mathbf{c}^{(i)}$$

$$\mathbf{b}^{(j)}_{\mathbf{C}} = b^{\mathbf{C}}_{1j} \mathbf{c}^{(1)} + b^{\mathbf{C}}_{2j} \mathbf{c}^{(2)} + \cdots + b^{\mathbf{C}}_{nj} \mathbf{c}^{(n)} = \sum_{i=1}^{n} b^{\mathbf{C}}_{ij} \mathbf{c}^{(i)} \quad j = 1, 2, \cdots, n$$

then

$$p^{\mathbf{C}} = (b_{\mathbf{C}}^{(1)}, b_{\mathbf{C}}^{(2)}, \cdots, b_{\mathbf{C}}^{(n)})p^{\mathbf{B}}. \tag{12.33}$$

[This is a generalization of (6.5) to the n-dimensional case.]

20. Prove: If $a = (a_1, a_2, \cdots, a_n)$ and $b = (b_1, b_2, \cdots, b_n)$ are two n-tuples of real numbers, then

$$a \cdot b = ab,$$

provided that a is interpreted as a row and b as a column.

21. Prove for sequences x, y, z of equal length and a number α, (a) $x \cdot y = y \cdot x$; (b) $x \cdot (y + z) = x \cdot y + x \cdot z$; (c) $\alpha(x \cdot y) = (\alpha x) \cdot y$.

22. Prove in detail, by referring to the relevant definitions and rules, that the system (8.1) can be abbreviated in the form

$$\sum_{i=1}^{n} a^{(i)}x_i + b = 0 \tag{12.34}$$

where

$$a^{(i)} = \begin{bmatrix} a_{1i} \\ a_{2i} \\ \vdots \\ a_{mi} \end{bmatrix} \quad \text{for} \quad i = 1, \cdots, n \quad \text{and} \quad b = \begin{bmatrix} b_1 \\ b_2 \\ \vdots \\ b_m \end{bmatrix}.$$

23. Prove: If B is an $(m \times n)$-matrix and $A = (a_{\downarrow}^{(1)}, a_{\downarrow}^{(2)}, \cdots, a_{\downarrow}^{(k)})$ is a matrix of k columns of n-tuples, then

$$BA = (Ba^{(1)}, Ba^{(2)}, \cdots, Ba^{(k)}).$$

24. Let B, C, D, E be submatrices of a (real) matrix A such that $A = \begin{bmatrix} B & C \\ D & E \end{bmatrix}$. Let B and D both have α columns (but not necessarily the same number of rows), and let C and E both have β columns. Let y and z be subcolumns, of lengths α and β, respectively, of a column x of elements of a vector space such that $x = \begin{bmatrix} y \\ z \end{bmatrix}$. Also let B and C have the same number of rows.

Prove:

$$Ax = \begin{bmatrix} By + Cz \\ Dy + Ez \end{bmatrix}.$$

25. Generalize the previous result to products of two matrices both of which are partitioned into suitable submatrices.

*26. Prove that the matrix multiplication of definition 12.5 can be generalized to those infinite (real or complex) double sequences $A = (a_{ij})_{(i,j) \epsilon I^+}$, (see Example 8 of Notations for the Images of an Element under a Mapping in Chapter 2) where (a) in *every* row and in *every* column there exist only finitely many numbers different from zero,

or (b) $\sum_{i=1}^{\infty} |a_{ij}|^2 < \infty$ every for $j \epsilon I^+$ and simultaneously $\sum_{j=1}^{\infty} |a_{ij}|^2 < \infty$

for every $i \epsilon I^+$.

27. The calculus of matrices was developed in this chapter under the assumption that the matrices act as left operators on column vectors whose "coordinates" are elements of a vector space V. Show that the whole calculus of matrices can be developed in a similar way, yielding the same definitions and theorems, if the matrices are *defined* to act as right operators on n-tuples of elements of a vector space V, provided that these n-tuples are interpreted as *row* vectors. More precisely, adopt first the following definition.

Definition 12.8: Let A be a matrix of n rows and m columns and let x be an n-tuple, written as a row, whose coordinates x_i are elements of a vector space V. Then the m-tuple, written as a row, whose ith column is the linear combination $\sum_{i=1}^{m} x_i a_{ji}$, is called *the product of x by the right-operator A* and is denoted by xA.

Now show that the definition of matrix multiplication by $x(AB) = (xA)B$ leads to definition 12.5 and that the definition of matrix addition by $x(A + B) = xA + xB$ leads to definition 12.6 as well as to the formula $(y + z)F = yF + zF$ (provided that both sides are defined).

13

Special Matrices

Matrices have not been introduced as an additional playground for lovers of numerical computation, but, on the contrary, to avoid lengthy, boring calculations and to replace them by a few short symbols that indicate suggestively the essence of a mathematical situation and point implicitly to a method of handling it. Competence in computing products of matrices without hesitation or strain is certainly necessary in order to solve explicitly *concrete numerical* problems whose *abstract symbolic* answers are given in the language of matrices; but the importance of this ability should not be overestimated. For these *abstract* answers should be obtained from *abstract* arguments, by application of the properties of matrices and their interpretation as left or right operators. A student who fails, for example, to see how matrices induce mappings or to understand what matrix formulas mean is better off without them, especially if he is a fast and efficient computer.

In this chapter some finer tools of matrix theory will be introduced, which can be applied to a variety of situations within and outside mathematics. Acquaintance with various types of matrices is needed if one is to master their calculus and apply them skillfully as operators to *alter* given matrices in a prescribed manner. Successive alteration of the matrix of coefficients was the essential process used to reduce a system of linear polynomials to echelon form, and the matrices inducing such alterations by left or right multiplication will be included in the discussion.

Suppose an $(m \times n)$-matrix A is interpreted as the matrix of coefficients of a system of m linear polynomials in n variables. Then *left* multiplication of A by a matrix B (of m columns) produces a matrix BA, which is the matrix of coefficients of a system *of linear combinations* of the original polynomials. Thus, the process of adding multiples of polynomials to obtain new sets of polynomials corresponds to *left* multiplication of the matrix of coefficients by a suitable matrix. Because of lemma 8.1, the transformed system admits the zeros of the old system *as zeros* but may have additional zeros.

It is harder to give a similar interpretation for the *right* multiplication of a matrix of coefficients by a matrix acting as an operator. We confine ourselves to the case in which the corresponding system is homogeneous. Suppose again that the system is given by Ax, where A is a matrix of m rows and n columns. If B is a matrix of n rows and, say, p columns and if y is a p-tuple of variables y_i written as a column vector, then By is a column vector of n linear combinations of the y's. Suppose we change our variables by identifying $x = By$; that is, by interpreting every old variable x_i as a certain linear combination of new variables y_i. Then we have $Ax = A(By) = (AB)y$. In other words, AB becomes the matrix of coefficients of a new system obtained from the old system by replacing the old variables by *linear combinations* of new variables. In general, the new system will have quite different zeros than the old system. If, in particular, we consider the case $n = p = 3$ (or $= 2$ or $= 1$) and interpret the x_i and y_i as coordinates of the points of $\Re^3$ (or $\Re^2$ or $\Re^1$), then it follows from Chapter 6 that the right multiplication of A by B corresponds to a *change of the base translations*.

Thus *left* multiplication of the matrix of coefficients of a system corresponds to a transition to another system having at least the same zeros as the old one, whereas *right* multiplication corresponds to a change of variables (or to a change of the coordinate system in the geometric interpretation). This remark may help to visualize the effect of the operators to be introduced.

In most cases we shall deal with *square matrices*. If they have n rows, then they can be interpreted as inducing mappings from the vector space R^n of all n-tuples of real numbers into itself. The easiest mapping of this type is that which maps every n-tuple x onto itself, that is, the so-called *identity mapping*. The image of x must then be the following n-tuple: In the first row we have 1 times x_1, in the second row 1 times x_2, $\cdots$, in the kth row 1 times x_k, and so forth. The matrix that produces these particular linear combinations obviously has the form

$$I = I_n = \begin{bmatrix} 1 & 0 & 0 & \cdot & \cdot & \cdot & 0 & 0 \\ 0 & 1 & 0 & \cdot & \cdot & \cdot & 0 & 0 \\ 0 & 0 & 1 & \cdot & \cdot & \cdot & 0 & 0 \\ & & & 1 & & & & \\ & & \mathbf{O} & & \cdot & & \mathbf{O} & \\ & & & & & 1 & & \\ 0 & 0 & 0 & \cdot & \cdot & \cdot & 1 & 0 \\ 0 & 0 & 0 & \cdot & \cdot & \cdot & 0 & 1 \end{bmatrix} \cdot \tag{13.1}$$

The big circles, first introduced in Chapter 8, indicate here and in some of the following formulas that certain parts of a matrix have only zeros as elements. The subscript n in I_n is to denote the *order* of (13.1). I_n reproduces any square matrix of order n not only by *left* multiplication but also by *right* multiplication.

Another easy type of mapping of R^n into itself is induced by the matrix tI_n for any real number t; that is,

$$tI_n = \begin{bmatrix} t & 0 & 0 & \cdots & 0 & 0 \\ 0 & t & 0 & \cdots & 0 & 0 \\ 0 & 0 & t & \cdots & 0 & 0 \\ & & & t & & \\ & & & & t & \\ 0 & 0 & 0 & \cdots & t & 0 \\ 0 & 0 & 0 & \cdots & 0 & t \end{bmatrix} . \tag{13.2}$$

If A is any square matrix of order n, then we have $(tI_n)A = t(I_nA) = tA$ and (because $tI_n = I_nt$) also $A(tI_n) = (At)I_n = At = tA$. In other words, both *left* and *right* multiplication of a matrix A of order n by a matrix tI_n have the same effect as multiplying every element of A by the number t.

Generalizing further, we consider the matrix D of which at most the elements of the form $d_{ii}(i = 1, \cdots n)$ are different from zero; these elements we shall then abbreviate d_i:

$$D = \begin{bmatrix} d_1 & 0 & 0 & \cdots & 0 & 0 \\ 0 & d_2 & 0 & \cdots & 0 & 0 \\ & & d_3 & & & \\ & & & \ddots & & \\ & & & & d_{n-2} & \\ 0 & 0 & 0 & \cdots & d_{n-1} & 0 \\ 0 & 0 & 0 & \cdots & 0 & d_n \end{bmatrix} . \tag{13.3}$$

If A is again a square matrix of order n, then the element in the ith row and kth column of the product DA is obtained as the inner product of the ith row of D, in which the ith coordinate is equal to d_i and all other coordinates are equal to zero, and the kth column of A. This element is obviously d_ia_{ik}:

$$(0,0,\cdots,0,d_i,0,\cdots,0)\cdot\begin{bmatrix}a_{1k}\\a_{2k}\\\vdots\\a_{ik}\\\vdots\\a_{nk}\end{bmatrix}=d_ia_{ik}.$$

Writing down all elements of DA (for all $i=1,\cdots,n$ and $k=1,\cdots,n$), we obtain

$$DA=\begin{bmatrix}d_1a_{11}&d_1a_{12}&\cdots&d_1a_{1n}\\d_2a_{21}&d_2a_{22}&\cdots&d_2a_{2n}\\\vdots&\vdots&&\vdots\\d_na_{n1}&d_na_{n2}&\cdots&d_na_{nn}\end{bmatrix}.$$

In other words, *left* multiplication of A by D has the effect that every *row* matrix of A is multiplied by a scalar; that is, the ith row is multiplied by d_i.

By a similar computation it can be seen that *right* multiplication of A by D has the effect that every *column* matrix of A is multiplied by a scalar; that is, the kth column is multiplied by the scalar d_k:

$$AD=\begin{bmatrix}d_1a_{11}&d_2a_{12}&\cdots&d_na_{1n}\\d_1a_{21}&d_2a_{22}&\cdots&d_na_{2n}\\\vdots&\vdots&&\vdots\\d_1a_{n1}&d_2a_{n2}&\cdots&d_na_{nn}\end{bmatrix}.$$

To start a vocabulary on special matrices we introduce the following terms.

Definition 13.1: If A is any matrix with elements a_{ij}, then the set of all elements of the form a_{kk}, that is, the set of all elements for which the two subscripts are alike, is called *the principal diagonal of A*. The sum of the elements of the principal diagonal is called *the trace of A* and is abbreviated $\tau(A)$. A matrix is called a *diagonal matrix* if all its elements outside the principal diagonal are equal to zero. A diagonal square matrix is called a *scalar matrix* if all elements in the principal diagonal are equal. The scalar matrix of order n whose elements in the principal diagonal are equal to 1 is called the *identity matrix (of order n)* and is denoted by I_n, or by I if no confusion with the set of integers is possible.

Note: Equation (13.1) defines the identity matrix of order n. (13.2) defines the scalar matrix that has the same effect as the scalar t. But (13.3) does not give the most general kind of diagonal matrix; for diagonal matrices that are not square may occur occasionally.

Now let us turn to the matrices that correspond to the processes involved in reducing a linear system to echelon form except for the process of canceling zero polynomials.

In the elimination process, a scalar multiple of one polynomial is added to *another* polynomial of the system. For the matrix A of coefficients, this means that to one row a multiple of another row is added. Suppose we want to add to the ith row of A the jth row multiplied by by the scalar α. Let $M_{ij}(\alpha)$ be an abbreviation for the matrix that produces this change by left multiplication. Then all rows except the ith are reproduced in their respective places; that is, $M_{ij}(\alpha)$ looks like the identity matrix in all rows except the ith. To obtain α times the old jth row in the new ith row, we must have α as the element in the ith row and jth column of $M_{ij}(\alpha)$, as well as the element 1 in the diagonal. According to whether $j < i$ or $j > i$, the required operator will have different representations:

$$\text{For } j < i; \quad M_{ij}(\alpha) = \begin{bmatrix} 1 & & & & & & & \\ & 1 & & & & & & \\ & & \ddots & & & & & \\ & & & 1 & & & & \\ & & & & \ddots & & & \\ \cdots\cdots\cdot\alpha & & & & & 1 & & \\ & & & & & & \ddots & \\ & & & & & & & 1 \end{bmatrix} \cdot$$

ith row $\rightarrow$

$\uparrow$
jth column   (13.4)

$$\text{For } j > i; \quad M_{ij}(\alpha) = \begin{bmatrix} 1 & & & & & & & \\ & 1 & & & & & & \\ & & \ddots & & & & & \\ & & & 1 & \alpha\cdots & & & \\ & & & & \ddots & & & \\ & & & & & 1 & & \\ & & & & & & \ddots & \\ & & & & & & & 1 \end{bmatrix} \leftarrow \begin{array}{l} i\text{th} \\ \text{row} \end{array}$$

$\uparrow$
jth column

Here the convention is adopted that every element not written down shall be equal to zero, except for the elements in the principal diagonal, which then, without exception, are equal to 1 (see exercise 12.5 for a concrete case).

$M_{ij}(\alpha)$ is so constructed that, as a *left* operator, it adds α times the jth row to the ith row of any matrix it is to act upon. It is easy to see that, as a *right*-operator, $M_{ij}(\alpha)$ adds α times the ith *column* to the jth *column* of a matrix A.

Normalization of the ith polynomial of a system corresponds to left multiplication of the matrix of coefficients by the diagonal matrix

$$
N_i(\alpha) =
\begin{bmatrix}
1 & & & & & & & \\
 & 1 & & & & & & \\
 & & 1 & & & & & \\
 & & & \ddots & & & & \\
 & & & & 1 & & & \\
 & & & & & \alpha & \cdots\cdots & \leftarrow i\text{th row} \\
 & & & & & & 1 & \\
 & & & & & & & \ddots \\
 & & & & & & & & 1
\end{bmatrix}
\qquad (13.5)
$$

in which all elements of the principal diagonal are equal to 1, except the element in the ith row, which is α. Again, all elements of (13.5), except those in the principal diagonal, are supposed to be equal to zero.

The exchange of the ith and jth coordinates $(i < j)$ of a column x of n variables x_k $(k = 1, \cdots , n)$ corresponds to left multiplication of x by the matrix obtained from the identity matrix by interchanging the ith and jth rows:

$$
E_{ij} =
\begin{bmatrix}
1 & & & & & & \\
 & 1 & \ddots & & & & \\
 & & \ddots & & & & \\
 & & & 1 & & & \\
 & & & 0\cdots\cdots 1\cdots\cdots & & & \leftarrow i\text{th row} \\
 & & & \vdots\, 1 \ddots\; \vdots & & & \\
 & & & \vdots\quad\; \ddots\; \vdots & & & \\
 & & & \vdots\quad\quad 1\, \vdots & & & \\
 & & & 1\cdots\cdots 0\cdots\cdots & & & \leftarrow j\text{th row} \\
 & & & \vdots\quad\; \ddots 1 & & & \\
 & & & \vdots\quad\quad \vdots\; \ddots & & & \\
 & & & \vdots\quad\quad \vdots\quad\; & & & 1
\end{bmatrix}
\qquad (13.6)
$$

$$\uparrow \qquad \uparrow$$
$$i\text{th column} \quad j\text{th column}$$

Hence, the system Ax with matrix of coefficients A is changed to the system $A(E_{ij}x) = (AE_{ij})x$ by exchange of the subscripts i and j (see exercise 12.2 for a concrete case). On the other hand, *left* multiplication of A by (13.6) exchanges the ith and jth *rows* of A.

For the square matrices corresponding to elimination, normalization, and exchange, the following terminology is customary.

Definition 13.2: A square matrix is called *elementary* if it is of one of the forms (13.4), (13.5), and (13.6).

Cancellation of the ith polynomial in a system corresponds to left multiplication of the matrix of coefficients by the matrix $I^{i;\phi}$ obtained from the identity matrix by cancellation of the ith row.

The whole reduction procedure of Chapter 8 can now be performed on the matrix of coefficients of a system without any reference to the variables, by the successive application of operators that are either elementary matrices or matrices of the form $I^{i;\phi}$. This process, too, is called *reduction of a matrix to echelon form* (or *to an echelon matrix*).

Products of matrices of the form (13.6) lead to the following type of matrices (see exercise 12.10).

Definition 13.3: Every *square* matrix that contains in every row one 1 and the rest zeros and, simultaneously, in every column one 1 and the rest zeros is called a *permuting matrix*.

It is not difficult to see that all those and only those matrices are permuting matrices that are obtainable from an identity matrix by exchanges of rows. Suitable products of matrices of the form (13.4) and (13.5) lead to the following types of matrices (see exercise 12.11).

Definition 13.4: Any matrix all of whose elements *above* the principal diagonal are equal to zero is called a *lower triangular matrix*. Any matrix all of whose elements *below* the principal diagonal are equal to zero is called an *upper triangular matrix*. A triangular matrix all of whose elements in the principal diagonal are equal to 1 is called *normalized*.

Note: A triangular matrix need not be square, but usually it will be. The choice of words "upper" and "lower" indicates where possible nonzero elements lie and *not* where the zeros are, because frequently the zeros are left out when a matrix is written out in detail. The following matrices are a lower triangular matrix and a normalized lower triangular matrix, respectively:

$$
\begin{bmatrix}
a_{11} & & & & \\
a_{21} & a_{22} & & \mathcal{O} & \\
a_{31} & a_{32} & a_{33} & & \\
\vdots & \vdots & \vdots & \ddots & \\
a_{n1} & a_{n2} & a_{n3} & \cdots & a_{nn}
\end{bmatrix},
\quad
\begin{bmatrix}
1 & & & & \\
a_{21} & 1 & & \mathcal{O} & \\
a_{31} & a_{32} & 1 & & \\
\vdots & \vdots & \vdots & \ddots & \\
a_{n1} & a_{n2} & a_{n3} & \cdots & 1
\end{bmatrix}.
\tag{13.7}
$$

On the other hand, the matrices

$$\begin{bmatrix} a_{11} & a_{12} & a_{13} & \cdots & a_{1n} \\ & a_{22} & a_{23} & \cdots & a_{2n} \\ & & a_{33} & \cdots & a_{3n} \\ & \mathbf{O} & & \ddots & \vdots \\ & & & & a_{nn} \end{bmatrix}, \quad \begin{bmatrix} 1 & a_{12} & a_{13} & \cdots & a_{1n} \\ & 1 & a_{23} & \cdots & a_{2n} \\ & & 1 & \cdots & a_{3n} \\ & \mathbf{O} & & \ddots & \vdots \\ & & & & 1 \end{bmatrix} \qquad (13.8)$$

are an upper triangular matrix and a normalized upper triangular matrix respectively.

It is now possible to show that, for any square matrix B defined by definitions 13.1, 13.2, and 13.4 and satisfying the additional condition that no element in the principal diagonal is equal to zero, there exists a matrix $\bar{B}$ such that $B\bar{B} = I$. From this proof it is only a small step to verify the following theorem.

Theorem 13:1: *The following sets of square matrices of order n are groups relative to matrix multiplication: (1) the set of all nonzero scalar matrices; (2) the set of all diagonal matrices without zeros in the principal diagonal; (3) the set of all normalized lower triangular matrices and (4) the set of all normalized upper triangular matrices; (5) the set of all lower and (6) the set of all upper triangular matrices without zero elements in the principal diagonals.*

Square matrices B for which there exist elements $\bar{B}$ (that is, *opposite* elements in a slight generalization of the concept introduced in definition 4.3) such that $B\bar{B} = \bar{B}B = I$, will be important in the calculus of matrices. Therefore, we increase our vocabulary as follows.

Definition 13.5: Any square matrix B for which there exists an opposite matrix $\bar{B}$ with $B\bar{B} = \bar{B}B = I$ is called *regular* (or *nonsingular*, or *invertible*). Any matrix that is not regular is called *singular* (or *nonregular*, or *noninvertible*). If such a matrix $\bar{B}$ exists, it is called *the inverse of B* and is usually denoted by B^{-1}.

If a matrix B has two inverses $\bar{B}$ and $\bar{\bar{B}}$ then they are equal because of $\bar{B} = \bar{B}(B\bar{\bar{B}}) = (\bar{B}B)\bar{\bar{B}} = \bar{\bar{B}}$; therefore, the wording of the last part of definition 13.5 is justified.

Lemma 13.1: *If A and B are two invertible matrices of order n, then*

$$(AB)^{-1} = B^{-1}A^{-1}. \qquad (13.9)$$

PROOF: We have $(AB)(B^{-1}A^{-1}) = A(BB^{-1})A^{-1} = AA^{-1} = I_n$. This shows that $B^{-1}A^{-1}$ is a right inverse of AB. As the right opposite is always a left opposite, by the proof of theorem 4.1, the matrix $B^{-1}A^{-1}$ is *the inverse of AB*.

Theorem 13.2:   *The set of all regular matrices of order n forms a group under multiplication, which (for $n > 1$) is not commutative.*

Proof: The associativity of matrix multiplication follows from lemma 12.1. The product of two regular matrices is regular by lemma 13.1. I_n is regular. The inverse of a regular matrix is regular.

If the inverse A^{-1} of a matrix A exists and if all elements of A^{-1} are *explicitly* known, then the solutions of *any* linear system having A as the matrix of coefficients *of the unknowns* can be written down immediately. For suppose we have a nonhomogeneous system written in the form

$$Ax = b, \qquad (13.10)$$

where A is an invertible matrix of order n, x a column of n unknowns $x_1, \cdots, x_n$, and b the column of the right-hand sides of the equations of the system (13.10). Then, by left multiplication by some matrix of n columns, we change (13.10) to some system that has *at least* all the n-tuples that solve (13.10) as solutions, but perhaps some additional solutions. If we choose A^{-1} as a left operator, we have $A^{-1}(Ax) = A^{-1}b$ as the new system, which can be written in the shorter form $x = A^{-1}b$. Obviously, this system has $A^{-1}b$ as the *only* solution; hence, $A^{-1}b$ is the only solution of (13.10), too.

Note: The knowledge of the inverse A^{-1} is very economical, for $A^{-1}b$ is the solution of (13.10) for *any* choice of the right-hand sides. In many applications of equations to fields outside mathematics, for example, economics, many systems have to be solved one after another where the coefficients of the unknowns are *always* the same and only the right-hand sides change from system to system. The formula $A^{-1}b$ for the solution indicates the effect of the change in the right-hand sides upon the explicit solution.

The preceding arguments even give a method (though not necessarily the best or fastest method) of *computing* the inverse of a matrix A: Write down a system of equations of the type (13.10), and leave the right-hand sides unspecified; that is, leave undetermined objects $b_1, \cdots, b_n$ on the right-hand sides. Then use the procedure of Chapter 8 to solve this system. The unique solution must be an n-tuple of linear combinations of the unspecified b's. The *matrix of coefficients* of these linear combinations must be the desired inverse of A. An alternative method of computing the inverse of a matrix A of order n (if it exists) is as follows: Reduce A to an echelon matrix by successive left multiplications of elementary matrices, but perform this process on the matrix (A, I), where I is the identity matrix of order n. The transformation that takes A into the identity matrix will take I into the inverse of A. This follows immediately from $B(A,I) = (BA,B) = (I,B)$ if $BA = I$.

The inverse of a matrix is defined only for certain matrices, not even for all square matrices. We turn now to another type of matrix, which can be constructed from *any* given matrix A in a very easy manner regardless of whether A is regular or square. Let A be interpreted as a row of columns in the form (12.5). If the column n-tuples are rewritten as a system of *rows* in the same order, a different matrix is obtained, in general. If this process is applied twice, we return to the original matrix. The following is an example of a matrix and the matrix obtained from it by this interchange of rows and columns:

$$\begin{bmatrix} a_{11} & a_{12} & \cdots & a_{1n} \\ a_{21} & a_{22} & \cdots & a_{2n} \\ \cdot & \cdot & & \cdot \\ \cdot & \cdot & & \cdot \\ \cdot & \cdot & & \cdot \\ a_{m1} & a_{m2} & \cdots & a_{mn} \end{bmatrix}, \quad \begin{bmatrix} a_{11} & a_{21} & \cdots & a_{m1} \\ a_{12} & a_{22} & \cdots & a_{m2} \\ \cdot & \cdot & & \cdot \\ \cdot & \cdot & & \cdot \\ \cdot & \cdot & & \cdot \\ a_{1n} & a_{2n} & \cdots & a_{mn} \end{bmatrix}. \qquad (13.11)$$

Definition 13.6: If A is any matrix, then the matrix obtained from A by writing all columns of A as rows, in the same order as the columns were listed, is called *the transpose of A* and is denoted by A'. The mapping $A \rightarrow A'$ is called *transposition*. Any matrix that is equal to its transpose is called *symmetric*. Any matrix whose transpose is equal to its inverse is called *orthogonal*.

The significance of the concepts here introduced cannot be understood fully now. The transpose of a matrix or, more specifically, of a column vector x, can be used to describe the inner product $x \cdot y$ of two n-tuples of Chapter 12 in matrix notation. If x and y are n-tuples written as columns, then x' is a row; hence, the matrix product $x'y$ is defined and equal to a matrix of one row and one column whose single element is the inner product $x \cdot y$. Since we identify (1×1)-matrices with their elements, by definition 12.1, we have

$$x'y = x \cdot y \quad \text{if} \quad x, y \, \varepsilon \, R^n, \quad \text{with } x \text{ and } y \text{ written as columns.} \quad (13.12)$$

For the transpose of a product we have the following rule, an example of which was exhibited in exercise 12.8:

Lemma 13.2: *If the product of two matrices A and B is defined, then*

$$(AB)' = B'A'. \qquad (13.13)$$

In Part IV, symmetric matrices will play an important role in the representation by matrix equations of *conic sections* (ellipses, hyperbolas, and parabolas) and certain surfaces called *quadrics*.

Orthogonal matrices correspond, in geometry, to mappings of a point space onto itself that *leave distances* and *angles unaltered* (corollary 15.2); these are later seen to be intimately connected with *rotations* of the space around some axis.

EXERCISES

1. State a necessary and sufficient condition that a diagonal matrix (13.3) be invertible, and give the inverse of such a matrix *explicitly*.

2. Give *explicitly* the inverses of the matrices (13.4), (13.5), and (13.6).

3. Prove that every permuting matrix is a product of matrices of the form (13.6) and that every *normalized* triangular square matrix is a product of matrices of the form (13.4).

4. Use lemma 13.1 and the results of exercises 1, 2, and 3 to prove theorem 13.1.

5. Compute the inverses of the following matrices, provided that they exist:

(a) $\begin{bmatrix} 3 & 1 & 2 \\ 4 & 1 & 1 \\ 3 & 1 & 3 \end{bmatrix}$,   (b) $\begin{bmatrix} 1 & 2 & 3 \\ 3 & 1 & 2 \\ 2 & 3 & 1 \end{bmatrix}$,   (c) $\begin{bmatrix} 1 & 1 & 2 \\ 0 & 2 & 1 \\ 2 & 1 & 1 \end{bmatrix}$,

(d) $\begin{bmatrix} 1 & 0 & 0 & 2 \\ 2 & 1 & 1 & 1 \\ 3 & 2 & -1 & 2 \\ 0 & 0 & 1 & 0 \end{bmatrix}$,   (e) $\begin{bmatrix} 1 & 0 & 0 & 0 \\ 2 & 1 & 0 & 0 \\ 3 & 4 & 1 & 0 \\ 0 & 0 & 0 & 1 \end{bmatrix}$,   (f) $\begin{bmatrix} 0 & 3 & 0 & 0 \\ 2 & 0 & 0 & 0 \\ 0 & 0 & 4 & 0 \\ 1 & 0 & 0 & 5 \end{bmatrix}$.

6. Prove: If a square matrix B induces a change $x \rightarrow Bx$ from old coordinates relative to a set of old base vectors to new coordinates relative to a set of new base vectors, then the matrix that induces the change from the new to the old coordinates is B^{-1}.

7. Prove: $(A')' = A$; $(AB)'$ (if defined) $= B'A'$; and $(A + B)'$ (if defined) $= A' + B'$. Define, for every matrix A, a matrix A^* obtained from A by interchange of rows and columns (as in the definition of A') *and* reversal of the order of appearance of all elements in every row and every column. Prove that $(A^*)^* = A$ and that $(AB)^*$ (if defined) $= B^*A^*$.

8. Prove: Every real orthogonal matrix of order 2 has either the form
$\begin{bmatrix} \cos\alpha & -\sin\alpha \\ \sin\alpha & \cos\alpha \end{bmatrix}$ or the form $\begin{bmatrix} \cos\alpha & \sin\alpha \\ \sin\alpha & -\cos\alpha \end{bmatrix}$ for a suitable $\alpha \in R$.

9. Prove: If A is symmetric and T is orthogonal, then $T^{-1}AT$ is symmetric.

10. Prove that every matrix (13.6) is orthogonal.

11. Prove that a triangular matrix that is symmetric must be diagonal.

12. Prove that a triangular matrix that is orthogonal must be the identity matrix.

13. A matrix B is called skew-symmetric if $B = -B'$. Prove: Every matrix is the (unique) sum of a symmetric matrix and a skew-symmetric matrix.

14. Let $A = (a_{ij})$, $B = (b_{ij})$, $C = (c_{ij})$ be three upper (or three lower) triangular matrices of order n such that $AB = C$. Prove: $a_{ii}b_{ii} = c_{ii}$ for $i = 1, \cdots, n$.

15. Let A be a square matrix of order n, let x be a column of length n, and let λ be a real or complex scalar. Prove: The systems $Ax = \lambda x$ and $(A - \lambda I)x = 0$ have exactly the same solutions.

16. Define, for a square matrix A,

$$A^i = \begin{cases} I & \text{for } j = 0 \\ (A^{i-1})A & \text{for } j > 0 \end{cases}$$

as usual in mathematics. Prove: If $A^n = 0$ for some positive integer n, then $I - A$ has $\displaystyle\sum_{j=0}^{n-1} A^i$ as its inverse.

17. Prove: A square matrix $A = (a^{(1)}, a^{(2)}, \cdots, a^{(n)})$ is orthogonal if and only if the following equations are satisfied for all couples of columns of A:

$$a^{(i)} \cdot a^{(j)} = \begin{cases} 1 & \text{if } i = j, \\ 0 & \text{if } i \neq j. \end{cases} \qquad (13.14)$$

Prove also that this proposition remains true if the reference to columns is changed to rows.

18. Let $a^{(1)}$ be a real (or complex) n-tuple, written as a row, whose inner square is equal to 1. Prove: It is always possible to find $n-1$ n-tuples, $a^{(2)}, \cdots, a^{(n)}$, each of whose inner squares is equal to 1, such that

$$\begin{pmatrix} a^{(1)} \\ a^{(2)} \\ \vdots \\ a^{(n)} \end{pmatrix}$$

is an orthogonal matrix.

Hint: Use formula (13.14). Prove at first that there exists an $x = a^{(2)}$, with inner square equal to 1, such that $\displaystyle\sum_{i=1}^{n} a_i^{(1)} x_i = 0$ and then proceed by induction.

19. Find an orthogonal matrix whose first row is $a^{(1)} = (\frac{3}{13}, \frac{4}{13}, \frac{12}{13})$.

 Hint: Find a nonzero triple x^* that satisfies $\frac{3}{13}x_1 + \frac{4}{13}x_2 + \frac{12}{13}x_3 = 0$, and take $a^{(2)} = (1/\sqrt{x^{*2}})x^*$, whose inner square is 1. Then find a solution x^{**} of the system

$$\frac{3}{13} x_1 + \frac{4}{13} x_2 + \frac{12}{13} x_3 = 0$$

$$a_1^{(2)}x_1 + a_2^{(2)}x_2 + a_3^{(2)}x_3 = 0,$$

and take $a^{(3)} = (1/\sqrt{x^{**2}})x^{**}$.

20. Let x and y be (real or complex) columns of length n, and let A be an orthogonal matrix of order n. Prove: $x \cdot y = (Ax) \cdot (Ay)$.

21. Let x and y be (real or complex) columns of length n, and let A be a symmetric matrix of order n. Prove: $(Ax) \cdot y = x \cdot (Ay)$.

14

Linear Mappings

Linear mappings are the most natural tools for comparing vector spaces and their subspaces, because they assign to the composites of one vector space the corresponding composites of the other. By exercise 9.16, they even map flocks into flocks. This means, in the two- or the three-dimensional geometric case, that they map a line on a line or on a single point, and a plane on a plane or on a line or on a point.

In this chapter it will be shown how closely matrices are related to linear mappings of vector spaces in which bases have been chosen, how matrices can represent changes in the coordinate system, and how matrices change if the bases are altered. We will restrict ourselves to *real* matrices and *real* vector spaces, but the results can be generalized automatically to the *complex* case. It will also frequently be assumed, without further mention, that the dimensions of the vector spaces considered are positive, in order to avoid uninteresting trivial cases.

Theorem 14.1: *The premultiplication $x \to Ax$ of real columns of length q by a real matrix A of p rows and q columns ($p \neq q$ or $p = q$) is a linear mapping of R^q into R^p, and every linear mapping of R^q into R^p is induced by a matrix.*

PROOF: 1.   If $x, y \; \varepsilon \; R^q$, then $A(x + y) = Ax + Ay$, by (12.22). If $\alpha \; \varepsilon \; R$ and $x \; \varepsilon \; R^q$, then $A(\alpha x) = (A\alpha)x = (\alpha A)x = \alpha(Ax)$, by definition 12.7. Hence every matrix induces a linear mapping.

2.   Let us now assume that μ is a linear mapping of R^q into R^p. Then,

by (5.15), the μ-image of *every* element of R^q can be determined if the μ-images of the elements of some basis of R^q are known. Suppose we know that the natural basis

$$e^{(1)} = \begin{bmatrix} 1 \\ 0 \\ \vdots \\ 0 \end{bmatrix}, \quad e^{(2)} = \begin{bmatrix} 0 \\ 1 \\ 0 \\ \vdots \\ 0 \end{bmatrix}, \quad \cdots, \quad e^{(q)} = \begin{bmatrix} 0 \\ 0 \\ \vdots \\ 0 \\ 1 \end{bmatrix}$$

has the following μ-images in R^p (where μ is used as a left operator):

$$\mu e^{(1)} = \begin{bmatrix} m_{11} \\ m_{21} \\ \vdots \\ m_{p1} \end{bmatrix}, \quad \mu e^{(2)} = \begin{bmatrix} m_{12} \\ m_{22} \\ \vdots \\ m_{p2} \end{bmatrix}, \quad \cdots, \quad \mu e^{(q)} = \begin{bmatrix} m_{1q} \\ m_{2q} \\ \vdots \\ m_{pq} \end{bmatrix}.$$

Then, by (5.15), the μ-image of an arbitrary element

$$u = u_1 e^{(1)} + u_2 e^{(2)} + \cdots + u_q e^{(q)}$$

of R^q is given by

$$\mu u = u_1(\mu e^{(1)}) + u_2(\mu e^{(2)}) + \cdots + u_q(\mu e^{(q)})$$

$$= u_1 \begin{bmatrix} m_{11} \\ m_{21} \\ \vdots \\ m_{p1} \end{bmatrix} + u_2 \begin{bmatrix} m_{12} \\ m_{22} \\ \vdots \\ m_{p2} \end{bmatrix} + \cdots + u_q \begin{bmatrix} m_{1q} \\ m_{2q} \\ \vdots \\ m_{pq} \end{bmatrix}$$

$$= \begin{bmatrix} m_{11}u_1 + m_{12}u_2 + \cdots + m_{1q}u_q \\ m_{21}u_1 + m_{22}u_2 + \cdots + m_{2q}u_q \\ \vdots \qquad\qquad \vdots \\ m_{p1}u_1 + m_{p2}u_2 + \cdots + m_{pq}u_q \end{bmatrix}$$

$$= Mu \quad \text{with} \quad M = \begin{bmatrix} m_{11} & m_{12} & \cdots & m_{1q} \\ m_{21} & m_{22} & \cdots & m_{2q} \\ \vdots & \vdots & & \vdots \\ m_{p1} & m_{p2} & \cdots & m_{pq} \end{bmatrix}.$$

Hence, every linear mapping of R^q into R^p is induced by a matrix A. This completes the second part of the proof.

Note: Because of this close relationship between matrices and linear mappings of finite sequence spaces, we shall sometimes use *the same symbol* to denote *both* the linear mapping of R^q into R^p and the matrix that induces that mapping:

$$M : u \to Mu, \qquad u \, \varepsilon \, R^q, \; Mu \, \varepsilon \, R^p. \tag{14.1}$$

Next we shall investigate the relationship between real matrices and linear mappings of *arbitrary* finite-dimensional real vector spaces. In preparation, we extend definition 6.3 to the *n*-dimensional case.

Definition 14.1: Let $\mathbf{B} = (\mathbf{b}^{(1)}, \cdots, \mathbf{b}^{(q)})$ be a basis of a real vector space $\mathbf{V}$. The mapping

$$\mathbf{v} = v_1 \mathbf{b}^{(1)} + v_2 \mathbf{b}^{(2)} + \cdots + v_q \mathbf{b}^{(q)} \to v = (v_1, v_2, \cdots, v_q) \tag{14.2}$$

assigning to every element $\mathbf{v}$ of $\mathbf{V}$, expressed as a (unique) linear combination of $\mathbf{B}$, its sequence $v = (v_1, \cdots, v_q)$ of coefficients is called the *transition from $\mathbf{V}$ to the coordinate space*. The opposite mapping

$$v = (v_1, v_2, \cdots, v_q) \to \mathbf{v} = v_1 \mathbf{b}^{(1)} + v_2 \mathbf{b}^{(2)} + \cdots + v_q \mathbf{b}^{(q)} \tag{14.3}$$

is called the *return from the coordinate space to $\mathbf{V}$*.

Note: Both mappings (14.2) and (14.3) are *isomorphisms* (see theorem 5.2 for the first case).

Since vectors can be represented by sequences of numbers, linear mappings of one vector space into another (or into itself) can be represented by double sequences. We restrict the discussion to the finite-dimensional real case, but the result can be generalized to any vector space.

Let us consider the following problem: Given a linear mapping $\mathbf{M}$ of a *q*-dimensional real vector space $\mathbf{U}$, with basis $\mathbf{B} = (\mathbf{b}^{(1)}, \mathbf{b}^{(2)}, \cdots, \mathbf{b}^{(q)})$ into a *p*-dimensional real vector space $\mathbf{V}$, with basis $\mathbf{C} = (\mathbf{c}^{(1)}, \mathbf{c}^{(2)}, \cdots, \mathbf{c}^{(p)})$. If the coordinate vector $(\varepsilon \, R^q)$ of an element of $\mathbf{U}$ is given, how can we determine the coordinate vector $(\varepsilon \, R^p)$ of its $\mathbf{M}$-image in $\mathbf{V}$? Or, in a different formulation: What kind of a mapping M does $\mathbf{M}$ induce from the coordinate space R^q of $\mathbf{U}$ into the coordinate space R^p of $\mathbf{V}$?

Let r be the return from R^q to $\mathbf{U}$, and let t be the transition from $\mathbf{V}$ to R^p. Then the mapping M of R^q into R^p, induced by $\mathbf{M}$ in the above sense, is defined by the equation

$$M = t \circ \mathbf{M} \circ r \tag{14.4}$$

(see Fig. 14.1). This is a triple composite of linear mappings. Hence, M is linear, by exercise 5.25, and induced by a matrix, by theorem 14.1; this matrix we shall then denote by M, too. We summarize.

Corollary 14.1: *Let $\mathbf{M}$ be a linear mapping of a real vector space $\mathbf{U}$ of dimension q with a given basis into a real vector space $\mathbf{V}$ of dimension p with a given basis. Let M be the corresponding mapping of R^q into R^p, assigning* to every coordinate vector $u = (u_1, u_2, \cdots, u_q)$ ($\varepsilon\ R^q$) of $\mathbf{u}\ \varepsilon\ \mathbf{U}$ the coordinate vector $v = (v_1, v_2, \cdots, v_p)$ ($\varepsilon\ R^p$) of $\mathbf{v} = \mathbf{Mu}$ ($\varepsilon\ \mathbf{V}$). Then M is induced by a real matrix, and every real $(p \times q)$-matrix induces such a mapping M.

One might wonder why theorems 5.2 and 9.1 and corollary 14.1 together do not present a strong case for abandoning the abstract finite-dimensional vector spaces and their linear mappings and working exclusively with vector spaces of sequences and with matrices. But many properties of vector spaces and linear mappings are not dependent on the bases chosen. If these properties were proved to hold with reference to particular co-ordinate systems, then the independence of the results from the bases chosen would have to be shown separately in every case. Also, the presentation of a result in terms of coordinate vectors will frequently distract from its essence. How much easier the coordinate-free treatment is may be witnessed in this text, and, as a matter of fact, later in this chapter. For all these reasons, the use of bases should be avoided as much as possible. It suffices to know what changes are to be made if coordinate systems have to be introduced. This chapter will give some answers with respect to linear mappings.

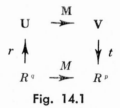

Fig. 14.1

There are two important special cases of corollary 14.1:
1. Let $\mathbf{M}$ be a *one-to-one* linear mapping of $\mathbf{U}$ with some basis *onto* $\mathbf{U}$ with the same basis, that is, an automorphism of $\mathbf{U}$.
2. Let $\mathbf{M}$ be the identity mapping of $\mathbf{U}$ with some basis onto the same vector space $\mathbf{U}$ *with some other basis*. In this case the corresponding mapping M induces the change from one basis to the other.

For these two cases the following corollary follows from corollary 14.1.

Corollary 14.2: *Every automorphism of a vector space of dimension n and every change of its basis are induced by a regular matrix of order n acting on the coordinate vectors. Every regular matrix of order n induces a mapping of the coordinate space corresponding to an automorphism or to a change of the basis of the vector space.*

Note: The regularity of the matrix is needed, because $\mathbf{M}$ is *one-to-one* and *onto* and, hence, must have an inverse. The ambiguity in the second part of the corollary means that the effect of the premultiplication by a regular matrix can be interpreted *in two different ways*: Either the matrix multiplication produces an *active transformation*, that is, assigns to the vectors (in general) other vectors of the same vector space as images; or a *passive transformation*, that is, merely a change in the coordinate system. Both types of interpretation will be used in applications to $\mathfrak{R}^2$ and $\mathfrak{R}^3$ (via $\mathbf{R}^2$ and $\mathbf{R}^3$, of course).

The next question that comes up naturally is: How is the matrix (14.4), corresponding to the linear mapping $\mathbf{M}$, changed if the bases of $\mathbf{U}$ and $\mathbf{V}$ are changed?

Let the *old* coordinates of elements $\mathbf{u} \ \varepsilon \ \mathbf{U}$ and $\mathbf{v} \ \varepsilon \ \mathbf{V}$ be denoted by $u = (u_1, \cdots, u_q)$ and $v = (v_1, \cdots v_p)$ and their *new* coordinates by $\bar{u} = (\bar{u}_1, \cdots, \bar{u}_q)$ and $\bar{v} = (\bar{v}_1, \cdots, \bar{v}_p)$, respectively. Let $\bar{R}^q$ and $\bar{R}^p$ be the new coordinate spaces (which, of course, are formally distinct from R^q and R^p only in order to simplify the discussion). Apply the suffix $\mathbf{U}$ or $\mathbf{V}$ to indicate to which vector space the transitions and returns refer, and use an overbar to indicate the transition, return, or linear mapping with respect to the new bases. Then the whole situation may be illustrated by the diagram in Fig. 14.2. We have, obviously,

$$\bar{M} = (\bar{l}_V \circ r_V) \circ M \circ (t_U \circ \bar{r}_U). \tag{14.5}$$

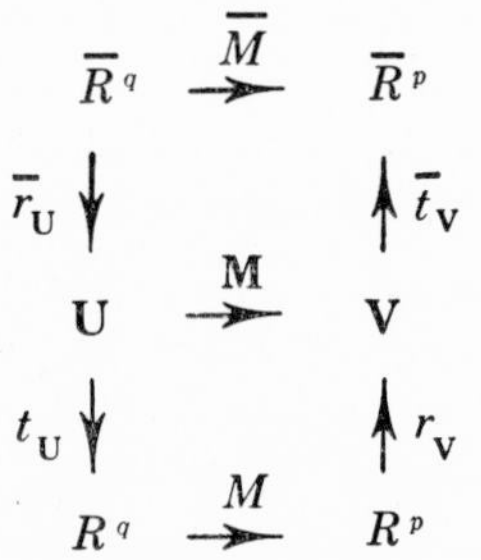

Fig. 14.2 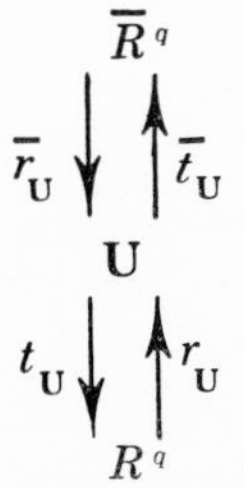   Fig. 14.3

Since transitions and returns are linear mappings, the mapping $t_U \circ \bar{r}_U$ of $\bar{R}^q$ into R^q must be linear and, hence, must be induced by a square matrix A. Since $\bar{l}_U \circ r_U$ is the opposite mapping of $t_U \circ \bar{r}_U$ (see Fig. 14.3), the matrix A must be regular. In similar fashion it can be seen that $\bar{l}_V \circ r_V$ is induced by a regular matrix B. Hence we have

$$\bar{M} = BMA \tag{14.6}$$

(see Fig. 14.4).

An important special case that comes up frequently is that in which $\mathbf{M}$ is a linear mapping of $\mathbf{U}$ into $\mathbf{U}$ with the same basis chosen in both cases (Fig. 14.5). In this case we have $\bar{M} = (\bar{l}_U \circ r_U) \circ M \circ (t_U \circ \bar{r}_U)$ and $(\bar{l}_U \circ r_U) \circ (t_U \circ \bar{r}_U) =$ the identity mapping. Hence the matrix inducing

$t_U \circ r_U$ must be the inverse of the matrix A that induces $t_U \circ \bar{r}_U$. Therefore,

$$\bar{M} = A^{-1}MA. \tag{14.7}$$

To express the preceding results in a short form, the following terminology is introduced.

Definition 14.2: Two matrices M and $\bar{M}$, both of p rows and q columns, are called *equivalent* if there exist a regular matrix B of order p and a regular matrix A of order q such that $\bar{M} = BMA$ holds. Two *square* matrices M and $\bar{M}$ of order q are called *similar* if there exists a regular matrix A of the same order such that $\bar{M} = A^{-1}MA$ holds.

Note: Both equivalence and similarity of matrices are easily seen to define equivalence relations in the sense of Chapter 2.

Theorem 14.2: *Two matrices of p rows and q columns are equivalent if and only if they correspond to the same linear mapping of a q-dimensional vector space into a p-dimensional vector space, but relative to different bases in these vector spaces. Two square matrices of order q are similar if and only if they correspond to the same linear mapping of a vector space of dimension q into itself, but relative to different bases.*

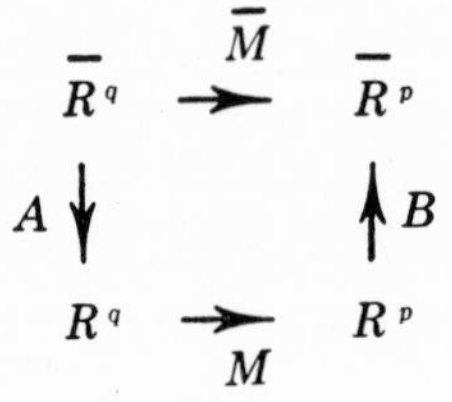

Fig. 14.4 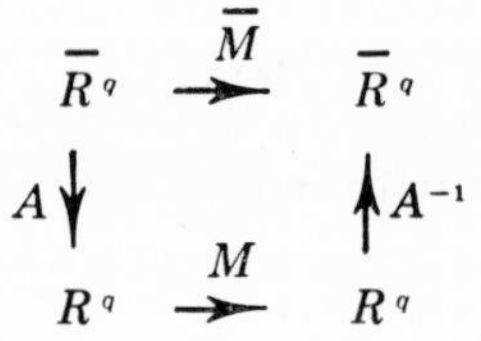   Fig. 14.5

It is not easy to find a practical, numerical criterion for two matrices to be *similar*; this text will give only an incomplete answer even in the very special case where the matrices M, $\bar{M}$ are *real symmetric* and A is *orthogonal* (see corollary 22.2). But it is not hard to obtain a necessary and sufficient criterion for two matrices to be *equivalent*. In preparation, we introduce two subspaces connected with a given linear mapping **M** and their dimensions.

Definition 14.3: The subspace of all elements mapped on zero by a linear mapping **M** is called the *null space of* **M**. Its dimension is called the *nullity of* **M** and is denoted by $\nu(\mathbf{M})$. The range of **M** is also called the *rank space of* **M**. Its dimension is called the *rank of* **M** and denoted by $\rho(\mathbf{M})$. If M is a matrix corresponding to **M** after introduction of bases, then $\nu(\mathbf{M})$ and $\rho(\mathbf{M})$ are also called the *nullity* and *rank* of M, respectively, and are denoted by $\nu(M)$ and $\rho(M)$.

It is easy to see that both the null space and the rank space of a linear mapping are subspaces, and it is obvious that neither depends on the choice of bases, provided that bases have been selected at all. It is also clear that equivalent matrices must have the same rank and the same nullity. But we shall find also the remarkable fact that equality of rank (or equality of nullity) suffices for two $(p \times q)$-matrices to be equivalent.

Lemma 14.1: *For every $(p \times q)$-matrix M, there exist regular matrices B and A such that BMA is a diagonal matrix having only 1's and 0's in the principal diagonal. The number of 1's is equal to the rank of M.*

PROOF: Let x be a column of q variables x_i. Reduce the linear system Mx to echelon form, but instead of canceling zero polynomials exchange the order of polynomials in such a way that zero polynomials come last. Then the new system has the matrix

$$\begin{bmatrix} I_\rho & R \\ 0 & 0 \end{bmatrix} \tag{14.8}$$

as coefficients, where I_ρ is the identity matrix of order ρ, R an arbitrary matrix (not necessarily square) of ρ rows and the two 0's stand for suitable zero matrices (not necessarily square). (14.8) is obtained from M by left and right multiplications by elementary matrices (which are regular). Now the (possibly) nonzero elements of the submatrix R can be eliminated by successive right multiplications by matrices of the type (13.4). Hence regular matrices B and A can be found such that

$$BMA = \begin{bmatrix} I_\rho & 0 \\ 0 & 0 \end{bmatrix}. \tag{14.9}$$

The dimension of the range of BMA is obviously ρ; hence the rank of M is ρ.

Theorem 14.3: *Two $(p \times q)$-matrices are equivalent if and only if they have the same rank.*

PROOF: The necessity of the condition is obvious. To prove sufficiency, let us assume that two $(p \times q)$-matrices M and N have the same rank. Then, by lemma 14.1, regular matrices A, B, C, and D can be found such that

$$BMA = \begin{bmatrix} I & 0 \\ 0 & 0 \end{bmatrix} = DNC.$$

Hence, $M = (B^{-1}D)N(CA^{-1})$; that is, M is equivalent to N.

Corollary 14.3: $\rho(M) = \rho(M')$.

PROOF: By transposing (14.9) we see that $BMA = A'M'B'$ from which $(A')^{-1}BMA(B')^{-1} = M'$ follows. Therefore, M and M' are equivalent and have the same rank by theorem 14.3.

Theorem 14.4:   *Let M be a $(p \times q)$-matrix, and let x be a column of q variables. The rank and nullity of M are equal to the rank and nullity, respectively, of the linear system Mx.*

PROOF: This is obvious for the nullity, by definition. For the rank, the statement of the theorem follows from the proof of lemma 14.1.

Corollary 14.4:   *The rank of a matrix M is equal to the maximum number of linearly independent rows of M, and also equal to the maximum number of linearly independent columns of M.*

PROOF: The statement about rows is but a restatement of the rank equality of theorem 14.4. That this property also holds for the columns follows then from corollary 14.3.

Corollary 14.5:   *A nonhomogeneous linear system $Ax = b$ is solvable if and only if $\rho(A) = \rho((A,b))$.*

PROOF: Either $\rho(A) = \rho((A,b))$ or $\rho((A,b)) = \rho(A) + 1$. If and only if $\rho((A,b)) = \rho(A) + 1$, b is *not* a linear combination of the columns of $A = (a^{(1)}, a^{(2)}, \cdots, a^{(n)})$, by application of corollary 14.4 to columns; that is, $\sum\limits_{j=1}^{n} a^{(i)}x_j = b$ is impossible.

EXERCISES

1. Suppose $r = (r_1, r_2, \cdots, r_n) \; \varepsilon \; R^n$ and $x = (x_1, x_2, \cdots, x_n)$. Prove: The mapping $x \to r \cdot x$ of R^n into itself, is linear.

2. Let V be the real vector space of dimension $n + 1$ of all real polynomials $p(x)$ of degree $\leq n$ in one variable x. Let α be a given real number. Prove: The mapping of V into R, defined by $p(x) \to p(\alpha)$, is linear. Determine the matrix corresponding to this mapping if the following bases are chosen: (a) $(1, x\; x^2, \cdots, x^n)$ for V, and 1 for R; (b) $(x + 1, x - 1, x^2 - 1, x^3 - 1, \cdots, x^n - 1)$ for V, and $1/3$ for R.

3. Interpret the mapping

$$\begin{bmatrix} x_1 \\ x_2 \\ x_3 \end{bmatrix} \to \begin{bmatrix} 1 & 2 & 3 \\ 2 & 1 & 1 \\ 1 & 0 & 4 \end{bmatrix} \begin{bmatrix} x_1 \\ x_2 \\ x_3 \end{bmatrix}$$

as a change from the natural basis $\begin{bmatrix} 1 \\ 0 \\ 0 \end{bmatrix}, \begin{bmatrix} 0 \\ 1 \\ 0 \end{bmatrix}, \begin{bmatrix} 0 \\ 0 \\ 1 \end{bmatrix}$ of R^3 to some other basis. What is the new basis?

4. Find the linear mapping of R^2 into itself that maps the basis $\begin{bmatrix} 1 \\ 0 \end{bmatrix}, \begin{bmatrix} 0 \\ 1 \end{bmatrix}$

on the basis $\begin{bmatrix} 1/\sqrt{2} \\ 1/\sqrt{2} \end{bmatrix}, \begin{bmatrix} 1/\sqrt{2} \\ -1/\sqrt{2} \end{bmatrix}$.

5. The matrix $\begin{bmatrix} 2 & 1 & 1 \\ 1 & 3 & 2 \end{bmatrix}$ induces a linear mapping of R^3 into R^2 with respect to their natural bases. What matrix induces the same mapping relative to the new bases

$$\begin{bmatrix} 1 \\ 2 \\ 3 \end{bmatrix}, \quad \begin{bmatrix} 1 \\ 1 \\ 0 \end{bmatrix}, \quad \begin{bmatrix} 0 \\ 1 \\ 4 \end{bmatrix} \quad \text{and} \quad \begin{bmatrix} 1 \\ 1 \end{bmatrix}, \quad \begin{bmatrix} 1 \\ -1 \end{bmatrix}$$

in R^3 and R^2, respectively?

6. Prove that equivalence and similarity of matrices are equivalence relations in the sense of Chapter 2.

7. Let **M** be a linear mapping of a vector space of finite dimension. Prove directly from definition 14.3:

$$\rho(\mathbf{M}) + \nu(\mathbf{M}) = q.$$

8. Spell out the proofs of theorem 14.4 and its two corollaries in detail.

9. Prove: The rank of a product of two matrices does not exceed the rank of either factor.

10. Prove: Two $(p \times g)$-matrices are equivalent if and only if they have the same nullity.

*11. Let V be the vector space of all real polynomials of degree $\leq n$ in one variable x. Prove: The mapping of V into itself defined by

$$\frac{d}{dx} : \quad \sum_{i=0}^{n} p_i x^i \rightarrow \sum_{i=0}^{n} i p_i x^{i-1}$$

is linear. What are its rank and nullity? Which matrix induces the same mapping with respect to the basis $(1, x, x^2, \cdots, x^n)$?

*12. Let V be the real vector space of all real functions of one variable x having derivatives of arbitrarily high order in a given interval. Prove:

$\sum_{i=0}^{n} \alpha_i \frac{d^i}{dx^i}$ (in the usual sense, with $\frac{d^0}{dx^0}$ as identity operator) induces a linear mapping of V into itself.

*13. Let V be the real vector space of all real polynomials of degree $< n$ in one variable x, and let W be the real vector space of all real polynomials of degree $\leq n$. Prove that the mapping of V into W defined by

$$\int_0^x dx : \qquad \sum_{i=0}^{n-1} p_i x^i \rightarrow \sum_{i=0}^{n-1} \frac{p_i}{i+1} x^{i+1}$$

is linear. Determine its null space and rank space. Find the matrix that induces the same mapping relative to the bases $\{x^i\}_{0 \leq i < n}$ and $\{x^i\}_{0 \leq i \leq n}$.

PART III

Multilinear Geometry and Algebra

Various geometric and algebraic properties are based on or connected with so-called *multilinear mappings* of *sequences of vectors*, that is, the mappings that are linear with respect to every vector in the sequence. The inner product of definition 12.4 is a typical example; so is the determinant of a square matrix.

15

Length and Angle

The methods developed in Part I and elaborated in Part II are sufficient to check whether a point lies on a line, a line lies on a plane, what points two lines or a line and a plane have in common, and so forth, or to find the ratio of the lengths of two translations having the same or opposite direction. But in analytic geometry one also wants to compute the length of a translation and the angle between two translations. This is particularly easy if a Cartesian coordinate system is chosen; hence, we shall assume Cartesian coordinates, *unless otherwise stated*, throughout this chapter.

Definition 15.1: If $\mathbf{x}$ and $\mathbf{y}$ are two translations of $\mathbf{R}^n (n = 1, 2, 3)$ and if $x = (x_1, \cdots, x_n)$ and $y = (y_1, \cdots, y_n)$ are their coordinate vectors with respect to some *Cartesian* coordinate system, then the inner product $x \cdot y$ is also called the *inner product of* $\mathbf{x}$ and $\mathbf{y}$ and is denoted by $\mathbf{x} \cdot \mathbf{y}$. Thus,

$$\mathbf{x} \cdot \mathbf{y} = x_1 y_1 + \cdots + x_n y_n, \tag{15.1}$$

and, in particular,

$$\mathbf{x}^2 = x_1^2 + \cdots + x_n^2. \tag{15.2}$$

If $\mathbf{x}^2 = 1$, then $\mathbf{x}$ is called a *unit translation*.

This definition is justified only if the expressions (15.1) and (15.2) are independent of the choice of Cartesian coordinate system. This will be shown now by giving a geometric interpretation of both formulas, which does not depend on the coordinate system as long as it is *Cartesian*.

Theorem 15.1:   *If $\mathbf{x}$ is a translation of $\mathbf{R}^n$ ($n = 1, 2, 3$), then $|\mathbf{x}| = \sqrt{\mathbf{x}^2}$.*

Note: (1). $\sqrt{\mathbf{x}^2}$ is not equal to $\mathbf{x}$ (which is not even always true for numbers), but $\sqrt{\mathbf{x}^2} = \sqrt{x_1^2 + x_2^2 + x_3^2}$ for $n = 3$. (2). The unit translations are those of length 1. (3). If $\mathbf{y} \neq \mathbf{0}$, then $(1/\sqrt{\mathbf{y}^2})\mathbf{y}$ is a *unit* translation in the same direction as $\mathbf{y}$.

PROOF FOR $n = 3$ (Fig. 15.1): If $(\mathbf{b}^{(i)})_{1 \leq i \leq 3}$ is a Cartesian basis of $\mathbf{R}^3$, then $\mathbf{x} = x_1\mathbf{b}^{(1)} + x_2\mathbf{b}^{(2)} + x_3\mathbf{b}^{(3)}$. Let us assume $x_1 \neq 0$, $x_2 \neq 0$, and $x_3 \neq 0$. Suppose we have representative line segments OX_1, OX_2, OP, OX such that $\overrightarrow{OX_1} = x_1\mathbf{b}^{(1)}$, $\overrightarrow{OX_2} = x_2\mathbf{b}^{(2)}$, $\overrightarrow{OP} = x_1\mathbf{b}^{(1)} + x_2\mathbf{b}^{(2)}$, and $\overrightarrow{OX} = x_1\mathbf{b}^{(1)} + x_2\mathbf{b}^{(2)} + x_3\mathbf{b}^{(3)}$. Since the base translations are of length 1, we have $|OX_1| = |x_1|$, $|OX_2| = |x_2|$. Since the first two base translations are perpendicular, we have

$$|OP| = |x_1\mathbf{b}^{(1)} + x_2\mathbf{b}^{(2)}| = \sqrt{|OX_1|^2 + |OX_2|^2} = \sqrt{x_1^2 + x_2^2}, \qquad (15.3)$$

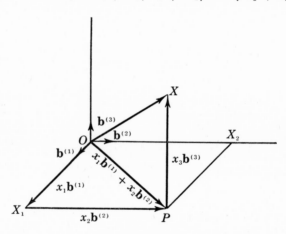

Fig. 15.1

by the Pythagorean theorem. Since $\overrightarrow{PX} = x_3\mathbf{b}^{(3)}$ is perpendicular to $\overrightarrow{OP}$, we may apply the Pythagorean theorem again to the right triangle OPX and obtain

$$|OX| = \sqrt{|OP|^2 + |PX|^2} = \sqrt{x_1^2 + x_2^2 + x_3^2},$$

by (15.3). If one or two of the coordinates of $\mathbf{x}$ are equal to zero or, what amounts essentially to the same thing, if $n = 2$ or $n = 1$, this proof can be simplified.

Corollary 15.1:   *If x and y are the Cartesian coordinate vectors of points X and Y respectively then the distance between X and Y is equal to $\sqrt{(x - y)^2}$.*

Theorem 15.2:   *If $\mathbf{x}$ and $\mathbf{y}$ are translations of $\mathbf{R}^n$ ($n = 1, 2, 3$), then*

$$\mathbf{x} \cdot \mathbf{y} = \begin{cases} |\mathbf{x}| \cdot |\mathbf{y}| \cos(\mathbf{x}, \mathbf{y}) & \text{if} \quad \mathbf{x} \neq 0 \quad \text{and} \quad \mathbf{y} \neq 0 \\ 0 & \text{if} \quad \mathbf{x} = 0 \quad \text{or} \quad \mathbf{y} = 0. \end{cases}$$

Here cos $(\mathbf{x}, \mathbf{y})$ *is the cosine of the angle* $\sphericalangle XOY$.

Note: This implies, for nonzero translations $\mathbf{x}$ *and* $\mathbf{y}$, *that they are perpendicular if and only if their inner product is equal to zero.*

PROOF: The second part is obvious. To prove the first part, consider the proper triangle XOY (Fig. 15.2). Let x and y be the Cartesian coordinate vectors of X and Y, respectively, with origin O. From exercise 12.21 it follows for the *inner square* of $x - y$ that

$$(x - y)^2 = x^2 + y^2 - 2x \cdot y.$$

By corollary 15.1, this reduces to

$$|YX|^2 = |OX|^2 + |OY|^2 - 2x \cdot y.$$

From the rule of cosines, applied to the triangle OXY, it follows that

$$|YX|^2 = |OX|^2 + |OY|^2 - 2|OX| \cdot |OY| \cos(\sphericalangle XOY).$$

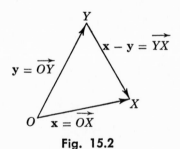

Fig. 15.2

A comparison of the last two equations proves the first part of the theorem, unless $\mathbf{x}$ and $\mathbf{y}$ are linearly dependent. But it is very easy to find the proof if $\{\mathbf{x}, \mathbf{y}\}$ is a linearly dependent set.

If the translations are interpreted as position vectors of points, then the following corollary follows from theorem 15.2 in conjunction with exercise 13.20.

Corollary 15.2:   *Let* Ω *be an orthogonal matrix of order* $n = 2$ *or* 3 *The mapping* $X \rightarrow \bar{X}$, *of* $\mathfrak{R}^n$ *into itself, induced by the mapping* $x \rightarrow \bar{x} = \Omega x$ *of the Cartesian coordinate vectors, leaves distances and cosines of angles unaltered.*

The purely geometric notion of perpendicularity is defined only for nonzero translations or for line segments. To avoid exceptional cases and to combine both parts of theorem 15.2, it is useful to generalize as follows.

Definition 15.2: Two *arbitrary* translations $\mathbf{x}$, $\mathbf{y}$ of $\mathbf{R}^n$ ($n = 1, 2, 3$) are called *perpendicular* if $\mathbf{x} \cdot \mathbf{y} = 0$.

Note: This includes the case in which one of the vectors is the zero vector.

Definition 15.3: Let a translation $\mathbf{a}$ be equal to the sum of a translation $\mathbf{x}$, having the same or opposite direction as a given nonzero translation $\mathbf{b}$ (if $\mathbf{x} \neq 0$), and a translation $\mathbf{y}$ perpendicular to $\mathbf{b}$. Then $\mathbf{x}$ is called the *perpendicular projection of* $\mathbf{a}$ *on* (*the direction of*) $\mathbf{b}$ and is denoted by $\mathbf{a_b}$.

Note: This perpendicular projection always exists and is unique. For take a Cartesian basis $(\mathbf{b}^{(i)})_{1 \leq i \leq n}$ such that $\mathbf{b}$ and $\mathbf{b}^{(1)}$ have the same direction. Then we have $\mathbf{a} = a_1 \mathbf{b}^{(1)} + a_2 \mathbf{b}^{(2)}$ in the two-dimensional case (Fig. 15.3), where, obviously,

$$\mathbf{a_b} = a_1 \mathbf{b}^{(1)} \qquad \text{with} \qquad \mathbf{b}^{(1)} = \frac{1}{|\mathbf{b}|} \mathbf{b}.$$

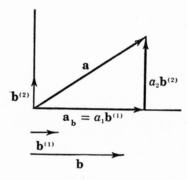

Fig. 15.3

If $\mathbf{a}$ and $\mathbf{b}$ are perpendicular, then $a_1 = 0$. If $\cos(\mathbf{a},\mathbf{b}) > 0$, then $\mathbf{a_b}$ and $\mathbf{b}$ have the same direction; if $\cos(\mathbf{a},\mathbf{b}) < 0$, then they have opposite directions. From trigonometry it follows that

$$|a_1 \mathbf{b}^{(1)}| = |a_1| = |a| \, |\cos(\mathbf{a}, \mathbf{b})| = |a| \, |\cos(\mathbf{a}, \mathbf{b}^{(1)})|.$$

Since $\mathbf{a} \cdot \mathbf{b}^{(1)} = |a| \cos(\mathbf{a},\mathbf{b}^{(1)})$, we have $a_1 = \mathbf{a} \cdot \mathbf{b}^{(1)}$. This result may be expressed in the following form.

Corollary 15.3: *If* $\mathbf{a}$ *is a translation and* $\mathbf{u}$ *is a unit translation of* $\mathbf{R}^n$ ($n = 2, 3$), *then*

$$\mathbf{a_u} = (\mathbf{a} \cdot \mathbf{u})\mathbf{u},$$

hence,

$$|\mathbf{a_u}| = |a \cdot u|.$$

The geometric notions of *length, cosine of an angle, perpendicularity, perpendicular projections* can be transferred to vector spaces R^n of n-tuples in a natural way as follows.

Definition 15.4:   If $x \,\varepsilon\, R^n$, then $\sqrt{x^2}$ is called *the length of x*.† If $x\ (\neq 0)$, $y\ (\neq 0)\ \varepsilon\ R^n$, then

$$\frac{x\cdot y}{\sqrt{x^2}\ \sqrt{y^2}}$$

is called *the cosine between x and y* and is sometimes denoted by $\cos\ (x,y)$. If $x,\ y\ \varepsilon\ R^n$ and $x\cdot y\ =\ 0$, then x and y are called *perpendicular*. A basis $(b^{(i)})_{1\leq i\leq n}$ of R^n is called *Cartesian* if each base vector has length 1 and any two base vectors are perpendicular. If $x\ =\ a\ +\ b,\ a\ =\ \alpha y\ (x,\ y,\ a,\ b\ \varepsilon\ R^n$ and $\alpha\ \varepsilon\ R)$ and $y\cdot b\ =\ 0$, then a is called the *perpendicular projection* of x on y and is denoted by x_y.

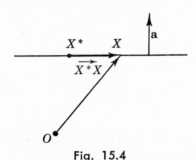

Fig. 15.4

The notation of the inner product can be applied very usefully to find an equation that the Cartesian coordinates of a line or plane have to satisfy. First we introduce

Definition 15.5:   A *nonzero* translation is called *normal* to a line or plane if it is perpendicular to (the extension of) every translation of that line or plane.

Theorem 15.3:   *Relative to a Cartesian coordinate system, an equation of the line through a point X^* with normal translation* **a** *is given by*

$$a_1(x_1\ -\ x_1^*)\ +\ a_2(x_2\ -\ x_2^*)\ =\ 0, \tag{15.4}$$

called a normal equation of the line. Relative to a Cartesian coordinate system, an equation of the plane through a point X^* with normal translation **a** *is given by*

$$a_1(x_1\ -\ x_1^*)\ +\ a_2(x_2\ -\ x_2^*)\ +\ a_3(x_3\ -\ x_3^*)\ =\ 0, \tag{15.5}$$

called a normal equation of the plane.

† If the context prevents confusion with "length of sequence" defined on p. 16.

Note: Both (15.4) and (15.5) are special cases of

$$a \cdot (x - x^*) = 0. \tag{15.6}$$

PROOF IN THE TWO-DIMENSIONAL CASE (Fig. 15.4): If X is a point on the line in question, then a is perpendicular to $\overrightarrow{X^*X}$, by definition 15.5; hence, (15.6) holds for their Cartesian coordinates by theorem 15.2. If Y is a point *not* on this line, then $|X^*Y| \neq 0$, $|a| \neq 0$, and $\cos (a, \overrightarrow{X^*Y}) \neq 0$; hence, $\overrightarrow{X^*Y}$ cannot be perpendicular to a. The three-dimensional extension is easily obtained.

Corollary 15.4: *A line whose Cartesian coordinates satisfy*

$$a_1 x_1 + a_2 x_2 + a_0 = 0 \tag{15.7}$$

has the translation with coordinates (a_1, a_2) as a normal. A plane whose Cartesian coordinates satisfy

$$a_1 x_1 + a_2 x_2 + a_3 x_3 + a_0 = 0 \tag{15.8}$$

has the translation with coordinates (a_1, a_2, a_3) as a normal.

PROOF IN THE TWO-DIMENSIONAL CASE: If X^* is a point on the line, then $a_1 x_1^* + a_2 x_2^* + a_0 = 0$. By subtracting this equation from (15.7) we obtain (15.4).

The preceding notions make it possible to give an easy method of determining the (shortest) distance of a point from a line or plane. We will treat the two cases together.

Theorem 15.4: *If Cartesian coordinates are chosen, then the distance of the point Z^* from the line*

$$c_1 x_1 + c_2 x_2 + c_0 = 0 \quad \text{with} \quad c_1^2 + c_2^2 = 1 \tag{15.9}$$

is given by the absolute value of

$$c_1 z_1^* + c_2 f_2^* + c_0. \tag{15.10}$$

If Cartesian coordinates are chosen, then the distance of the point Z^* from the plane

$$c_1 x_1 + c_2 x_2 + c_3 x_3 + c_0 = 0 \quad \text{with} \quad c_1^2 + c_2^2 + c_3^2 = 1 \tag{15.11}$$

is given by the absolute value of

$$c_1 z_1^* + c_2 z_2^* + c_3 z_3^* + c_0. \tag{15.12}$$

If the distance is different from zero, then (15.10) or (15.12) are positive if and only if Z^* lies on that side of the line or plane to which a representative line segment of the translation c points if it begins at some point on the line or plane.

Note: (15.7) and (15.9) and, likewise, (15.8) and (15.10) differ by the requirement in the theorem that the normal translations **c** must be *unit* translations. If they are not, as in the corollary, the division by $\sqrt{a_1^2 + a_2^2}$ will transform (15.7) into (15.9) with the abbreviations

$$c_1 = \frac{a_1}{\sqrt{a_1^2 + a_2^2}}, \qquad c_2 = \frac{a_2}{\sqrt{a_1^2 + a_2^2}}, \qquad c_0 = \frac{a_0}{\sqrt{a_1^2 + a_2^2}};$$

and division by $\sqrt{a_1^2 + a_2^2 + a_3^2}$ will transform (15.8) into (15.11).

PROOF IN THE THREE-DIMENSIONAL CASE (Fig. 15.5): If F is the foot of the perpendicular to the plane through the point Z^*, then the required

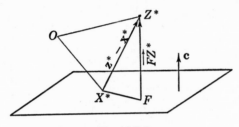

Fig. 15.5

distance d is equal to $|FZ^*|$. Now $\overrightarrow{FZ^*}$ is the projection of $\overrightarrow{X^*Z^*}$ on the unit normal **c** with Cartesian coordinates (c_1, c_2, c_3). Hence,

$$d = |(\mathbf{z}^* - \mathbf{x}^*)_c| = |\mathbf{c} \cdot (\mathbf{z}^* - \mathbf{x}^*)| = |\mathbf{c} \cdot \mathbf{z}^* - \mathbf{c} \cdot \mathbf{x}^*| \qquad (15.13)$$

by corollary 15.3. Since X^* lies on the plane, we have

$$-\mathbf{c} \cdot \mathbf{x}^* = -(c_1 x_1^* + c_2 x_2^* + c_3 x_3^*) = c_0. \qquad (15.14)$$

The substitution of c_0 for $-\mathbf{c} \cdot \mathbf{x}^*$ in (15.13) shows that d is equal to the absolute value of (15.12). Since $\mathbf{c} \cdot (\mathbf{z}^* - \mathbf{x}^*)$ is positive if and only if both $\overrightarrow{FZ^*}$ and $\overrightarrow{X^*Z^*}$ point to the same side of the plane, the expression (15.12) is positive exactly in this case.

EXAMPLES OF COMPUTATION OF DISTANCES

1. *What is the distance of the point* (2,3) *from the line*

$$3x_1 + 4x_2 - 2 = 0$$

if the coordinate system is Cartesian (Fig. 15.6)? By corollary 15.4, the translation (3,4) is normal to this line. The unit translation **c** of the same direction has a coordinate vector c, which is obtained from (3,4) by scalar multiplication by the inverse of the length of (3,4). Hence,

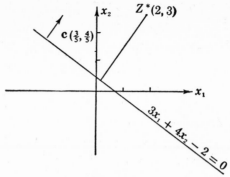

Fig. 15.6

$$c = \frac{1}{\sqrt{3^2 + 4^2}}(3, 4) = (\tfrac{3}{5}, \tfrac{4}{5}).$$

Therefore, the line in question *also* has the equation

$$\tfrac{3}{5}x_1 + \tfrac{4}{5}x_2 - \tfrac{2}{5} = 0,$$

which is of the required form (15.9). Consequently, the distance d is obtained by

$$d = |\tfrac{3}{5}\cdot 2 + \tfrac{4}{5}\cdot 3 - \tfrac{2}{5}| = \frac{16}{5}.$$

2. *What is the distance of the point* (1,2,3) *from the plane*

$$-12x_1 + 4x_2 + 3x_3 - 13 = 0$$

if the coordinate system is Cartesian? By corollary 15.4, the translation $(-12,4,3)$ is normal to this plane. The unit translation c of the same direction has the coordinate vector

$$\frac{1}{\sqrt{12^2 + 4^2 + 3^2}}(-12, 4, 3) = \left(\frac{-12}{13}, \frac{4}{13}, \frac{3}{13}\right).$$

Hence the plane under consideration also has the equation

$$-\frac{12}{13}x_1 + \frac{4}{13}x_2 + \frac{3}{13}x_3 - 1 = 0,$$

which is of the required form (15.11). Consequently, the distance d is obtained by

$$d = \left|-\frac{12}{13}\cdot 1 + \frac{4}{13}\cdot 2 + \frac{3}{13}\cdot 3 - 1\right| = \frac{8}{13}.$$

EXERCISES

Note: All coordinate systems are assumed to be Cartesian.

1. Prove: If $x \ \varepsilon \ R^n$, then $x^2 = 0$ if and only if x is the zero vector. Show that this is not true if $x \ \varepsilon \ C^n$.
   Hint: Compute x^2 for $x = (1,i)$.

2. Prove: If $\mathbf{u}$ is a unit translation of $\mathbf{R}^3$ and if $(\mathbf{b}^{(i)})_{1 \leq i \leq 3}$ is a basis of $\mathbf{R}^3$, then the coordinates of $\mathbf{u}$ are obtained by

$$u_i = \mathbf{u} \cdot \mathbf{b}^{(i)} = \cos(\mathbf{u}, \mathbf{b}^{(i)}), \quad i = 1, 2, 3.$$

   Therefore, the coordinates of a unit translation are sometimes called *direction cosines*.

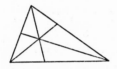

Fig. 15.7

3. Which couples of the following vectors are perpendicular? $(3,4,12)$, $(4,3,12)$, $(4,-12,3)$, $(12,-4,-3)$, $(3,12,-4)$.

4. Let $(\mathbf{u},\mathbf{v},\mathbf{w})$ be a Cartesian basis of $\mathbf{R}^3$ and let $\mathbf{a} = \alpha\mathbf{u} + \beta\mathbf{v} + \gamma\mathbf{w}$ be a translation. Prove $\mathbf{a}_\mathbf{u} = (\mathbf{a} \cdot \mathbf{u})\mathbf{u}$ directly from the above representation of $\mathbf{a}$ as a linear combination.

5. Prove:

$$\mathbf{a}_\mathbf{u} = \frac{\mathbf{a} \cdot \mathbf{u}}{\mathbf{u}^2} \mathbf{u} \quad \text{if} \quad \mathbf{u} \neq 0.$$

6. Prove theorem 15.1 for $n = 2$.

7. Prove: If $B = (b^{(1)}, b^{(2)}, \cdots, b^{(n)})$ is a basis of R^n, it is Cartesian if and only if B is orthogonal as a matrix.

8. Prove: If A is a square matrix of order n, then the mapping $x \to Ax$ of R^n into itself maps a Cartesian basis into a Cartesian basis if and only if A is orthogonal.

9. Prove: If $\mathbf{u}$ is a nonzero translation, then $(\mathbf{v}_\mathbf{u})_\mathbf{u} = \mathbf{v}_\mathbf{u}$.

10. Prove that the three bisectors of the angles of a triangle have a point in common (Fig. 15.7).

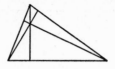

Fig. 15.8

11. Prove that the three altitudes of a triangle have a point in common (Fig. 15.8).

12. Find the equations of the lines
    (a) through (1,2) normal to (1,2);
    (b) through (1,3) normal to (3,−5);
    (c) through (2,−1) normal to (1,1);
    (d) through (1,0) normal to (1,1);
    (e) through (0,0) normal to (0,1).

13. Find the equation of the planes:
    (a) through (1,2,3) normal to (1,2,3);
    (b) through (1,3,3) normal to (3,2,−5);
    (c) through (1,0,0) normal to (1,1,1);
    (d) through (0,0,0) normal to (0,1,0).

14. Prove theorem 15.3 in the three-dimensional case.

15. What is the distance of the origin from the line $a_1x_1 + a_2x_2 + a_0 = 0$ and from the plane $a_1x_1 + a_2x_2 + a_3x_3 + a_0 = 0$?

16. What is the distance of the point (2,3,4) from the planes:
    (a) $2x_1 + 3x_2 + 4x_3 - 29 = 0$;
    (b) $x_1 - x_2 + x_3 - 3 = 0$;
    (c) $x_1 + x_2 + x_3 + 2 = 0$;
    (d) $3x_1 - 2x_2 - x_3 - 5 = 0$.

17. Prove *Schwarz's inequality*: $(\mathbf{u} \cdot \mathbf{v})^2 \leq \mathbf{u}^2\mathbf{v}^2$ for translations $\mathbf{u}$, $\mathbf{v}$.

18. Prove the triangular inequality $|\mathbf{u} + \mathbf{v}| \leq |\mathbf{u}| + |\mathbf{v}|$ for translations $\mathbf{u}$, $\mathbf{v}$. Prove also $|\mathbf{u} - \mathbf{v}| \leq |\mathbf{u}| + |\mathbf{v}|$ and $|\mathbf{u} - \mathbf{v}| \geq ||\mathbf{u}| - |\mathbf{v}||$.

16

Euclidean and Unitary Vector Spaces

In the previous chapter the inner multiplication was applied to *construct* formulas for the length of a translation and for the angle between two nonzero translations and to *define* corresponding concepts in R^n. In this chapter these notions will be further generalized to arbitrary real and complex vector spaces of *finite* dimension.

As a basis for the discussion, some definitions will be given in more general terms than really necessary at this stage. This generality, however, will be valuable later and will also indicate to the reader our reasons for choosing as we have the title of Part III.

Definition 16.1: Let V and W be vector spaces. A mapping f of the set of *all m-tuples of elements of* V into W is called *multilinear* (or *bilinear* for $m = 2$) if

$$f(v^{(1)}, \cdots, v^{(j-1)}, y + z, v^{(j+1)}, \cdots, v^{(m)})$$

$$= f(v^{(1)}, \cdots, v^{(j-1)}, y, v^{(j+1)}, \cdots, v^{(m)})$$

$$+ f(v^{(1)}, \cdots, v^{(j-1)}, z, v^{(j+1)}, \cdots v^{(m)}) \qquad (16.1)$$

and

$$f(v^{(1)}, \cdots, v^{(j-1)}, \alpha y, v^{(j+1)}, \cdots, v^{(m)})$$

$$= \alpha f(v^{(1)}, \cdots, v^{(j-1)}, y, v^{(j+1)}, \cdots, v^{(m)}) \qquad (16.2)$$

hold for *all* elements $v^{(1)}, \cdots, v^{(j-1)}, v^{(j+1)}, \cdots, v^{(m)}, y, z \; \varepsilon \; V$, every scalar α, and every $j = 1, 2, \cdots, m$. f is called *symmetric* if the exchange of two arbitrary distinct indices in $f(v^{(1)}, \cdots, v^{(m)})$ leaves that image unaltered, and *skew-symmetric* if every such exchange alters the sign of this image. A bilinear mapping **f** into R is called *positive definite* if, for every $\mathbf{v}^* \neq \mathbf{0}$, $\mathbf{f}(\mathbf{v}^*, \mathbf{v}^*) > 0$.

The multilinearity of a mapping **f** means *linearity of* **f** *with respect to every coordinate* $\mathbf{v}^{(i)}$. In other words, if all coordinates but one of a sequence of m elements of **V** are specified and if one is left variable, then a multilinear **f** is linear with respect to this coordinate. In this chapter we shall deal with *bilinearity* only.

Let **f** be a bilinear mapping of an n-dimensional vector space $\mathbf{V}^n$ with basis $(\mathbf{b}^{(i)})_{1 \leq i \leq n}$. Then the conditions (16.1) and (16.2) imply, for two

vectors $\mathbf{u} = \sum\limits_{i=1}^{n} u_i \mathbf{b}^{(i)}$ and $\mathbf{v} = \sum\limits_{i=1}^{n} v_i \mathbf{b}^{(i)}$ that

$$\mathbf{f}(\mathbf{u}, \mathbf{v}) = \sum_{i=1}^{n} \sum_{j=1}^{n} u_i v_j \mathbf{f}(\mathbf{b}^{(i)}, \mathbf{b}^{(j)}). \tag{16.3}$$

Hence the **f**-image of every couple $(\mathbf{u}, \mathbf{v})$ of elements of $\mathbf{V}^n$ is known if the coordinate vectors of **u** and **v** are given and the images $\mathbf{f}(\mathbf{b}^{(i)}, \mathbf{b}^{(j)})$ $(i, j = 1, \cdots, n)$ of all possible couples of base vectors are known.

If, in particular, **f** is a mapping into the set of real numbers, then we may define a real polynomial $f(u,v) = f(u_1, u_2, \cdots, u_n, v_1, v_2, \cdots, v_n)$ in $2n$ variables by

$$f(u, v) = \sum_{i=1}^{n} \sum_{j=1}^{n} \mathbf{f}(\mathbf{b}^{(i)}, \mathbf{b}^{(j)}) u_i v_j, \tag{16.4}$$

which implies, in conjunction with (16.3), that

$$\mathbf{f}(\mathbf{u}, \mathbf{v}) = f(u, v). \tag{16.5}$$

This means that, relative to a basis of $\mathbf{V}^n$, the **f**-image of every couple $(\mathbf{u}, \mathbf{v})$ of elements of $\mathbf{V}^n$ can be obtained by substitution of the coordinate vectors u, v of **u** and **v**, respectively, in the ordinary real polynomial (16.4).

After this general discussion, let us return to the inner products $u \cdot v$ and $\mathbf{u} \cdot \mathbf{v}$ introduced in definitions 12.4 and 15.1. By exercises 12.21 and 15.1, the mappings $(u,v) \rightarrow u \cdot v$ $(u, v \ \varepsilon \ R^n)$ and $(\mathbf{u}, \mathbf{v}) \rightarrow \mathbf{u} \cdot \mathbf{v}$ $(\mathbf{u}, \mathbf{v} \ \varepsilon \ \mathbf{R}^n$, $n = 1, 2, 3)$ are *positive definite symmetric bilinear mappings into* R. The idea of inner multiplication is now generalized to arbitrary real vector spaces of finite dimension as follows.

Definition 16.2: A finite-dimensional real vector space **V** together with a given positive definite symmetric bilinear mapping **f** of $\mathbf{V} \times \mathbf{V}$ into the set R of all real numbers is called a *Euclidean vector space* and is denoted by $\{\mathbf{V}, \mathbf{f}\}$. For every $\mathbf{v} \ \varepsilon \ \mathbf{V}$, the real number, denoted by $|\mathbf{v}|$,

$$|\mathbf{v}| = \sqrt{\mathbf{f}(\mathbf{v}, \mathbf{v})} \tag{16.6}$$

is called *the length of* **v**. $|\mathbf{u} - \mathbf{v}|$ is called *the distance between* **u** *and* **v**. The real number, denoted by cos (**u**,**v**),

$$\cos (\mathbf{u}, \mathbf{v}) = \frac{\mathbf{f(u, v)}}{\sqrt{\mathbf{f(u, u)}} \ \sqrt{\mathbf{f(v, v)}}} \qquad (16.7)$$

is called *the cosine of the angle between* **u** *and* **v**. Two elements **u** and **v** are called *perpendicular* if $\mathbf{f(u,v)} = 0$.

Note: **f** is a mapping into the set R of all *real* numbers.

If an angle $\measuredangle$ (**u**,**v**) is to be determined by (16.7) for two nonzero vectors **u** and **v** in the sense of trigonometry, the right-hand side of (16.7) must have an absolute value ≤ 1. That this is always true is a consequence of the following important inequality.

Theorem 16.1: (*Schwarz's inequality*)†: *If* **u** *and* **v** *are elements of a Euclidean vector space* { **V**,**f**}, *then*

$$(\mathbf{f(u, v)})^2 \leq \mathbf{f(u, u)f(v, v)}. \qquad (16.8)$$

PROOF: 1. From the properties of a bilinear mapping it can be concluded easily that the *equality sign* holds in (16.8) if $\mathbf{u} = \alpha\mathbf{v}$ for some scalar α. 2. Let us now assume that **u** and **v** are linearly independent. Then we shall see that the inequality

$$(\mathbf{f(u, v)})^2 - \mathbf{f(u, u)f(v, v)} \geq 0 \qquad (16.9)$$

cannot hold. Since $\mathbf{f(u,v)}$, $\mathbf{f(u,u)}$, and $\mathbf{f(v,v)}$ are all *real numbers*, we may consider an algebraic equation, in the unknown ξ, which has these numbers as coefficients:

$$\mathbf{f(u, u)}\xi^2 + 2\mathbf{f(u, v)}\xi + \mathbf{f(v, v)} = 0. \qquad (16.10)$$

Since $\mathbf{u} \neq \mathbf{0}$ and since **f** is *positive definite*, (16.10) is a *quadratic* equation in ξ. If (16.9) were true, then the two solutions ξ^*, ξ^{**} of (16.10) would have to be *real* numbers. Applying the rules for a symmetric bilinear mapping, we conclude from (16.10) that

$$0 = \xi^{*2}\mathbf{f(u, u)} + 2\xi^*\mathbf{f(u, v)} + \mathbf{f(v, v)}$$

$$= \mathbf{f}(\xi^*\mathbf{u}, \xi^*\mathbf{u}) + \mathbf{f}(\xi^*\mathbf{u}, \mathbf{v}) + \mathbf{f}(\mathbf{v}, \xi^*\mathbf{u}) + \mathbf{f(v, v)}$$

$$= \mathbf{f}(\xi^*\mathbf{u} + \mathbf{v}, \xi^*\mathbf{u} + \mathbf{v}) \qquad (16.11)$$

holds. Since **u** and **v** are linearly independent, we would have $\xi^*\mathbf{u} + \mathbf{v} \neq \mathbf{0}$; hence $\mathbf{f}(\xi^*\mathbf{u} + \mathbf{v}, \xi^*\mathbf{u} + \mathbf{v}) > 0$. But this contradicts (16.11); so we must really have

$$(\mathbf{f(u, v)})^2 < \mathbf{f(u, u)f(v, v)}. \qquad (16.12)$$

† Named after the German mathematician *Hermann Amandus Schwarz* (1843–1921).

Let us check this proof again. The bilinearity of **f** was applied several times, its positive definiteness twice, and its symmetry once. None of the conditions for **f** can be left out in proving Schwarz's inequality. By the way, the symmetry of **f** has another convenient consequence, namely,

$$\cos(\mathbf{u}, \mathbf{v}) = \cos(\mathbf{v}, \mathbf{u}). \tag{16.13}$$

Turning next to formula (16.6), we shall see that the following properties hold for the lengths of the vectors.

Theorem 16.2: *If* **u** *and* **v** *are elements of a Euclidean vector space* {**V**,**f**} *and* α *is any scalar, then*

$$|\alpha\mathbf{u}| = |\alpha|\,|\mathbf{u}|,$$
$$|\mathbf{u} + \mathbf{v}| \leq |\mathbf{u}| + |\mathbf{v}|.$$

PROOF: The first formula is immediately clear. The second one follows from Schwarz's inequality.

There is still another very remarkable property of Euclidean vector spaces, which will lead us back to the *inner product* we started from.

Theorem 16.3: *In every Euclidean vector space of dimension* $n > 0$ {**V**^{n},**f**} *there exists a Cartesian basis* $(\mathbf{b}^{(i)})_{1 \leq i \leq n}$, *that is, a basis all of whose elements have length* 1 *and, if* $n > 1$, *are perpendicular in pairs.*

PROOF: We assume $n \geq 1$. Take any nonzero vector $\mathbf{a}^{(1)}$ of **V**^{n} and define $\mathbf{b}^{(1)} = (1/|\mathbf{a}^{(1)}|)\mathbf{a}^{(1)}$. Then *one* vector $\mathbf{b}^{(1)}$ of length 1 is constructed. Suppose we have already found k $(< n)$ vectors $\mathbf{b}^{(1)}, \mathbf{b}^{(2)}, \cdots, \mathbf{b}^{(k)}$ of length 1 and perpendicular in pairs. Then we can always find an additional vector $\mathbf{b}^{(k+1)}$ such that the set $\mathbf{b}^{(1)}, \mathbf{b}^{(2)}, \cdots, \mathbf{b}^{(k)}, \mathbf{b}^{(k+1)}$ still consists of vectors of length 1 that are perpendicular in pairs, by the following *Gram-Schmidt orthogonalization process*:†

Let **c** be any vector that is not a linear combination of $\mathbf{b}^{(1)}, \mathbf{b}^{(2)}, \cdots, \mathbf{b}^{(k)}$, and consider all vectors of the form

$$\beta_1\mathbf{b}^{(1)} + \beta_2\mathbf{b}^{(2)} + \cdots + \beta_k\mathbf{b}^{(k)} + \mathbf{c}, \qquad \beta_1, \beta_2, \cdots, \beta_k \text{ scalars}. \tag{16.14}$$

We claim that, for a suitable choice of the coefficients $\beta_1, \beta_2, \cdots, \beta_k$, (16.14) is a vector perpendicular to all $\mathbf{b}^{(1)}, \mathbf{b}^{(2)}, \cdots, \mathbf{b}^{(k)}$. A necessary condition for this to happen is that, for every $j = 1, 2, \cdots, k$,

$$0 = \mathbf{f}(\beta_1\mathbf{b}^{(1)} + \beta_2\mathbf{b}^{(2)} + \cdots + \beta_k\mathbf{b}^{(k)} + \mathbf{c}, \mathbf{b}^{(j)})$$
$$= \sum_{i=1}^{k} \beta_i\mathbf{f}(\mathbf{b}^{(i)}, \mathbf{b}^{(j)}) + \mathbf{f}(\mathbf{c}, \mathbf{b}^{(j)}).$$

Because of the hypothesis $\mathbf{f}(\mathbf{b}^{(i)}, \mathbf{b}^{(j)}) = 0$ for $i \neq j$ and $\mathbf{f}(\mathbf{b}^{(i)}, \mathbf{b}^{(j)}) = 1$

† Named after the Danish mathematician *J. P. Gram* (1850-1916) and the German mathematician *Erhard Schmidt* (1876-).

for $i = j$, this reduces to the k conditions

$$0 = \beta_i + f(c, b^{(i)}), \quad \text{or} \quad \beta_i = -f(c, b^{(i)})$$

$$\text{for} \quad j = 1, 2, \cdots, k. \quad (16.15)$$

But these conditions (16.15) are also sufficient for the vector (16.14) to be perpendicular to all $b^{(1)}, b^{(2)}, \cdots, b^{(k)}$; for we have, for every $j = 1, \cdots, k$,

$$f\left(\sum_{i=1}^{k} - f(c, b^{(i)})b^{(i)} + c, b^{(j)}\right) = \sum_{i=1}^{k} - f(c, b^{(i)})f(b^{(i)}, b^{(j)}) + f(c, b^{(j)}),$$

which reduces to zero, because $f(b^{(i)}, b^{(j)}) = 0$ for $i \neq j$ and $f(b^{(i)}, b^{(i)}) = 1$. Denote this vector (16.14) with (16.15) by $a^{(k+1)}$. Then $b^{(k+1)} = (1/|a^{(k+1)}|)a^{(k+1)}$ is also perpendicular to all $b^{(i)}$ with $i = 1, \cdots, k$, but $b^{(k+1)}$ has length 1. Hence the enlarged set $b^{(1)}, b^{(2)}, \cdots, b^{(k)}, b^{(k+1)}$ consists again of unit vectors perpendicular in pairs. After a finite number of steps the Cartesian basis is completed.

Corollary 16.1: *Every Euclidean vector space* $\{V^n, f\}$ ($n > 0$) *has a basis such that* $f(u, v)$ *reduces, for any* $u, v \in V^n$, *to the ordinary inner product* $u \cdot v$ *of their coordinates* u *and* v, *respectively, relative to this basis:*

$$f(u, v) = u \cdot v.$$

PROOF: Choose a Cartesian basis, which is possible by theorem 16.3, and apply formula (16.3).

Thus every positive definite symmetric bilinear mapping into R

$$f: (u, v) \to f(u, v)$$

corresponds to the mapping

$$f: (u, v) \to u \cdot v$$

if a suitable basis (namely, a Cartesian basis) is chosen for V^n.

Theorem 16.3 also implies

Corollary 16.2: *If* a *is a nonzero element of a Euclidean vector space* $\{V, f\}$ *of dimension* $n > 1$, *then the set of all vectors* v *of* V *satisfying* $f(a, v) = 0$ (*or* $a \cdot v = 0$ *with respect to a Cartesian basis) is a hyperplane of* V.

This completes the circle of our investigations about inner products and their generalizations to higher-dimensional *real* vector spaces.

The case of *complex* vector spaces is somewhat more complicated. It was observed in exercise 15.1 [by the example $(1, i)^2 = 1 + i^2 = 0$] that the ordinary inner square $x^2 = \sum_{i=1}^{n} x_i^2$ loses the property of being positive definite if $x \, \varepsilon \, C^n$. In fact, the inner square need not even be a real number in the case of C^n. Looking to $C = C^1$ for guidance, we find from high school algebra that the absolute value of a complex number $\gamma = \gamma_1 + \gamma_2 i$ $(\gamma_1, \gamma_2 \, \varepsilon \, R, i^2 = -1)$ is defined by $|\gamma| = \sqrt{\gamma_1^2 + \gamma_2^2} = \gamma\bar{\gamma}$ where $\bar{\gamma} = \gamma_1 - \gamma_2 i$ is the complex conjugate of γ. This leads to the idea of *defining* an absolute value or *length* for the complex n-tuple $c = (c_1, c_2, \cdots, c_n) = (\gamma_{11} + \gamma_{12}i, \gamma_{21} + \gamma_{22}i, \cdots, \gamma_{n1} + \gamma_{n2}i) \, \varepsilon \, C^n \, (\gamma_{ij} \, \varepsilon \, R)$ by

$$|c| = \sqrt{\sum_{i=1}^{n} c_i \bar{c}_i} = \sqrt{\sum_{i=1}^{n} (\gamma_{i1}^2 + \gamma_{i2}^2)}.$$

The square of this expression has the form

$$c_1 \bar{c}_1 + c_2 \bar{c}_2 + \cdots + c_n \bar{c}_n. \tag{16.16}$$

Just as the inner square corresponds to the inner product in the case of real n-tuples, so (16.16) corresponds to a bilinear expression, which is introduced as follows.

Definition 16.3: If $x = (x_1, \cdots, x_n)$ and $y = (y_1, \cdots, y_n)$ are n-tuples of complex numbers and if $\bar{y} = (\bar{y}_1, \cdots, \bar{y}_n)$ is defined by conjugation, coordinate by coordinate, then the complex number, denoted by $x \cdot y$

$$x \cdot y = x_1 \bar{y}_1 + \cdots + x_n \bar{y}_n = \sum_{i=1}^{n} x_i \bar{y}_i, \tag{16.17}$$

is called *the complex inner product of x and y.*

This complex inner product is easily seen to have the four properties:

$$x \cdot y = \overline{y \cdot x}, \tag{16.18}$$

$$x \cdot (y + z) = x \cdot y + x \cdot z, \tag{16.19}$$

$$(\alpha x) \cdot y = \alpha (x \cdot y), \tag{16.20}$$

$$x \cdot x \geq 0, \quad \text{and} \quad x \cdot x = 0 \quad \text{only if} \quad x = 0, \tag{16.21}$$

for all $x, y, z \, \varepsilon \, C^n$ and $\alpha \, \varepsilon \, C$.

In the complex vector space C^n with the complex inner product (16.17), the notions *length* and *perpendicularity*, *Cartesian basis* and *perpendicular projection* can be introduced in analogy with definition 15.4. But the generalization of the concept of a cosine leads to complex angles in general.

The four properties (16.18) to (16.21) are used to define the analog of the Euclidean vector space in the complex case.

Definition 16.4: A finite-dimensional *complex* vector space **C** together with a given mapping **f**: $\mathbf{C} \times \mathbf{C} \to C$ satisfying, for all **x, y, z** ϵ **C**, $\alpha \, \epsilon \, C$, $\mathbf{f(x,y)} = \overline{\mathbf{f(y,x)}}$, $\mathbf{f(x,y + z)} = \mathbf{f(x,y)} + \mathbf{f(x,z)}$, $\mathbf{f(\alpha x, y)} = \alpha \mathbf{f(x,y)}$, $\mathbf{f(x,x)} \geq 0$ and $= 0$ *only if* $\mathbf{x} = \mathbf{0}$ is called a *unitary vector space* and is denoted by $\{\mathbf{C, f}\}$.

For generalizations of theorems 16.1, 16.2, and 16.3 and corollary 16.1 we refer the reader to some of the exercises below.

EXERCISES

1. Prove formula (16.3) for a bilinear mapping.

2. Prove the second formula of theorem 16.2.

3. Let x and y be real n-tuples, and let A be a square matrix of order n. Prove: (a) $(Ax) \cdot (Ay) = x \cdot y$ only if A is orthogonal; (b) $(Ax) \cdot y = x \cdot (Ay)$ only if A is symmetric.

4. Prove that the distance $\delta(\mathbf{u},\mathbf{v}) = |\mathbf{u} - \mathbf{v}|$ between two vectors, as introduced in definition 16.2, has the property $\delta(\mathbf{u},\mathbf{v}) = \delta(\mathbf{u} + \mathbf{w}, \mathbf{v} + \mathbf{w})$ for every $\mathbf{w} \; \varepsilon \; V$.

5. Prove corollary 16.1.

6. Prove corollary 16.2.

7. If A is a complex matrix, then denote by $\bar{A}$ the matrix obtained from A by replacing every element by its complex conjugate. A complex square matrix is called *unitary* if $A\bar{A}' = \bar{A}'A = I$ and *Hermitian†* if $A = \bar{A}'$. Prove for the complex inner product (16.17):
   (a) $(Ax) \cdot (Ay) = x \cdot y$ if and only if A is unitary;
   (b) $(Ax) \cdot y = x \cdot (Ay)$ if and only if A is Hermitian.

8. Prove that definition 16.3 implies (16.18), (16.19), (16.20), and (16.21).

9. Prove Schwarz's inequality $|\mathbf{f}(\mathbf{u},\mathbf{v})|^2 \leq \mathbf{f}(\mathbf{u},\mathbf{u})\mathbf{f}(\mathbf{v},\mathbf{v})$ for unitary vector spaces.

10. Generalize theorem 16.3 and its two corollaries to unitary vector spaces.

*11. Let H_R be the set of all real infinite sequences $a = (a_i)_{i \varepsilon I^+}$ with $\sum_{i=1}^{\infty} a_i^2 < \infty$ (Note that this is a subset of $\overline{R^\infty}$ and a superset of R^∞). Prove: (1) The restrictions of the two composition laws of $\overline{R^\infty}$ to H_R are composition laws for H_R. (2) $|\sum_{i=1}^{\infty} a_i b_i| < \infty$ for $a = (a_i)_{i \varepsilon I^+}$, $b = (b_i)_{i \varepsilon I^+} \; \epsilon \; H_R$ (*Hint*: Extend Schwarz's inequality to H_R.). (3) The set of all infinite sequences of the form $(1,0,\cdots 0,\cdots)$, $(0,1,0,\cdots,0,\cdots)$, $\cdots$, $(0,\cdots,0,1,0,\cdots)$, $\cdots$ is *not* a basis of H_R *in the sense of definition* 9.2.

Note: If a mapping f of $H_R \times H_R$ into R and an "inner product" $a \cdot b$ are defined by $f: (a,b) \to a \cdot b = \sum_{i=1}^{\infty} a_i b_i$ then $\{H_R,f\}$ is a generalization of a Euclidean vector space to an *infinite-dimensional* real vector space.

† Named after the French mathematician *Charles Hermite* (1822–1905).

*12. Generalize the results of the previous exercise to the set H_C of all complex infinite sequences $a = (a_i)_{i \epsilon I^+}$ with $\sum_{i=1}^{\infty} |a_i|^2 < \infty$. *Hint*: Define a "complex inner product" by $a \cdot b = \sum_{i=1}^{\infty} a_i \bar{b}_i$ and show that for $a, b \epsilon H_C$, $a \cdot b$ converges. Both vector spaces H_R and H_C, together with their respective inner products, are simple examples of *Hilbert Spaces*.†

† Named after the German mathematician *David Hilbert* (1862–1943).

17

A Recursive Definition of the Determinant

This chapter will present a definition of a certain interesting expression in the elements of a square matrix, the so-called *determinant*. Ever since the German mathematician and philosopher *Gottfried Wilhelm Leibniz* (1646–1716) invented the concept of determinants, mathematicians as well as laymen have been fascinated by their striking properties and have enjoyed studying them. Determinants are very convenient for numerical computations of solutions of linear systems and for elegant formulation of theorems concerning linear dependence and independence. But in this century it has been realized that their importance has been overestimated, probably because of their aesthetic appeal to the mathematical intellect. We shall, therefore, confine ourselves to an outline of their essential properties and choose not the most beautiful, but a practical way of introducing them.

A formula that reduces a definition depending on a positive integer n to that definition for the integer $n - 1$ is called a *recursion formula*. From any recursion formula the *explicit* formula for a particular $n = k$ can be found after $k - 1$ successive applications of that formula for decreasing integers, provided that the formula is given explicitly for $n = 1$. This process is called *recursion*.

We shall give the definition of the determinant of a square matrix of order n *recursively* in terms of determinants of square matrices of order $n - 1$. This definition will be a special case of the recursive definition of the expansion of a determinant by some row or column. We shall see then that all these expansions are equal so that each of them could have been taken as the definition of a determinant.

Definition 17.1: Let

$$A = \begin{bmatrix} a_{11} & \cdots & a_{1n} \\ \vdots & & \vdots \\ a_{n1} & \cdots & a_{nn} \end{bmatrix}$$

be a square matrix of order n whose elements are real (complex) numbers or real (complex) polynomials.† If $n = 1$, the element a_{11} (itself) is called the *determinant of* A and is denoted by $|A|$. Suppose now that $n > 1$ and that the determinant of every square matrix of order $n - 1$ has been defined previously. Then the following expression is called the *determinant of* A and is denoted by $|A|$:

$$|A| = \sum_{i=1}^{n} (-1)^{i+1} a_{i1} |A^{i;1}|. \tag{17.1}$$

For $j = 1, 2, \cdots, n$, the expression

$$\sum_{i=1}^{n} (-1)^{i+j} a_{ij} |A^{i;j}| \tag{17.2}$$

is called the *expansion of* $|A|$ *by the jth column*. For $i = 1, 2, \cdots, n$, the expression

$$\sum_{j=1}^{n} (-1)^{i+j} a_{ij} |A^{i;j}| \tag{17.3}$$

is called the *expansion of* $|A|$ *by the ith row*. The positive integer n is called the *order of the determinant*. The determinant of any square submatrix of a matrix B (not necessarily a square matrix) is called a *subdeterminant of B*.

If the square matrix A of order $n > 1$ is given in one of the forms

$$\begin{bmatrix} a_{11} & \cdots & a_{1n} \\ \vdots & & \vdots \\ a_{n1} & \cdots & a_{nn} \end{bmatrix}, \quad \begin{bmatrix} a \overset{(1)}{\longrightarrow} \\ \vdots \\ a \overset{(n)}{\longrightarrow} \end{bmatrix}, \quad (a \overset{(1)}{\downarrow}, \cdots, a \overset{(n)}{\downarrow})$$

then its determinant is also denoted by

---

† Like the concept introduced in definition 12.5, the concept of a determinant can be generalized to more general matrices, for example, to matrices whose elements are differential operators (exercise 18.31), to matrices in which one column (or row) consists of vectors and all others of scalars (see note to definition 19.2), or to matrices whose elements belong to a *commutative ring* in the sense of algebra.

$$\begin{vmatrix} a_{11} & \cdots & a_{1n} \\ \vdots & & \vdots \\ a_{n1} & \cdots & a_{nn} \end{vmatrix}, \quad \begin{vmatrix} a \xrightarrow{(1)} \\ \vdots \\ a \xrightarrow{(n)} \end{vmatrix}, \quad \begin{vmatrix} a \!\!\underset{(1)}{\downarrow}, & \cdots, & a \!\!\underset{(n)}{\downarrow} \end{vmatrix}.$$

The evaluation of formulas (17.1) and (17.2) can be obtained easily in the following manner. Take a square matrix S of order n of alternating plus and minus signs beginning with plus in the first row and first column:

$$S = (s_{ij}) = \begin{bmatrix} + & - & + & - & \cdot & \cdot & \cdot \\ - & + & - & + & \cdot & \cdot & \cdot \\ + & - & + & - & \cdot & \cdot & \cdot \\ - & + & - & + & \cdot & \cdot & \cdot \\ \cdot & \cdot & \cdot & \cdot & \cdot & \cdot & \cdot \\ \cdot & \cdot & \cdot & \cdot & \cdot & \cdot & \cdot \\ \cdot & \cdot & \cdot & \cdot & \cdot & \cdot & \cdot \end{bmatrix}$$

Now the expansion of $|A|$ by the ith row is composed as follows. Take every element a_{ij} of the ith row, multiply it by the determinant of order $n-1$ obtained by cancellation of that row and that column in which a_{ij} lies, change the sign of the product if $s_{ij} =$ minus, and add all n products of this type. The expansion of $|A|$ by the jth column, in particular, the determinant of A itself, is composed in a similar fashion.

EXAMPLES OF EXPANSIONS OF A DETERMINANT

1. Expansion of the determinant of $\quad A = \begin{bmatrix} 1 & 2 \\ 3 & 4 \end{bmatrix}$

   by the first row:

$$1 \begin{vmatrix} 1 & 2 \\ 3 & 4 \end{vmatrix} - 2 \begin{vmatrix} 1 & 2 \\ 3 & 4 \end{vmatrix} = 1.4 - 2.3 = -2,$$

   by the second row:

$$-3 \begin{vmatrix} 1 & 2 \\ 3 & 4 \end{vmatrix} + 4 \begin{vmatrix} 1 & 2 \\ 3 & 4 \end{vmatrix} = -3.2 + 4.1 = -2,$$

   by the first column:

$$1 \begin{vmatrix} 1 & 2 \\ 3 & 4 \end{vmatrix} - 3 \begin{vmatrix} 1 & 2 \\ 3 & 4 \end{vmatrix} = 1.4 - 3.2 = -2,$$

by the second column:

$$-2\begin{vmatrix}1 & 2 \\ 3 & 4\end{vmatrix} + 4\begin{vmatrix}1 & 2 \\ 3 & 4\end{vmatrix} = -2.3 + 4.1 = -2.$$

2. Expansion of the determinant of

$$A = \begin{bmatrix}1 & 2 & 3 \\ 4 & 5 & 6 \\ 7 & 8 & 9\end{bmatrix}$$

by the second row:

$$-4\begin{vmatrix}1 & 2 & 3 \\ 4 & 5 & 6 \\ 7 & 8 & 9\end{vmatrix} + 5\begin{vmatrix}1 & 2 & 3 \\ 4 & 5 & 6 \\ 7 & 8 & 9\end{vmatrix} - 6\begin{vmatrix}1 & 2 & 3 \\ 4 & 5 & 6 \\ 7 & 8 & 9\end{vmatrix}$$

$$= -4\begin{vmatrix}2 & 3 \\ 8 & 9\end{vmatrix} + 5\begin{vmatrix}1 & 3 \\ 7 & 9\end{vmatrix} - 6\begin{vmatrix}1 & 2 \\ 7 & 8\end{vmatrix},$$

by the second column:

$$-2\begin{vmatrix}1 & 2 & 3 \\ 4 & 5 & 6 \\ 7 & 8 & 9\end{vmatrix} + 5\begin{vmatrix}1 & 2 & 3 \\ 4 & 5 & 6 \\ 7 & 8 & 9\end{vmatrix} - 8\begin{vmatrix}1 & 2 & 3 \\ 4 & 5 & 6 \\ 7 & 8 & 9\end{vmatrix}$$

$$= -2\begin{vmatrix}4 & 6 \\ 7 & 9\end{vmatrix} + 5\begin{vmatrix}1 & 3 \\ 7 & 9\end{vmatrix} - 8\begin{vmatrix}1 & 3 \\ 4 & 6\end{vmatrix}.$$

Note: For a complete evaluation the second-order subdeterminants have still to be expanded by the first column.

EXAMPLES OF DETERMINANTS

1.
$$\begin{vmatrix}a_{11} & a_{12} \\ a_{21} & a_{22}\end{vmatrix} = a_{11}a_{22} - a_{21}a_{12}.$$

2.
$$\begin{vmatrix}a_{11} & a_{12} & a_{13} \\ a_{21} & a_{22} & a_{23} \\ a_{31} & a_{32} & a_{33}\end{vmatrix} = a_{11}\begin{vmatrix}a_{22} & a_{23} \\ a_{32} & a_{33}\end{vmatrix} - a_{21}\begin{vmatrix}a_{12} & a_{13} \\ a_{32} & a_{33}\end{vmatrix} + a_{31}\begin{vmatrix}a_{12} & a_{13} \\ a_{22} & a_{23}\end{vmatrix}$$

$$= a_{11}(a_{22}a_{33} - a_{32}a_{23}) - a_{21}(a_{12}a_{33} - a_{32}a_{13}) + a_{31}(a_{12}a_{23} - a_{22}a_{13})$$

$$= \begin{cases}+ a_{11}a_{22}a_{33} + a_{21}a_{32}a_{13} + a_{31}a_{12}a_{23} \\ - a_{11}a_{32}a_{23} - a_{21}a_{12}a_{33} - a_{31}a_{22}a_{13}.\end{cases}$$

The recursive definition of a determinant and its expansions will make it particularly convenient to prove propositions about determinants by mathematical induction.

Lemma 17.1:   *The expansion of a determinant by some column is equal to its expansion by any other column.*

PROOF: It suffices to show that for any square matrix A of order $n \geq 2$

$$\sum_{i=1}^{n} (-1)^{i+k} a_{ik} |A^{i;k}| = \sum_{j=1}^{n} (-1)^{j+k+1} a_{j,k+1} |A^{j;k+1}|$$

(17.4)

$$\text{for} \quad k = 1, 2, \cdots, n - 1.$$

It is very easy to see that this equation is satisfied for $n = 2$. Suppose that (17.4) is true for all $n \leq N$ (where N is some unspecified integer ≥ 2); that is, suppose that the determinant of any square matrix A of order $n \leq N$ can be expressed by any of the n expressions (17.2). We want to show that, under this induction assumption, (17.4) remains true for the case $n = N + 1$.

Let us explain the idea of the proof first. In (17.4) we replace the number n by the number $N + 1$, cancel the equality sign, and consider each side separately. On the left-hand side we expand the subdeterminants by their kth column (which is the $(k + 1)$st column of A). On the right-hand side we expand the subdeterminants by their kth column. In this way we obtain two expressions "by successive expansion by the kth and (original) $(k + 1)$st column," only in different order of procedure. It is plausible to expect these two expressions to be equal, but checking whether corresponding terms have the right signs takes some time.

By induction, the determinant of a submatrix $B = A^{\alpha;\beta}$ of a matrix A of order $N + 1$ is equal to its expansion by *every* column. Hence, making use of (12.31) and (12.32), we have

$$|A^{\alpha;\beta}| = |B| = \sum_{\gamma=1}^{N} (-1)^{\gamma+\delta} b_{\gamma\delta} |B^{\gamma;\delta}|$$

$$= \begin{cases} \displaystyle\sum_{\gamma=1}^{\alpha-1} (-1)^{\gamma+\delta} a_{\gamma\delta} |A^{\alpha,\gamma;\beta,\delta}| + \sum_{\gamma=\alpha}^{N} (-1)^{\gamma+\delta} a_{\gamma+1,\delta} |A^{\alpha,\gamma+1;\beta,\delta}| \\ \qquad\qquad\qquad \textit{for all} \quad \delta < \beta, \qquad\qquad\qquad\qquad (17.5) \\ \displaystyle\sum_{\gamma=1}^{\alpha-1} (-1)^{\gamma+\delta} a_{\gamma,\delta+1} |A^{\alpha,\gamma;\beta,\delta+1}| + \sum_{\gamma=\alpha}^{N} (-1)^{\gamma+\delta} a_{\gamma+1,\delta+1} |A^{\alpha,\gamma+1;\beta,\delta+1}| \\ \qquad\qquad\qquad \textit{for all} \quad \delta \geq \beta. \end{cases}$$

To expand the determinant $|A^{i;k}|$ on the left-hand side of (17.4) by the (new) kth column (that is, by the original $(k + 1)$st column of A)

we apply (17.5) with $\alpha = i$, $\beta = k$, $\delta = k$, and the additional substitutions $\gamma = j$ for the summation index in the *first* sum of (17.5), but $\gamma + 1 = j$ in the *second* sum. Then we have the case $\delta \geq \beta$; hence

$$|A^{i;k}| = \sum_{j=1}^{i-1} (-1)^{j+k} a_{j,k+1} |A^{i,j;k,k+1}|$$

$$+ \sum_{j=i+1}^{N+1} (-1)^{j-1+k} a_{j,k+1} |A^{i,j;k,k+1}|. \qquad (17.6)$$

To expand $|A^{j;k+1}|$ on the right-hand side of (17.4) by the (new and old) kth column, we apply (17.5) with $\alpha = j$, $\beta = k + 1$, $\delta = k$, and the additional substitutions $\gamma = i$ for the summation index in the *first* sum of (17.5), but $\gamma + 1 = i$ in the *second* sum. Then we have the case $\delta < \beta$; hence

$$|A^{j,k+1}| = \sum_{i=1}^{j-1} (-1)^{i+k} a_{ik} |A^{j,i;k+1,k}|$$

$$+ \sum_{i=j+1}^{N+1} (-1)^{i-1+k} a_{ik} |A^{j,i;k+1,k}|. \qquad (17.7)$$

But the substitutions (17.6) and (17.7) on the respective sides of (17.4) *in both cases* give

$$\sum_{\substack{i,j=1 \\ i<i}}^{N+1} (-1)^{i+j} a_{ik} a_{j,k+1} |A^{i,j;k,k+1}| + \sum_{\substack{i,j=1 \\ j>i}}^{N+1} (-1)^{i+j+1} a_{ik} a_{j,k+1} |A^{i;j;k,k+1}|.$$

Hence, the left- and right-hand sides of (17.4) are equal for $n = N + 1$, provided that they were equal for $n = N$, and the induction proof is completed.

Theorem 17.1:   *Transposition of a square matrix leaves its determinant unaltered:*

$$|A| = |A'|. \qquad (17.8)$$

Proof: If $n = 1$, then $A = A'$, and the theorem is trivially true. Suppose that the theorem is true for all determinants of order N, where N is some unspecified positive integer. Let A be a square matrix *of order* $N + 1$, and let B be its transpose: $A' = B$. Then,

$$a_{ij} = b_{ji} \quad \text{for every} \quad i, j = 1, \cdots, N + 1 \qquad (17.9)$$

and likewise

$$A^{i;i} = (B^{i;i})' \quad \text{for every} \quad i, j = 1, \cdots, N + 1. \qquad (17.10)$$

Since, by the induction assumption, the theorem is true for all square matrices of order N and since (17.10) consists of such square matrices, we conclude

$$|A^{i;i}| = |B^{i;i}|. \qquad (17.11)$$

From lemma 17.1 it follows that

$$|B| = \sum_{j=1}^{N+1} (-1)^{i+j} b_{ji} |B^{j;i}| \quad \text{for} \quad i = 1, 2, \cdots, N+1.$$

If we add these $N + 1$ equations, we obtain

$$(N + 1) |B| = \sum_{i=1}^{N+1} \sum_{j=1}^{N+1} (-1)^{i+j} b_{ji} |B^{j;i}|. \tag{17.12}$$

On the other hand, we have also by lemma 17.1

$$|A| = \sum_{i=1}^{N+1} a_{ij} |A^{i;j}| \quad \text{for} \quad j = 1, 2, \cdots, N+1.$$

If we add these $N + 1$ equations, we obtain

$$(N + 1) |A| = \sum_{j=1}^{N+1} \sum_{i=1}^{N+1} (-1)^{i+j} a_{ij} |A^{i;j}|. \tag{17.13}$$

But from (17.9) and (17.11) it follows that the right-hand sides of (17.12) and (17.13) are equal. Hence we have $(N + 1) |B| = (N + 1) |A|$ or $|B| = |A|$, because $N + 1$ is a positive integer and, therefore, never equal to zero.

Since transposition of a matrix changes columns to rows and vice versa, theorem 17.1 implies immediately

Corollary 17.1:   *The expansion of a determinant by any row is equal to its expansion by any column.*

Thus we may summarize:

Theorem 17.2:   *The determinant of a square matrix A is equal to its expansion by any row or column.*

EXERCISES

1. Compute the following determinants by expansion by the first and third column:

$$\begin{vmatrix} 1 & 2 & 3 & 4 \\ 4 & 3 & 2 & 1 \\ 3 & 1 & 4 & 2 \\ 2 & 4 & 1 & 3 \end{vmatrix}, \quad \begin{vmatrix} 1 & 4 & 3 & 2 \\ 2 & 3 & 1 & 4 \\ 3 & 2 & 4 & 1 \\ 4 & 1 & 2 & 3 \end{vmatrix}, \quad \begin{vmatrix} 2 & -1 & 1 \\ 1 & 1 & -1 \\ 2 & 1 & 0 \end{vmatrix}, \quad \begin{vmatrix} 2 & 1 & 2 \\ -1 & 1 & 1 \\ 1 & -1 & 0 \end{vmatrix},$$

$$\begin{vmatrix} 1 & 1 & 1 \\ a & a & a \\ a^2 & a^2 & a^2 \end{vmatrix}, \quad \begin{vmatrix} 1 & a & a^2 \\ 1 & b & b^2 \\ 1 & c & c^2 \end{vmatrix}, \quad \begin{vmatrix} a & b & c \\ c & a & b \\ b & c & a \end{vmatrix}, \quad \begin{vmatrix} a & c & b \\ b & a & c \\ c & b & a \end{vmatrix}.$$

Check that $|A| = |A'|$ is true for these cases.

2. Prove the following propositions:
   (a) $|tI| = t^n$ for any scalar matrix (13.2) of order n.
   (b) $|M_{ij}(\alpha)| = 1$ for any matrix (13.4).
   (c) $|N_i(\alpha)| = \alpha$ for any matrix (13.5).
   (d) $|E_{ij}| = -1$ for any matrix (13.6).
   (e) $|P| = \pm 1$ for any permuting matrix.

3. Prove: The determinant of any triangular matrix is equal to the product of its elements in the principal diagonal.

4. Let P be a permuting matrix having the number 1 in the nth row and jth column. Prove the formula $|P^{n;j}| = (-1)^{n+j} |P|$.

5. It can be shown that the following formula, due to Leibniz, is true:

$$|A| = \sum_{\alpha = P \begin{pmatrix} 1 \\ 2 \\ \vdots \\ n \end{pmatrix}} |P|\, a_{1\alpha_1} a_{2\alpha_2} \cdots a_{n\alpha_n}. \tag{17.14}$$

Here the sum on the right-hand side is to be extended over all n-tuples α, written as *column* matrices, that are obtained from the n-tuple $(1,2,3, \cdots, n)$, written as a *column*, by left multiplication by an arbitrary *permuting* matrix P of order n. The determinant of P appears as a factor of the corresponding term in the sum. Prove:

$$|A^{n;j}| = \sum_{\alpha = P \begin{pmatrix} 1 \\ 2 \\ \vdots \\ n \end{pmatrix}} |P^{n;j}|\, a_{1\alpha_1} \cdots a_{n-1,\alpha_{n-1}} \tag{17.15}$$

for all those P for which $\alpha_n = j$ holds. *Hint*: Use exercise 4.

6. Prove: If (17.14) is true for $n = k - 1$ (that is, for matrices A of order $k - 1$), then (17.14) is also true for $n = k$ (for matrices of order k). *Hint*: Use formula (17.15).

18

Basic Properties of a Determinant

The recursive definition of a determinant in terms of an expansion and the proposition that all expansions of a determinant are equal make it very easy to prove the basic properties of determinants. We shall, therefore, confine ourselves to short outlines of most of the proofs.

Theorem 18.1: *A determinant changes its sign if two of its rows or two of its columns are interchanged:*

$$|E_{ij}A| = |AE_{ij}| = -|A|. \tag{18.1}$$

This theorem can be proved in several ways, for example, by induction on the order or by "double expansion" (as in the proof of lemma 17.1) by the two critical rows (or columns).

EXAMPLE

$$\begin{vmatrix} 1 & 2 & 3 \\ 4 & 5 & 6 \\ 7 & 8 & 9 \end{vmatrix} = - \begin{vmatrix} 7 & 8 & 9 \\ 4 & 5 & 6 \\ 1 & 2 & 3 \end{vmatrix}.$$

Corollary 18.1: *A determinant vanishes if two of its rows or two of its columns are equal.*

This is an immediate consequence of theorem 18.1.
Hint: Change the two rows or columns that are equal.

EXAMPLE

$$\begin{vmatrix} 1 & 2 & 3 \\ 1 & 2 & 3 \\ 4 & 5 & 6 \end{vmatrix} = 0.$$

Theorem 18.2: *If a row or a column of a determinant is multiplied by a number t, then the determinant is multiplied by that factor:*

$$|a^{(1)},\cdots,a^{(i-1)},ta^{(i)},a^{(i+1)},\cdots,a^{(n)}| = t|A|, \qquad (18.2)$$

where the $a^{(i)}$ $(i = 1, \cdots, n)$ are either the rows or the columns of A.

Expand the left-hand side of (18.2) by the ith row (or column), and the proof follows at once.

EXAMPLE

$$\begin{vmatrix} 1 & 2 & 3 \\ 12 & 15 & 18 \\ 7 & 8 & 9 \end{vmatrix} = 3\begin{vmatrix} 1 & 2 & 3 \\ 4 & 5 & 6 \\ 7 & 8 & 9 \end{vmatrix}.$$

Corollary 18.2: *A determinant vanishes if all elements of a row or a column are equal to zero.*

This is an obvious consequence of (18.2).

EXAMPLE

$$\begin{vmatrix} 1 & 2 & 3 \\ 0 & 0 & 0 \\ 4 & 5 & 6 \end{vmatrix} = 0.$$

Theorem 18.3: *Let n be an integer > 1, and let i be an integer satisfying $1 \le i \le n$. If $a^{(1)}, \cdots, a^{(i-1)}, b, c, a^{(i+1)}, \cdots, a^{(n)}$ are $n + 1$ n-tuples, all written either as rows or as columns, then the following addition rule holds for determinants:*

$$|a^{(1)},\cdots,a^{(i-1)},b + c,a^{(i+1)},\cdots,a^{(n)}|$$
$$= |\cdots,a^{(i-1)},b,a^{(i+1)},\cdots| + |\cdots,a^{(i-1)},c,a^{(i+1)},\cdots|. \qquad (18.3)$$

The proof is obtained by expansion of all three determinants of (18.3) by the critical ith row or ith column.

EXAMPLE

$$\begin{vmatrix} 1 & 2 & 3 \\ 4 & 5 & 6 \\ 7 & 8 & 9 \end{vmatrix} + \begin{vmatrix} 1 & 2 & 3 \\ 4 & 5 & 6 \\ 10 & 11 & 12 \end{vmatrix} = \begin{vmatrix} 1 & 2 & 3 \\ 4 & 5 & 6 \\ 7+10, & 8+11, & 9+12 \end{vmatrix}.$$

Theorem 18.4: *A determinant remains unchanged if to any of its rows an arbitrary multiple of another row is added or if to any of its columns an arbitrary multiple of another column is added:*

$$|A| = |M_{ij}(\alpha) A| = |A M_{ij}(\alpha)|. \tag{18.4}$$

For the proof, apply theorems 18.3 and 18.2 and corollary 18.1.

EXAMPLE

$$\begin{vmatrix} 1 & 2 & 3 \\ 4 & 5 & 6 \\ 7 & 8 & 9 \end{vmatrix} = \begin{vmatrix} 1 & 2 & 3 \\ 4 & 5 & 6 \\ 7+4\cdot1 & 8+4\cdot2 & 9+4\cdot3 \end{vmatrix}.$$

By the use of definition 16.1, we may combine theorems 18.1, 18.2, and 18.3 in the following fashion.

Theorem 18.5: *The mapping $A \to |A|$ of the set of all real (or complex) square matrices of order n onto the set of all real (or complex) numbers is skew-symmetric and multilinear relative to the rows of the matrices and also relative to the columns of the matrices.*

In preparation for the important multiplication theorem for matrices, we need the following result on square matrices.

Lemma 18.1: *Every square matrix can be transformed into an upper (or into a lower) triangular matrix by left multiplication by a product of elementary matrices. It can also be transformed into an upper (or into a lower) triangular matrix by right multiplication by a product of elementary matrices.*

PROOF: We confine ourselves to the case of upper triangular matrices. The method will be similar to but not identical with the method described in Chapter 8 for systems of linear polynomials and analyzed in Chapter 13 for the matrices of their coefficients. For in this earlier construction *both* left and right multiplications by elementary matrices were used to obtain triangular form; here it will be obtained using left multiplications alone or right multiplications alone, in either case by matrices of the forms (13.4) and (13.6), *but not* (13.5).

We start with an inductive instruction to transform a square matrix A of order n into an upper triangular matrix $A^{(n)}$ (not necessarily normalized) by *left* multiplications alone. Suppose we have already obtained from A, by left multiplications by matrices of the forms (13.4) and (13.6), a matrix $A^{(j)}$ (where $1 \leq j \leq n$) in which all elements of the first, second, $\ldots$, up to the jth column that lie *below* the principal diagonal vanish.

$$
A^{(j)} = \begin{bmatrix}
a_{11}^{(j)} & a_{12}^{(j)} & \cdots & a_{1j}^{(j)} & a_{1,j+1}^{(j)} & \cdots & a_{1n}^{(j)} \\
 & a_{22}^{(j)} & \cdots & a_{2j}^{(j)} & a_{2,j+1}^{(j)} & \cdots & a_{2n}^{(j)} \\
 & & & \vdots & \vdots & & \vdots \\
 & & & a_{jj}^{(j)} & a_{j,j+1}^{(j)} & \cdots & a_{jn}^{(j)} \\
 & & & & a_{j+1,j+1}^{(j)} & \cdots & a_{j+1,n}^{(j)} \\
 & \mathbf{O} & & & \vdots & & \vdots \\
 & & & & a_{i,j+1}^{(j)} & \cdots & a_{in}^{(j)} \\
 & & & & \vdots & & \vdots \\
 & & & & a_{n,j+1}^{(j)} & \cdots & a_{nn}^{(j)}
\end{bmatrix} \quad \leftarrow i\text{th row}
$$

Then we shall give a procedure for obtaining from $A^{(j)}$, by left multiplications by elementary matrices (13.4) and (13.6), a matrix $A^{(j+1)}$ in which all elements of the $(j+1)$st column below the principal diagonal also vanish.

We distinguish two main cases: (1) All elements of the $(j+1)$st column of $A^{(j)}$ below the principal diagonal may vanish already. Then we simply take $A^{(j+1)} = I A^{(j)}$; that is, $A^{(j+1)} = A^{(j)}$. (2) Or we may have in $A^{(j)}$ (at least) one element $a_{i,j+1}^{(j)}$ with $i > j + 1$ (that is, below the principal diagonal) different from zero. In this case we have to distinguish two subcases:

First subcase: $a_{j+1,j+1}^{(j)} \neq 0$; that is, the element of $A^{(j)}$ of the $(j+1)$st column belonging to the principal diagonal does not vanish. In this case we proceed as in Chapter 8, except that we do not normalize the jth row. We left-multiply $A^{(j)}$ by $M_{i,j+1}(\alpha)$, where $\alpha = -a_{i,j+1}^{(j)}/a_{j+1,j+1}^{(j)}$ and $i > j + 1$. Then $M_{i,j+1}(\alpha) A^{(j)}$ is obtained from $A^{(j)}$ by adding to the ith row a multiple of the $(j+1)$st row such that the *new* element in the ith row and $(j+1)$st column equals zero. We repeat this process for all $i > j + 1$, until we have obtained zeros everywhere in the $(j+1)$st column below the principal diagonal. The matrix so obtained we call $A^{(j+1)}$.

Second subcase: $a_{j+1,j+1}^{(j)} = 0$; that is, the element of $A^{(j)}$ of the $(j+1)$st column belonging to the principal diagonal does vanish. In

Chapter 8 this case was handled by exchange of *columns*, that is, by *right* multiplications by matrices of the form (13.6). Here we simply exchange the $(j + 1)$st and ith *rows*; that is, apply $E_{i+1,i}$ as *left* operator, in order to get the element $a_{i,j+1}^{(i)}$ (which is *different from zero*, by assumption) into the principal diagonal. Thereafter, we use matrices (13.4) as left operators to change to zero any possible further nonzero elements of the $(j + 1)$st column below the principal diagonal. In this way we obtain $A^{(j+1)}$.

After $n - j - 1$ such steps we reach $A^{(n-1)}$, or $A^{(j)}$ with $j = n - 1$, which has upper triangular form. The *first* step is to bring all required elements in the *first* column to zero; the *second* step to bring all required elements in the *second* column to zero; and so forth.

The proof that a square matrix can be transformed into an upper triangular matrix by successive *right* multiplications by elementary matrices is similar. But now our *first* step is to bring all required elements in the nth (that is, the *last*) row to zero. If these zeros are not in the right places in the beginning, they can be brought there by suitable additions of multiples of the last column to earlier columns, after the columns, if necessary, have been so exchanged that the very last element in the last column is different from zero. The *second* step consists of bringing all required elements in the $(n - 1)$st row to zero. And so on. Again, upper diagonal form is reached after $n - 1$ steps, each succeeding step dealing with the next higher row.

Theorem 18.6: *If A and B are two square matrices of equal order, then*

$$|AB| = |A| \cdot |B|. \tag{18.5}$$

PROOF: Let P be a product of matrices E_{ij} and $M_{ii}(\alpha)$ of order n such that $PA = U$ is an upper triangular matrix. Let Q be a product of elementary matrices E_{ij} and $M_{ii}(\alpha)$ such that $BQ = V$ is an upper triangular matrix. Both P and Q exist (not necessarily uniquely), by lemma 18.1. Define the symbol $(-1)^P$ to mean $+1$ if the number of those factors in P that are of the form E_{ij} is *even* and to mean -1 if this number is odd. Define $(-1)^Q$ in a corresponding way. Then it follows from (18.1) and (18.4) that $|PA| = (-1)^P |A|$ and that $|BQ| = (-1)^Q |B|$; hence, we can conclude that

$$|A| \cdot |B| = (-1)^P (-1)^Q |U| \cdot |V|. \tag{18.6}$$

Similarly we can see that $|P(AB)Q| = (-1)^P (-1)^Q |AB|$; hence, we have also

$$|AB| = (-1)^P (-1)^Q |UV|. \tag{18.7}$$

But $|U| \cdot |V|$ and $|UV|$ are equal, because of exercise 17.3 and exercise 13.14. Hence the left-hand sides of (18.6) and (18.7) are equal, too.

Corollary 18.3:   *If a square matrix A is regular, then* $|A| \neq 0$.

PROOF: $|A| \cdot |A^{-1}| = |AA^{-1}| = |I| = 1$.

But the converse of corollary 18.3, namely the proposition that $|A| \neq 0$ implies the regularity of A, is likewise true, as we intend to show next. In preparation, we state a generalized expansion theorem (theorem 18.7) due to the French mathematician and astronomer *Pierre-Simon de Laplace* (1749–1827); and we make use of the following notation, which is due to the German mathematician *Leopold Kronecker* (1823–1891).

Definition 18.1:   Let i and j be two numbers (or, more generally, two elements of some set). The symbol δ_{ij} is defined to mean the number 1 if $i = j$ and the number zero if $i \neq j$ and is called the *Kronecker delta:*

$$\delta_{ij} = \begin{cases} 1 & \text{if } i = j, \\ 0 & \text{if } i \neq j. \end{cases} \tag{18.8}$$

Thus we have, for example, $\delta_{11} = 1$, $\delta_{66} = 1$, but $\delta_{13} = 0$, $\delta_{95} = 0$.

Theorem 18.7:   *Let A be a square matrix of order $n > 1$. Then*

$$\sum_{i=1}^{n} (-1)^{i+j} a_{ij} |A^{i;k}| = \delta_{jk} |A|, \tag{18.9}$$

$$\sum_{j=1}^{n} (-1)^{i+j} a_{ij} |A^{k;j}| = \delta_{ik} |A|. \tag{18.10}$$

PROOF: For $j = k$, the first equation is a restatement of lemma 17.1; for $i = k$, the second equation follows from theorem 17.2. Assume now that $j \neq k$. Let $a^{(1)}, a^{(2)}, \cdots, a^{(n)}$ be the columns of A. Construct from A a matrix B by replacing the kth column of A by $a^{(i)}$ but leaving all other columns (*including* the jth column) in their respective places:

$$B = (a^{(1)}, \cdots, a^{(k-1)}, a^{(i)}, a^{(k+1)}, \cdots, a^{(i-1)}, a^{(i)}, a^{(i+1)}, \cdots, a^{(n)})$$

Since in B the kth and jth columns are equal, the determinant of B vanishes, by corollary 18.1. On the other hand, expansion of B by *its* kth column yields (except possibly for sign) the left-hand side of (18.9).

In a similar way (18.10) can be proved.

From theorem 18.7 and the definition of matrix multiplication we can easily prove

Theorem 18.8:   *A square matrix A of order n has an inverse if and only if* $|A| \neq 0$. *If* $|A| \neq 0$ *and* $n > 1$, *then the matrix $\bar{A}$ with elements $\bar{a}_{ij}$ (in the ith row and jth column of $\bar{A}$) that satisfy*

$$\bar{a}_{ij} = (-1)^{i+j} \frac{|A^{j;i}|}{|A|} \qquad \text{for } i, j = 1, \cdots, n \tag{18.11}$$

is the inverse of A.

Attention: The reversal of i and j in the superscript on the right-hand side of (18.11) is no misprint, but essential. To obtain the element in the ith row and jth column of the inverse of A, one needs the sub-determinant of A obtained by cancellation of the jth row and ith column of A, as the proof of (18.11) shows. For the matrix multiplication demands inner products of rows by columns.

PROOF: First, $A\bar{A} = I$ may be verified; it is a simple consequence of the previous theorem. This formula *constructs* the inverse of A if $|A| \neq 0$ and $n > 1$. If $A = (a_{11})$ is of order 1 and if $a_{11} \neq 0$, then we obviously have $A^{-1} = (a_{11}^{-1})$. Hence, for *any* order n, the inverse exists if $|A| \neq 0$. That the inverse exists *only if* $|A| \neq 0$ is the assertion of corollary 18.3.

The following corollary, called *Cramer's rule*, is due to the Swiss mathematician *Gabriel Cramer* (1704–1752):

Corollary 18.4: *If* $A = (a_{\downarrow}^{(1)}, a_{\downarrow}^{(2)}, \cdots, a_{\downarrow}^{(n)})$ *is a regular square matrix of order* $n > 1$ *and if* x, b *are columns of length* n, *then the linear system*

$$Ax = b$$

has a unique solution x *with*

$$x_i = \frac{|a^{(1)}, \cdots, a^{(i-1)}, b, a^{(i+1)}, \cdots, a^{(n)}|}{|A|}. \tag{18.12}$$

PROOF: $Ax = b$ implies $x = A^{-1}b$, and vice versa; and $|A| \neq 0$, by theorem 18.8. Hence, the solution is unique. By theorem 18.8, the ith coordinate of $x = A^{-1}b$ is given by

$$x_i = \sum_{j=1}^{n} (-1)^{i+j} b_j \frac{|A^{j;i}|}{|A|}$$

which, apart from the denominator $|A|$, is equal to the expansion of $|a^{(1)}, \cdots, a^{(i-1)}, b, a^{(i+1)}, \cdots, a^{(n)}|$ by the ith column.

This corollary implies that a homogeneous system has *no* nontrivial solution if $|A| \neq 0$. But the converse is also true:

Theorem 18.9: *Let* A *be a square matrix of order* n *and let* x *be a column of length* n. *The homogeneous system* $Ax = 0$ *has a nontrivial solution if and only if* $|A| = 0$.

PROOF: By theorems 9.2, 14.3, 14.4 and exercise 10 the nullity of this solvable system is positive if and only if $|A| = 0$.

In various parts of mathematics, for example, in geometry (see Chapter 22), and in the applications of mathematics to physics, the question may arise whether a mapping $x \to Ax$ induced by a square matrix A may map a nonzero n-tuple x on a *multiple* λx of x. The answer to this question is an immediate consequence of theorem 18.9.

Corollary 18.5:   *Let A be a square matrix of order n, let x be a column of length n, and let λ be a real or complex number. The system $Ax = \lambda x$ has a solution $x \neq 0$ if and only if λ is a solution of $|A - \lambda I| = 0$.*

Definition 18.2:   A (real or complex) number λ is called an *eigenvalue*† (or *characteristic value*) of the square matrix A if $|A - \lambda I| = 0$. A (real or complex) nonzero sequence x, written as a column, is called *an eigenvector*† *of A for the eigenvalue λ if $Ax = \lambda x$.* The polynomial $|A - \lambda I|$ and the equation $|A - \lambda I| = 0$ are called the *characteristic polynomial* and the *characteristic equation* of A, respectively.

Note: Since λ is a solution of an algebraic equation, it may be a complex number even if all the elements of A are real. If A is real but an eigenvalue λ of A is complex, then every eigenvector of A for the eigenvalue λ must be complex, too. We shall see later (Chapter 22) that real symmetric matrices have only real eigenvalues.

We conclude this chapter with a few remarks about numerical computations of determinants *in practice*. Examples 1 and 2 of Determinants in Chapter 17 give explicit formulas for computing determinants of order 2 and 3. But, for determinants of higher orders, it does not pay to apply an explicit formula for numerical computation.

A more convenient way to find the determinant of a matrix A is to transform A to a triangular matrix (lower or upper, whichever is more convenient in the specific case) whose determinant is equal to the product of its diagonal elements. The required determinant then differs from this determinant at most by a sign; and, by careful registration of all exchanges of rows or of columns, the proper sign can be found at once. Frequently one is not even interested in computing a determinant explicitly, but wishes to know only whether it is equal to zero; in that case it is unnecessary to bother about signs. In obtaining triangular form, we need not keep to operations involving rows alone or columns alone, but may use *both* row and column operations *at pleasure*, that is, *both* left and right multiplications by E_{ij} and $M_{ij}(t)$.

EXERCISES

1. Prove theorem 18.1 in two different ways.
2. Prove (or supply the *parts* of the proofs omitted in the previous pages): theorems 18.2, 18.3, 18.4, and 18.8, corollaries 18.1, 18.2, and 18.4, and lemma 18.1.

---

† These are curiously coined but very popular hybrids, making use of the German word *eigen* (= proper, own), as in *Eigenwert* and *Eigenvektor*.

3. Prove: Three points X, Y, Z of $\Re^2$ lie on a straight line if and only if their coordinates satisfy

$$\begin{vmatrix} x_1 & y_1 & z_1 \\ x_2 & y_2 & z_2 \\ 1 & 1 & 1 \end{vmatrix} = 0.$$

4. Prove: Three vectors $\mathbf{u}$, $\mathbf{v}$, and $\mathbf{w}$ of $\mathbf{R}^3$ are linearly independent if and only if $|u,v,w| \neq 0$.

5. Prove: If $\mathbf{u}$ and $\mathbf{v}$ are elements of $\mathbf{R}^3$, then the vector $\mathbf{w}$ of $\mathbf{R}^3$ with Cartesian coordinates $w_i = (-1)^{i+1} |(u,v)^{i;\phi}|$ is perpendicular to both $\mathbf{u}$ and $\mathbf{v}$, and $\mathbf{w}$ is the zero vector if and only if $\mathbf{u}$ and $\mathbf{v}$ are linearly dependent.

6. Prove that n n-tuples of real numbers $v^{(1)}$, $\cdots$, $v^{(n)}$ form a basis of R^n if and only if $|v^{(1)}, \cdots , v^{(n)}| \neq 0$.

7. Prove that in $\Re^2$ the two lines $a \cdot x = \alpha$ and $b \cdot x = \beta$ have one and only one point in common if and only if $|a,b| \neq 0$. What is the corresponding condition that three planes, expressed in normal form, have one and only one point in common?

8. Prove: The rank of a matrix M is r if there exists (at least) one subdeterminant of M of order r that does not vanish but all sub-determinants of M of order $> r$ do vanish.

9. Prove that, for any two triples $x = (x_1,x_2,x_3)$ and $y = (y_1,y_2,y_3)$,

$$\begin{vmatrix} x_1 & y_1 \\ x_2 & y_2 \end{vmatrix}^2 + \begin{vmatrix} x_1 & y_1 \\ x_3 & y_3 \end{vmatrix}^2 + \begin{vmatrix} x_2 & y_2 \\ x_3 & y_3 \end{vmatrix}^2 = x^2 y^2 - (x \cdot y)^2 \qquad (18.13)$$

holds, and deduce from this result a proof of Schwarz's inequality.

10. Prove: A square matrix A of order n is equivalent to an identity matrix if and only if $|A| \neq 0$.

11. Compute the inverse of a square matrix of order 3 explicitly.

12. Prove: Every eigenvector of a real matrix A for a *nonreal* complex eigenvalue λ has at least one nonreal coordinate.

13. Prove that Vandermonde's determinant [after the French mathematician *Alexis Théophile Vandermonde* (1735–1796)]

$$\begin{vmatrix} 1 & x_1 & x_1^2 & \cdots & x_1^{n-1} \\ 1 & x_2 & x_2^2 & \cdots & x_2^{n-1} \\ \vdots & \vdots & \vdots & & \vdots \\ 1 & x_n & x_n^2 & \cdots & x_n^{n-1} \end{vmatrix}$$

is equal to the product of all differences $x_i - x_j$ with $i > j$. Hence prove: A polynomial $f(x)$ of degree n can be found whose graph passes through $n + 1$ given points if and only if no two first coordinates of these points are the same.

14. Prove: If M is orthogonal, then $|M|$ is equal to 1 or to -1.

15. Let M be an orthogonal matrix, and let I be the identity matrix of equal order. Prove: If $|M| = -1$, then $|M + I| = 0$. If the order of M is odd and $|M| = 1$, then $|M - I| = 0$.

16. Prove: There exist at most n different numbers λ such that $|A - \lambda I| = 0$ for a given matrix M of order n.

17. Let M be a real orthogonal matrix of order 3 with $|M| = 1$. The mapping $x \rightarrow Mx$ of R^3 into itself induces a mapping of $\mathfrak{R}^3$ into itself relative to a coordinate system that assigns to a point with coordinates x the point with coordinate Mx. Prove: There exists a straight line all of whose points are mapped onto themselves by this induced mapping.

    Hint: Apply exercise 15.

18. Prove: **Theorem 18.10:** *If f is a mapping of the set of all real square matrices A of order n into the real numbers that is skew-symmetric and multilinear relative to the rows of A and that satisfies $f(I) = 1$, then $f(A)$ is the determinant of A.* This theorem, due to the German mathematician *Karl Weierstrass* (1815–1897), can be used for an alternative definition of the determinant.

19. Determine the rank and nullity of a diagonal matrix.

20. What are the rank and nullity of an invertible matrix of order r?

21. Find an eigenvalue of a singular square matrix A.

22. Determine all eigenvalues of any triangular matrix.

23. Prove: If B is a regular square matrix and if A is a square matrix of equal order, then A and $B^{-1}AB$ have the same characteristic polynomial.

24. Let B be a regular square matrix, and let A be a square matrix of equal order. Set z be an eigenvector of $B^{-1}AB$ belonging to the eigenvalue λ. Find an eigenvector of A belonging to the same eigenvalue λ.

25. Prove: All *real* eigenvalues of a real matrix A satisfying $A = -A'$ are equal to zero.

26. Prove: If $A = -A'$ and if A is of odd order, then $|A| = 0$.

27. Prove: All eigenvalues λ of a *real* orthogonal matrix satisfy $|\lambda| = 1$.

28. Prove: If $B = (b^{(1)}, b^{(2)}, \cdots, b^{(n)})$ is an orthogonal matrix and if $b^{(1)}$ is an eigenvector of a symmetric matrix A for the eigenvalue λ^*, then

$$B'AB = \begin{bmatrix} \lambda & 0 & \cdots & 0 \\ 0 & & & \\ \vdots & & R & \\ \vdots & & & \\ 0 & & & \end{bmatrix}$$

with $(B'AB)^{1;1} = R$, where R is symmetric, too.

Hints: $B'B = I$ implies $b^{(1)}{}'B = (1,0,\cdots,0)$. Also

$$B'(AB) = \begin{bmatrix} b^{(1)}{}' \\ \vdots \\ b^{(n)}{}' \end{bmatrix} \begin{bmatrix} Ab^{(1)} & \cdots & Ab^{(n)} \end{bmatrix} =$$

$$(B'A)B = \begin{bmatrix} b^{(1)}{}'A \\ \vdots \\ b^{(n)}{}'A \end{bmatrix} \begin{bmatrix} b^{(1)} & \cdots & b^{(n)} \end{bmatrix} .$$

29. Prove: The coefficient of λ^{n-1} in the characteristic polynomial $|A - \lambda I|$ of a square matrix A of order n is equal to $(-1)^{n-1}\tau(A)$.

30. Prove: If B is a regular square matrix and if A is a matrix of equal order, then the *traces* of A and $B^{-1}AB$ are equal: $\tau(A) = \tau(B^{-1}AB)$.
    Hint: Apply exercises 23 and 29.

*31. Let $\mathfrak{D}$ be the set of all linear differential operators

$$a_0 + a_1 \frac{d}{dx} + a_2 \frac{d^2}{dx^2} + \cdots + a_m \frac{d^m}{dx^m}$$

with constant coefficients and arbitrary order m. Define in $\mathfrak{D}$ addition and multiplication as operator addition and multiplication, respectively. Let A be a square matrix of order $n > 1$ whose elements belong to $\mathfrak{D}$. Suppose the determinant of A, computed formally as in definition 17.1, is equal to the constant 1. Prove that in this case A has an inverse A^{-1} whose elements are given formally by (18.11).

*32. Define $\mathcal{D}$ and A as in the previous example. Let

$$y = \begin{bmatrix} y_1\,(x) \\ y_2\,(x) \\ \vdots \\ y_m(x) \end{bmatrix} \qquad \text{and} \qquad b = \begin{bmatrix} b_1\,(x) \\ b_2\,(x) \\ \vdots \\ b_m(x) \end{bmatrix}$$

be m-tuples of unknown functions $y_i(x)$ and of given functions $b_i(x)$, differentiable sufficiently often, respectively. Prove: If $|A| = 1$, then $Ay = b$ has the unique solution $y = A^{-1}b$.

33. Let $\mathbf{v}^{(1)}$, $\mathbf{v}^{(2)}$, $\cdots$, $\mathbf{v}^{(n)}$ be elements of a real vector space $\mathbf{V}$, and let a_{ij} (for $1 \leq i \leq n$, $1 \leq j \leq n - 1$) be real scalars. Define two *partial* internal composition laws in the set $\{\mathbf{V}, R\} = \mathbf{V} \cup R$, designated addition and multiplication, respectively, so that the following determinant is defined:

$$\Delta = \begin{vmatrix} a_{11} & a_{12} & \cdots & a_{1,n-1} & \mathbf{v}^{(1)} \\ a_{21} & a_{22} & \cdots & a_{2,n-1} & \mathbf{v}^{(2)} \\ \vdots & \vdots & & \vdots & \vdots \\ a_{n1} & a_{n2} & \cdots & a_{n,n-1} & \mathbf{v}^{(n)} \end{vmatrix}.$$

34. Prove: If the determinant Δ in the previous exercise is suitably defined, then the following laws hold formally:

$$|\Delta| = |\Delta'|, \qquad |E_{ij}\,\Delta| = -|\Delta|, \qquad |M_{ii}(\alpha)\,\Delta| = |\Delta|.$$

*35. Let $A = (a^{(1)}, a^{(2)}, \cdots, a^{(n)})$ be a square matrix of order n of differentiable functions of one variable x. Denote by $da^{(i)}/dx$ the column of derivatives of the elements of $a^{(i)}$:

$$\frac{da^{(i)}}{dx} = \begin{bmatrix} \dfrac{da_{1i}}{dx} \\ \dfrac{da_{2i}}{dx} \\ \vdots \\ \dfrac{da_{ni}}{dx} \end{bmatrix}.$$

Let A_i be the matrix obtained from A by replacing the ith column $a^{(i)}$ by the column of its derivatives $da^{(i)}/dx$. Prove:

$$\frac{d|A|}{dx} = \sum_{i=1}^{n} |A_i|.$$

19

Orientation, Area, Volume, Vector Product

Some of the exercises of the previous chapter show how geometric properties can be expressed algebraically by the vanishing or nonvanishing of certain determinants of the coordinate vectors involved. In this chapter some of these determinants themselves will be studiêd.

First, we shall look for a geometric interpretation of the *sign* and *absolute value* of determinants of order 2 or 3 made up of the Cartesian coordinate vectors of two or three points. Since a determinant changes its sign if two rows or two columns are interchanged, the sign of a determinant of coordinates depends on the order in which the coordinate vectors or the corresponding points are listed. This leads to the following geometric concepts:

Definition 19.1: The ordered triple (P,Q,R) of noncollinear points of $\mathfrak{R}^2$ is said to have *left* or *right orientation* if the interior of the triangle PQR lies on the left or right, respectively, when one moves along the directed line segments PQ, QR, and RP (Fig. 19.1). The ordered quadruple (P,Q,R,S) of noncoplanar points of $\mathfrak{R}^3$ is said to have *left* or *right orientation* if the ordered triple (Q,R,S) has left or right orientation, respectively, when one looks at it from point P (Fig. 19.2).

Note: This concept of orientation can be generalized immediately to triangles and tetrahedra if their vertices are given in a definite order. If an oriented (solid) triangle is moved *as a whole* in $\mathfrak{R}^2$, its orientation remains the same. If an oriented (solid) tetrahedron is moved *as a whole* in $\mathfrak{R}^3$, its orientation likewise remains the same. In particular, *a translation*

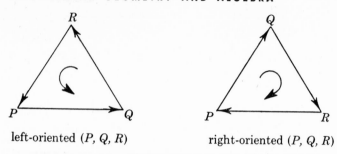

left-oriented (P, Q, R)　　　　　　right-oriented (P, Q, R)

Fig. 19.1

or a rotation of $\mathfrak{R}^n$ $(n = 2, 3)$ does not alter the orientation of a noncollinear or noncoplanar $(n + 1)$-tuple of points of $\mathfrak{R}^n$.

Lemma 19.1: *The orientation of an n-tuple $(n = 3, 4)$ of points changes if two points are interchanged in the sequence.*

PROOF: This is easily seen in the two-dimensional case, and also in the three-dimensional case provided that only two of the last three points are interchanged. (P,Q,R,S) and (Q,P,R,S) have opposite orientation as Fig. 19.3 shows where, on the right, PRS is viewed from below.

The geometric meaning of the determinant of Cartesian coordinate vectors can now be determined easily in the special case where the underlying matrix has triangular form.

Lemma 19.2: *Let the Cartesian coordinate vectors of an ordered couple of points $(T^{(1)}, T^{(2)})$ of $\mathfrak{R}^2$ be given by*

$$t^{(1)} = \begin{bmatrix} t_{11} \\ 0 \end{bmatrix}, \qquad t^{(2)} = \begin{bmatrix} t_{12} \\ t_{22} \end{bmatrix} \qquad \text{with} \qquad t_{11} > 0, \qquad t_{22} \neq 0. \qquad (19.1)$$

Then the absolute value of $\frac{1}{2} |t^{(1)}, t^{(2)}|$ is equal to the area of the triangle with vertices O, $T^{(1)}$, $T^{(2)}$, and the sign of this determinant is positive if and only if $(O,T^{(1)},T^{(2)})$ and $(O,B^{(1)},B^{(2)})$ have the same orientation, where $B^{(1)}$, $B^{(2)}$

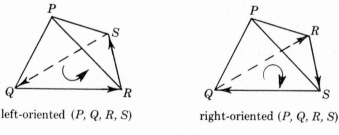

left-oriented (P, Q, R, S)　　　　　　right-oriented (P, Q, R, S)

Fig. 19.2

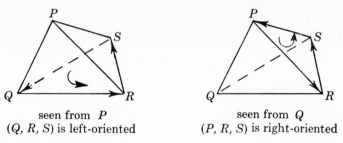

seen from P seen from Q
(Q, R, S) is left-oriented (P, R, S) is right-oriented

Fig. 19.3

are the base points of the chosen Cartesian coordinate system (Fig. 19.4). Let the Cartesian coordinate vectors of an ordered triple of points $(T^{(1)}, T^{(2)}, T^{(3)})$ of $\mathfrak{R}^3$ be given by

$$t^{(1)} = \begin{bmatrix} t_{11} \\ 0 \\ 0 \end{bmatrix}, \qquad t^{(2)} = \begin{bmatrix} t_{12} \\ t_{22} \\ 0 \end{bmatrix}, \qquad t^{(3)} = \begin{bmatrix} t_{13} \\ t_{23} \\ t_{33} \end{bmatrix} \qquad (19.2)$$

$$\text{with} \qquad t_{11} > 0, \qquad t_{22} > 0, \qquad t_{33} \neq 0.$$

Then the absolute value of $\frac{1}{6} |t^{(1)}, t^{(2)}, t^{(3)}|$ is equal to the volume of the tetrahedron with vertices O, $T^{(1)}$, $T^{(2)}$, $T^{(3)}$, and the sign of this determinant is positive if and only if $(O, T^{(1)}, T^{(2)}, T^{(3)})$ and $(O, B^{(1)}, B^{(2)}, B^{(3)})$ have the same orientation, where the $B^{(i)}$ are the base points (Fig. 19.5).

PROOF IN THE TWO-DIMENSIONAL CASE: Since the coordinate system is Cartesian, the length of $t^{(1)}$ is equal to t_{11}, and the distance of $T^{(2)}$ from the line through O and $T^{(1)}$ is equal to $|t_{22}|$. Consequently, the area of the triangle with vertices O, $T^{(1)}$, $T^{(2)}$ is equal to $\frac{1}{2} t_{11} \cdot |t_{22}| = \frac{1}{2} \|t^{(1)}, t^{(2)}\|$†.

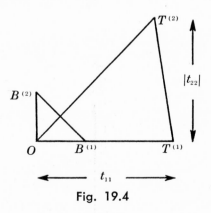

Fig. 19.4

† The vertical double bars indicate the absolute value of the determinant.

If and only if $t_{22} > 0$, the second base point $B^{(2)}$ and $T^{(2)}$ lie on the same side of the line through O and $T^{(1)}$. Hence, if and only if $|t^{(1)}, t^{(2)}|$ is positive, $(O, T^{(1)}, T^{(2)})$ and $(O, B^{(1)}, B^{(2)})$ have the same orientation.

PROOF IN THE THREE-DIMENSIONAL CASE: The length of $t^{(1)}$ is equal to t_{11}; the distance of the point $T^{(2)}$ from the line through O and $T^{(1)}$ is equal to t_{22}; and the distance of the point $T^{(3)}$ from the plane through O, $T^{(1)}$, and $T^{(2)}$ is equal to $|t_{33}|$. Consequently, the volume of the tetrahedron with vertices $O, T^{(1)}, T^{(2)}, T^{(3)}$ is equal to $\frac{1}{6} t_{11} \cdot t_{22} |t_{33}| = \frac{1}{6} \|t^{(1)}, t^{(2)}, t^{(3)}\|$.[†] If and only if $t_{33} > 0$, the third base point $B^{(3)}$ and $T^{(3)}$ lie on the same side of the plane through O, $T^{(1)}$, $T^{(2)}$. Hence, if and only if the determinant $|t^{(1)}, t^{(2)}, t^{(3)}|$ is positive, $(O, T^{(1)}, T^{(2)}, T^{(3)})$ and $(O, B^{(1)}, B^{(2)}, B^{(3)})$ have the same orientation.

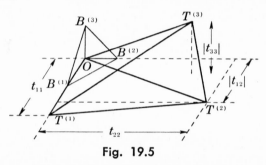

Fig. 19.5

It will be shown later that the Cartesian coordinates of any couple of points or of any triple of points can be brought to the form (19.1) or (19.2) (except for the conditions $t_{22} \neq 0$ or $t_{33} \neq 0$), respectively, *by a suitable rotation of the coordinate system.* Hence, the results of lemma 19.2 will turn out to be true in general. But first the matrices that induce or are induced by rotations must be characterized.

Theorem 19.1:   *A mapping $X \to \bar{X}$ of $\mathfrak{R}^n$ into itself $(n = 2, 3)$ induced by the mapping of coordinate vectors*

$$x \to \bar{x} = \Omega x \tag{19.3}$$

of R^n into itself is a rotation about a point (for $n = 2$) or about an axis (for $n = 3$) if and only if Ω is a real orthogonal matrix with $|\Omega| = 1$.

PROOF: For $n = 2$, the theorem follows from exercise 13.8 without difficulty. Therefore, we confine ourselves to the case $n = 3$.

1. Suppose Ω is a real orthogonal matrix. If $|\Omega| = 1$ it has the eigenvalue 1, by exercise 18.15. Hence, there exists an eigenvector z^* of Ω that satisfies

$$\Omega z^* = z^* \quad \text{and} \quad |z^*| = 1. \tag{19.4}$$

† The vertical double bars indicate the absolute value of the determinant.

Construct a real orthogonal matrix Z of order 3 whose first column is z^*:

$$Z = (z^*, z^{(2)}, z^{(3)}) = \begin{bmatrix} z_1^* & z_{12} & z_{13} \\ z_2^* & z_{22} & z_{23} \\ z_3^* & z_{32} & z_{33} \end{bmatrix}. \tag{19.5}$$

The existence of such an orthogonal Z, which is by no means unique, follows by applying the *Gram-Schmidt orthogonalization process*, explained in the proof of theorem 16.3 (see also exercises 13.18 and 13.19). Equation (19.4) and exercise 12.23 imply

$$\Omega Z = (\Omega z^*, \Omega z^{(2)}, \Omega z^{(3)}) = (z^*, \Omega z^{(2)}, \Omega z^{(3)}). \tag{19.6}$$

Since Z is orthogonal, we have $Z'Z = I$ and, hence, $Z'z^* = \begin{bmatrix} 1 \\ 0 \\ 0 \end{bmatrix}$. There-

fore, it follows from (19.6) that the matrix $Z'\Omega Z$ must have the form

$$Z'\Omega Z = \begin{bmatrix} 1 & \cdot & \cdot \\ 0 & \cdot & \cdot \\ 0 & \cdot & \cdot \end{bmatrix}.$$

Since $Z' \Omega Z$ is orthogonal, too, its first *row* must likewise be a unit vector. Consequently

$$Z'\Omega Z = \begin{bmatrix} 1 & 0 & 0 \\ 0 & R \\ 0 & \end{bmatrix},$$

where R is the matrix of the four remaining elements. It is now easy to see that R is also orthogonal and that $|R| = 1$ in view of $|Z' \Omega Z| = 1$. Hence, it follows from the two-dimensional case that

$$Z'\Omega Z = \begin{bmatrix} 1 & 0 & 0 \\ 0 & \cos\alpha & \sin\alpha \\ 0 & -\sin\alpha & \cos\alpha \end{bmatrix}. \tag{19.7}$$

The mapping $x \to \bar{\bar{x}}$ of $\mathbf{R}^3$ into itself, corresponding to the mapping $x \to \bar{x} = Z'\Omega Z x$ of coordinate vectors, has the following property (Fig. 19.6): It maps the first base translation into itself while it turns the second and third base translations through the angle α about the axis $x = te^{(1)}$. Hence, the corresponding mapping $X \to \bar{X}$ rotates $\mathbf{R}^3$ about this axis by this angle. Since $Z'\Omega Z = Z^{-1}\Omega Z$ and Ω are similar, they induce the same linear mapping, but relative to different bases. Since Z is orthogonal, the coordinate system to which Ω refers must also be Cartesian, by exercise 13.20. This proves that an orthogonal matrix of order 3 induces a rotation of $\mathbf{R}^3$.

2. Suppose that a rotation of $\mathbf{R}^3$ is given. Then it is induced by a matrix (19.7) relative to a suitable Cartesian coordinate system. Let M be this orthogonal matrix. By theorem 14.2 the matrix corresponding to the same rotation, but relative to another Cartesian coordinate system, has the form $A^{-1}MA$ where A is an orthogonal matrix by exercise 15.8. Then $A^{-1}MA$ is orthogonal by exercise 2; consequently, every rotation of $\mathbf{R}^3$ is induced by an orthogonal matrix.

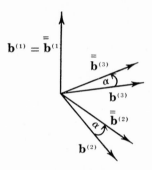

Fig. 19.6

Theorem 19.2:   *Let $u^{(1)}$ and $u^{(2)}$ be the Cartesian coordinates of two linearly independent position vectors $\mathbf{u}^{(1)}$ and $\mathbf{u}^{(2)}$ of $\mathbf{R}^2$, respectively. Then the absolute value of*

$$\tfrac{1}{2}\,|u^{(1)},u^{(2)}| \tag{19.8}$$

is equal to the area of the triangle with vertices O, $U^{(1)}$, and $U^{(2)}$. The sign of (19.8) is positive if and only if $(O,U^{(1)},U^{(2)})$ and $(O,B^{(1)},B^{(2)})$ have the same orientation, where the $B^{(i)}$ are the base points.

Let $u^{(1)}$, $u^{(2)}$, and $u^{(3)}$ be the Cartesian coordinates of three linearly independent position vectors $\mathbf{u}^{(1)}$, $\mathbf{u}^{(2)}$, and $\mathbf{u}^{(3)}$ of $\mathbf{R}^3$, respectively. Then the absolute value of

$$\tfrac{1}{6}\,|u^{(1)},u^{(2)},u^{(3)}| \tag{19.9}$$

is equal to the volume of the tetrahedron with vertices O, $U^{(1)}$, $U^{(2)}$, and $U^{(3)}$. The sign of (19.9) is positive if and only if $(O,U^{(1)},U^{(2)},U^{(3)})$ and $(O,B^{(1)},B^{(2)},B^{(3)})$ have the same orientation, where the $B^{(i)}$ are the base points.

PROOF IN THE THREE-DIMENSIONAL CASE: Our objective is to construct a real orthogonal matrix Ω with $|\Omega| = 1$ and such that $\Omega u^{(i)} = t^{(i)}$ $(i = 1,2,3)$ where the $t^{(i)}$ satisfy the conditions of (19.2). From

$|\Omega u^{(1)}, \Omega u^{(2)}, \Omega u^{(3)}| = |\Omega| \cdot |u^{(1)}, u^{(2)}, u^{(3)}|$ we have $|t^{(1)}, t^{(2)}, t^{(3)}| = |u^{(1)}, u^{(2)}, u^{(3)}|$ so that a rotation of the Cartesian coordinate system leaves (19.9) unaltered. The theorem then follows immediately from lemma 19.2.

We define the triple $a^{(1)}$ to be the unit vector $(1/|u^{(1)}|)u^{(1)}$. Then we define the scalar t_{11} by

$$u^{(1)} = t_{11}a^{(1)} \qquad \text{where} \qquad t_{11} > 0. \tag{19.10}$$

Next we define the triple $a^{(2)}$ as that unit vector which is a linear combination of $u^{(1)}$ and $u^{(2)}$, perpendicular to $a^{(1)}$, and for which the coefficient of $u^{(2)}$ is positive: $a^{(2)} = \alpha u^{(1)} + \beta u^{(2)}$ with $\beta > 0$. Then

$$u^{(2)} = t_{12}a^{(1)} + t_{22}a^{(2)} \qquad \text{with} \qquad t_{22} > 0 \tag{19.11}$$

defines scalars t_{12} and t_{22}. Finally, we choose the unit vector $a^{(3)}$ such that it is perpendicular to both $a^{(2)}$ and $a^{(1)}$, and

$$|a^{(1)}, a^{(2)}, a^{(3)}| = 1. \tag{19.12}$$

The $a^{(i)}$ are linearly independent by exercise 18.6. Hence there exist scalars t_{13}, t_{23}, t_{33} such that

$$u^{(3)} = t_{13}a^{(1)} + t_{23}a^{(2)} + t_{33}a^{(3)} \quad \text{where} \quad t_{33} \neq 0. \tag{19.13}$$

The scalar t_{33} is not equal to zero since the $u^{(i)}$ are assumed to be linearly independent. Equations (19.10), (19.11), and (19.13) may be combined into the matrix equation

$$(u^{(1)}, u^{(2)}, u^{(3)}) = (a^{(1)}, a^{(2)}, a^{(3)}) \begin{bmatrix} t_{11} & t_{12} & t_{13} \\ 0 & t_{22} & t_{23} \\ 0 & 0 & t_{33} \end{bmatrix}$$

$$\text{with} \qquad t_{11} > 0, \qquad t_{22} > 0, \qquad t_{33} \neq 0. \tag{19.14}$$

We can now define $\Omega^{-1} = (a^{(1)}, a^{(2)}, a^{(3)})$. Then Ω is orthogonal by construction, and (19.14) implies $\Omega u^{(i)} = t^{(i)}$ ($i = 1,2,3$) which completes the proof.

The proof in the two-dimensional case is left as exercise 3.

EXAMPLE OF THE CONSTRUCTION OF Ω

Suppose $u^{(1)\prime} = (3, 4, 12)$, $u^{(2)\prime} = (3, 1, 0)$, $u^{(3)\prime} = (2, -1, 1)$. Then $a^{(1)\prime} = (\frac{3}{13}, \frac{4}{13}, \frac{12}{13})$ and $u^{(1)\prime} = 13(\frac{3}{13}, \frac{4}{13}, \frac{12}{13})$; hence $t_{11} = 13$. Now scalars α and β have to be determined, such that

$$a^{(2)\prime} = \alpha(3, 4, 12) + \beta(3, 1, 0)$$

is a nonzero vector *perpendicular* to $a^{(1)\prime} = (\frac{3}{13}, \frac{4}{13}, \frac{12}{13})$. Hence, $0 = \alpha$ $(3, 4, 12)(\frac{3}{13}, \frac{4}{13}, \frac{12}{13}) + \beta(3, 1, 0)(\frac{3}{13}, \frac{4}{13}, \frac{12}{13}) = 13\,\alpha + \beta$, or $\beta = -13\alpha$. Therefore, $a^{(2)\prime}$ must be of the form

$$a^{(2)\prime} = \alpha(3, 4, 12) - 13\alpha(3, 1, 0) = \alpha(-36, -9, 12).$$

Since $a^{(2)}$ must be a unit vector, we have the further condition

$$1 = a^{(2)2} = \alpha^2(-36, -9, 12)^2 = 39^2\alpha^2.$$

Hence, $\alpha = \mp\frac{1}{39}$, $\beta \pm\frac{1}{3}$, and, therefore, $a^{(2)\prime} = (\pm\frac{12}{13}, \pm\frac{3}{13}, \mp\frac{4}{13})$. But

$$u^{(2)} = -\frac{\alpha}{\beta}u^{(1)} + \frac{1}{\beta}a^{(2)} = \frac{1}{13}u^{(1)} \pm 3a^{(2)}.$$

Since $1/\beta = t_{22} > 0$ is required, the upper signs have to be taken; hence

$$a^{(2)\prime} = -\frac{1}{39}(-36, -9, 12) = \left(\frac{12}{13}, \frac{3}{13}, -\frac{4}{13}\right).$$

Now $x = a^{(3)}$ is determined uniquely by the system

$$a^{(1)} \cdot x = 0$$
$$a^{(2)} \cdot x = 0$$
$$|a^{(1)}, a^{(2)}, x| = 1,$$

that is, by the system

$$3/13x_1 + 4/13x_2 + 12/13x_3 = 0$$
$$12/13x_1 + 3/13x_2 - 4/13x_3 = 0$$
$$-4/13x_1 + 12/13x_2 - 3/13x_3 = 1.$$

The unique solution of this system is $x' = a^{(3)\prime} = (-\frac{4}{13}, \frac{12}{13}, -\frac{3}{13})$. Therefore,

$$\Omega = (a^{(1)}, a^{(2)}, a^{(3)})' = \begin{bmatrix} \dfrac{3}{13} & \dfrac{4}{13} & \dfrac{12}{13} \\[2mm] \dfrac{12}{13} & \dfrac{3}{13} & -\dfrac{4}{13} \\[2mm] -\dfrac{4}{13} & \dfrac{12}{13} & -\dfrac{3}{13} \end{bmatrix}.$$

Theorem 19.2 makes it possible to establish easy proofs of the geometric properties of a particular three-dimensional translation whose Cartesian coordinates are made up of the Cartesian coordinates of two given translations in a special way and which is known as their *vector product*. Its algebraic counterpart will be introduced first:

Definition 19.2: If u and v are two triples of real numbers, then the triple

$$\left(\begin{vmatrix} u_2 & v_2 \\ u_3 & v_3 \end{vmatrix} ,\ -\begin{vmatrix} u_1 & v_1 \\ u_3 & v_3 \end{vmatrix} ,\ \begin{vmatrix} u_1 & v_1 \\ u_2 & v_2 \end{vmatrix} \right) \tag{19.15}$$

is called *the vector product of u and v* and is denoted by $u \times v$. If u and v are the Cartesian coordinate vectors of two translations **u** and **v** of $\mathbf{R}^3$, respectively, then the translation with Cartesian coordinate vector $u \times v$ is also called the vector product of **u** and **v** and denoted by $\mathbf{u} \times \mathbf{v}$.

Note: 1. If $\mathbf{b}^{(1)}$, $\mathbf{b}^{(2)}$, $\mathbf{b}^{(3)}$ are the base translations of $\mathbf{R}^3$, then (19.15) can be memorized as follows: Expand the formal expression

$$\begin{vmatrix} u_1 & v_1 & \mathbf{b}^{(1)} \\ u_2 & v_2 & \mathbf{b}^{(2)} \\ u_3 & v_3 & \mathbf{b}^{(3)} \end{vmatrix} \tag{19.16}$$

by the last column exactly as if it were a determinant. Then the three coefficients of $\mathbf{b}^{(1)}$, $\mathbf{b}^{(2)}$, $\mathbf{b}^{(3)}$, respectively, are the coordinates of the triple (19.15). This formal expansion leads, of course, to a perfectly legitimate translation, namely $\mathbf{u} \times \mathbf{v}$ itself.

2. The vector product of two translations may be dependent on the coordinate system.

Theorem 19.3: *If u, v, w are triples of real numbers and if α is a real number, then the following three rules hold:*

(a) $u \times v = -(v \times u)$,

(b) $(\alpha u) \times v = \alpha(u \times v)$,

(c) $u \times (v + w) = (u \times v) + (u \times w)$.

Corollary 19.1: *The mapping $(u, v) \to u \times v$ of R^3 into itself is bilinear and skewsymmetric.*

The proofs of the theorem and its corollary are left as exercises. We turn now to the interesting geometric property of the vector product.

Theorem 19.4: *If **u** and **v** are translations of $\mathbf{R}^3$, then the translation* $\mathbf{w} = \mathbf{u} \times \mathbf{v}$ *is perpendicular to both **u** and **v**. If **u** and **v** are linearly dependent, then the length of **w** is equal to zero. If **u** and **v** are linearly independent, then the length of **w** is equal to the area of the parallelogram whose vertices have coordinate vectors 0, u, v, $u + v$; and the direction of **w** is such that (O, U, V, W) and $(O, B^{(1)}, B^{(2)}, B^{(3)})$ have the same orientation (Fig. 19.7).*

Note: This theorem states, in particular, that the vector product does not depend on the choice of the Cartesian coordinate system, *except for its orientation*.

PROOF: Let u, v, w be the Cartesian coordinate vectors of $\mathbf{u}, \mathbf{v}, \mathbf{w}$, respectively. Then it follows from the definition of the inner product and note 1 below definition 19.2 that

$$(u \times v) \cdot u = |u, v, u| \tag{19.17}$$

holds, and this determinant vanishes because it has two equal columns. Hence, $\mathbf{w}$ is perpendicular to $\mathbf{u}$. In the same way $\mathbf{w}$ is also seen to be perpendicular to $\mathbf{v}$. If u and v are linearly dependent, then w is obviously the zero vector. Suppose now that u and v are linearly independent. Then it can easily be shown that w is not the zero vector and, hence, that u, v, w

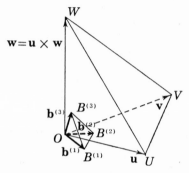

Fig. 19.7

are linearly independent. Therefore, the points O, U, V, W determine a tetrahedron (Fig. 19.7). By theorem 19.2, its volume β is equal to $\beta = \frac{1}{6} |u, v, w|$. Expanding this determinant by the third column and applying the definition of w, we obtain

$$\beta = \tfrac{1}{6} |u, v, w| = \tfrac{1}{6}(w_1^2 + w_2^2 + w_3^2) = \tfrac{1}{6} |w|^2 > 0. \tag{19.18}$$

This shows, in particular, that (O, U, V, W) and $(O, B^{(1)}, B^{(2)}, B^{(3)})$ have the same orientation. But, on the other hand, we know from elementary geometry that the volume of the tetrahedron under consideration is also equal to one-third of the product of the area α of the triangle with vertices O, U, V by the length of $\overrightarrow{OW} = \mathbf{w}$ (because $\mathbf{w}$ is perpendicular to the plane defined by this triangle):

$$\beta = \tfrac{1}{3}\alpha |w|. \tag{19.19}$$

A comparison of (19.18) and (19.19) shows that $|w| = |u \times v| = 2\alpha$. Hence, the length of $\mathbf{w}$ is equal to the area of the parallelogram whose vertices have coordinate vectors $0, u, v, u + v$.

This geometric theorem allows us to prove the following algebraic theorem in a roundabout way.

Theorem 19.5: *If Ω is an orthogonal matrix of order 3 with positive determinant and if u and v are triples of real numbers, then*

$$\Omega(u \times v) = \Omega u \times \Omega v. \tag{19.20}$$

PROOF: The rotation $\mathbf{x} \to \bar{\mathbf{x}}$ induced by the mapping $x \to \bar{x} = \Omega x$ leaves the area of a parallelogram and the orientation unaltered. Hence $\bar{\mathbf{u}} \times \bar{\mathbf{v}} = \bar{\mathbf{w}}$. Returning to coordinate vectors, we have $\bar{w} = \bar{u} \times \bar{v}$, which proves the theorem.

The introduction of the vector product allows us to frame a very short formula for the distance between two skew lines.

Theorem 19.6: *Let $\mathbf{x} = \mathbf{a} + \xi\,\mathbf{u}$ and $\mathbf{x} = \mathbf{b} + \xi\,\mathbf{v}$ be the equations for the position vectors of two skew lines. Then the shortest distance between them is equal to the absolute value of*

$$\frac{1}{|u \times v|}\,(b - a)\cdot(u \times v). \tag{19.21}$$

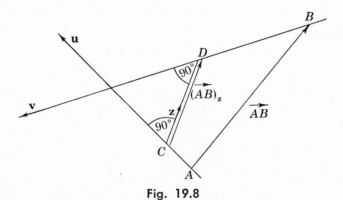

Fig. 19.8

PROOF: Let C and D be the two points on the two respective lines such that $|CD|$ is the shortest distance between these lines (Fig. 19.8). Then $\overrightarrow{CD}$ is perpendicular to both $\mathbf{u}$ and $\mathbf{v}$; hence $\overrightarrow{CD}$ is a multiple of the unit vector $\mathbf{z} = \dfrac{1}{|\mathbf{u} \times \mathbf{v}|}\,(\mathbf{u} \times \mathbf{v})$. If A and B are *any* points on the first and second line, respectively, then $\overrightarrow{CD} = (\overrightarrow{AB})_z = (\mathbf{b} - \mathbf{a})_z$. By corollary 15.3, the length of this vector is determined by

$$|(\mathbf{b} - \mathbf{a})_z| = |(\mathbf{b} - \mathbf{a})\cdot\mathbf{z}| = \frac{1}{|\mathbf{u} \times \mathbf{v}|}\,(\mathbf{b} - \mathbf{a})\cdot(\mathbf{u} \times \mathbf{v}).$$

because $|\mathbf{z}| = 1$. This proves the theorem.

We complete this section with a list of some useful identities linking *inner products*, *vector products*, and *determinants* of triples:

$$(u \times v) \cdot w = (v \times w) \cdot u = (w \times u) \cdot v = |u, v, w|. \qquad (19.22)$$

$$u \times (v \times w) = (u \cdot w)v - (u \cdot v)w. \qquad (19.23)$$

$$(u \times v) \cdot (y \times z) = (u \cdot y)(v \cdot z) - (u \cdot z)(v \cdot y). \qquad (19.24)$$

$$(u \times v) \times (y \times z) = |u, v, z| \, y - |u, v, y| \, z. \qquad (19.25)$$

Of course, all these equations remain true if the triples are replaced by translations of $\mathbf{R}^3$.

As a sample of the proofs of these identities we shall prove (19.23), but only for three *linearly independent* triples u, v, w. Our assumptions imply, in particular, $u \neq 0$ and $v \times w \neq 0$. The left-hand side of (19.23) is a triple that is perpendicular to $v \times w$. Now the set of *all* triples perpendicular to the nonzero triple $v \times w$ is a subspace of dimension 2; it contains the linearly independent triples v and w and, hence, is spanned by them. Therefore, $u \times (v \times w)$ must be expressible in the form

$$u \times (v \times w) = \alpha v + \beta w, \qquad (19.26)$$

where α and β are scalars. By inner multiplication of both sides of (19.26) with u, we obtain

$$u \cdot (u \times (v \times w)) = \alpha(u \cdot v) + \beta(u \cdot w).$$

Since u is perpendicular to $u \times (v \times w)$, the left-hand side of the last equation is equal to zero. Thus every solution (α, β) of the equation $\alpha(u \cdot v) + \beta(u \cdot w) = 0$ has the form $\alpha = \lambda(u \cdot w)$, $\beta = -\lambda(u \cdot v)$ for some scalar λ; hence (19.26) reduces to

$$u \times (v \times w) = \lambda((u \cdot w)v - (u \cdot v)w). \qquad (19.27)$$

It suffices to determine λ in the case where $|u| = 1$. Define a mapping $x \to \bar{x} = \Omega x$ with an orthogonal matrix Ω *of positive determinant*. Then, by exercise 13.20 and theorem 19.5, the formula (19.27) remains true if bars are put over all letters standing for vectors. Now choose Ω in such a way

that $\bar{u} = e^{(1)} = \begin{bmatrix} 1 \\ 0 \\ 0 \end{bmatrix}$. Then we have $\bar{u} \cdot \bar{w} = \bar{w}_1$ and $\bar{u} \cdot \bar{v} = \bar{v}_1$; hence (19.27)

with bars over the vectors implies

$$\bar{u} \times (\bar{v} \times \bar{w}) = \lambda(\bar{w}_1 \bar{v} - \bar{v}_1 \bar{w}).$$

Taking the second coordinate on both sides of this equation, we obtain

$$\bar{w}_1 \bar{v}_2 - \bar{v}_1 \bar{w}_2 = \lambda(\bar{w}_1 \bar{v}_2 - \bar{v}_1 \bar{w}_2). \qquad (19.28)$$

Since $\{\bar{u}, \bar{v}, \bar{w}\}$ is linearly independent, we have $|e^{(1)}, \bar{v}, \bar{w}| \neq 0$; hence $\bar{w}_1 \bar{v}_2 - \bar{v}_1 \bar{w}_2 \neq 0$. Therefore, (19.28) implies that $\lambda = 1$.

EXERCISES

1. Prove theorem 19.1 for the case $n = 2$.

2. Prove: (a) The product of orthogonal matrices of the same order is orthogonal. (b) If

$$M = \begin{bmatrix} 1 & 0 & \cdots & 0 \\ 0 & \multicolumn{3}{c}{} \\ \vdots & & R & \\ 0 & \multicolumn{3}{c}{} \end{bmatrix}$$

is orthogonal, then R is also orthogonal.

3. Prove theorem 19.2 in the two-dimensional case.

4. Find orthogonal matrices whose first columns are

(a) $\begin{bmatrix} 1/\sqrt{14} \\ -2/\sqrt{14} \\ 3/\sqrt{14} \end{bmatrix}$, (b) $\begin{bmatrix} 2/\sqrt{21} \\ 4/\sqrt{21} \\ -1/\sqrt{21} \end{bmatrix}$, (c) $\begin{bmatrix} -1/\sqrt{3} \\ 1/\sqrt{3} \\ 1/\sqrt{3} \end{bmatrix}$, (d) $\begin{bmatrix} 3/5 \\ 0 \\ 4/5 \end{bmatrix}$.

5. Prove: (a) The area of the triangle whose vertices have Cartesian coordinate vectors a, b, c is given by the absolute value of $\frac{1}{2} |a - b, a - c|$. (b) The volume of the tetrahedron whose vertices have Cartesian coordinate vectors a, b, c, d is given by the absolute value of $\frac{1}{6} |a - b, a - c, a - d|$.

6. Compute the area of the triangles whose vertices have the following Cartesian coordinates:

   (a) $(1, 2)$, $(3, 1)$, $(-2, 4)$;   (b) $(3, 3)$, $(2, 1)$, $(4, 9)$;

   (c) $(8, 12)$, $(3, 1)$, $(2, 2)$;   (d) $(1, 0)$, $(3, 2)$, $(4, 4)$.

7. Compute the volume of the tetrahedron whose vertices have the following Cartesian coordinate vectors:

   (a) $(1, 2, 2)$, $(3, 2, 1)$, $(-2, 4, 2)$, $(3, 3, 4)$;

   (b) $(-1, 1, 0)$, $(2, 2, 1)$, $(3, 1, 4)$, $(-2, -2, 6)$;

   (c) $(1, 2, 3)$, $(3, 2, 1)$, $(6, 1, 1)$, $(7, 5, -6)$.

8. Prove: If Ω is an orthogonal matrix of order 3 with *negative* determinant, then $\Omega(u \times v) = \Omega v \times \Omega u$.

9. Prove theorem 19.3, and show that the vector product is not associative. Also prove corollary 19.1.

10. Prove formula (19.22).

11. Prove formula (19.24), and deduce from it another proof of Schwarz's inequality in the three-dimensional case.

12. Prove formula (19.25).

13. Prove that the square of the area of a triangle is equal to $s(s - a)(s - b)(s - c)$ if $s = \frac{1}{2}(a + b + c)$ and if a, b, c are the lengths of its sides.

PART IV

Quadratic Geometry and Algebra

The point sets that have been considered in the first three parts are *linear* geometric objects; that is, their coordinates are zeros of linear systems. In this part sets of points will be investigated whose coordinates are determined by *quadratic* equations or by combinations of linear and quadratic equations. All coordinates systems employed will be Cartesian.

20

Circles and Spheres

In this chapter we shall deal with quadratic equations whose graphs are circles or spheres or their generalizations to arbitrary finite-dimensional vector spaces. The topics investigated and methods developed will serve as models for the theories of more complicated curves and surfaces to be established in the chapters that follow.

Definition 20.1: The set of all points X of $\mathfrak{R}^n$ at a given distance ρ from a given point C is called a *circle* (for $n = 2$) or a *sphere* (for $n = 3$) and is denoted by $\mathfrak{S}^n$. The point C is called the *center* of $\mathfrak{S}^n$. The non-negative number ρ is called the *radius* of $\mathfrak{S}^n$. If $\rho = 0$, then $\mathfrak{S}^n$ is called *degenerate*. If X^* ε $\mathfrak{S}^n$, then the translation $\mathbf{x} - \mathbf{c}$ is called a *radius vector* of $\mathfrak{S}^n$. A line that has one and only one point in common with a circle $\mathfrak{S}^2$ is called a *tangent* of $\mathfrak{S}^2$ and is denoted by $\mathfrak{T}_\mathfrak{S}$. A plane that has one and only one point in common with a sphere $\mathfrak{S}^3$ is called a *tangent plane* of $\mathfrak{S}^3$ and is denoted by $\mathfrak{T}_\mathfrak{S}^3$. The common point of $\mathfrak{S}^n$ and $\mathfrak{T}_\mathfrak{S}^n$ is called the *point of contact* (Fig. 20.1).

Note: If a Cartesian coordinate system is chosen, then, by corollary 15.1, a circle or a sphere is the graph of the equation

$$(x - c)^2 - \rho^2 = 0. \tag{20.1}$$

Theorem 20.1: *The radius vector from the center of $\mathfrak{S}^n$ to the point of contact of $\mathfrak{T}_\mathfrak{S}^n$ is perpendicular to $\mathfrak{T}_\mathfrak{S}^n$.*

PROOF IN THE CASE $n = 3$: Choose a Cartesian coordinate system such that the origin is the center of $\mathfrak{S}^3$ and such that the first base transla-

Fig. 20.1

tion $\mathbf{b}^{(1)}$ is a normal of the tangent plane $\mathbb{C}_{\mathfrak{S}}^{3}$ (Fig. 20.2). Then

$$x_1^2 + x_2^2 + x_3^2 = \rho^2 \tag{20.2}$$

is the equation of $\mathfrak{S}^3$. Let

$$x_1 - \sigma = 0 \tag{20.3}$$

be the equation of $\mathbb{C}_{\mathfrak{S}}^3$. If and only if $\sigma = \rho$ (20.2) and (20.3) have exactly one common real solution which then is $x^* = (\rho,0,0)$. In this case the radius vector from the center to the point of contact is $\mathbf{x}^* = \rho\mathbf{b}^{(1)}$ and hence is perpendicular to $\mathbb{C}_{\mathfrak{S}}^3$.

Theorem 20.2: *If $\mathfrak{S}^n$ is the graph of $(x - c)^2 - \rho^2 = 0$ and if $Z^* \,\varepsilon\, \mathbb{C}_{\mathfrak{S}}^n$, then the distance δ between Z^* and the point of contact of $\mathbb{C}_{\mathfrak{S}}^n$ is given by*

$$\delta = \sqrt{(z^* - c)^2 - \rho^2}.$$

PROOF (Fig. 20.3): Let X^* be the point of contact. Then

$$\delta^2 = (z^* - x^*)^2, \tag{20.4}$$

by corollary 15.1. By theorem 20. 1, the radius vector $\mathbf{x}^* - \mathbf{c}$ is perpendicular to $\mathbf{z}^* - \mathbf{x}^*$; hence

$$2(z^* - x^*) \cdot (x^* - c) = 0, \tag{20.5}$$

where the factor 2 is included for reasons to be seen shortly. The length of

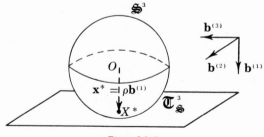

Fig. 20.2

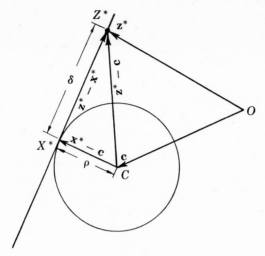

Fig. 20.3

the radius vector is equal to ρ; hence

$$(x^* - c)^2 - \rho^2 = 0. \tag{20.6}$$

Consequently, the addition of the left-hand sides of (20.5) and (20.6) to (20.4) does not contribute anything, since they are equal to zero. Thus

$$\delta^2 = (z^* - x^*)^2 + 2(z^* - x^*) \cdot (x^* - c) + (x^* - c)^2 - \rho^2 = 0.$$

By a well-known formula, this expression is equal to

$$((z^* - x^*) + (x^* - c))^2 - \rho^2 = (z^* - c)^2 - \rho^2,$$

which proves the theorem.

This type of proof is not "magic mathematics." Equations (20.4), (20.5) without the factor 2 and equation (20.6) are prerequisites for the proof anyway, and the idea of the proof is simply to eliminate the point of contact X^*. The straightforward elimination of x^* will lead to a very similar proof.

Theorem 20.3: *If $\mathfrak{S}^n$ is the graph of $(x - c)^2 - \rho^2 = 0$ ($\rho \neq 0$) and if X^* is the point of contact of $\mathfrak{T}_{\mathfrak{S}}^n$, then $\mathfrak{T}_{\mathfrak{S}}^n$ is the graph of*

$$(x^* - c) \cdot (x - c) - \rho^2 = 0 \quad \text{with} \quad \rho \neq 0. \tag{20.7}$$

Proof: $\mathfrak{T}_{\mathfrak{S}}^n$ has $x^* - c$ as a normal and passes through X^*; hence, its equation may be written

$$(x^* - c) \cdot (x - x^*) = 0, \tag{20.8}$$

by (15.6). The substitution $x - x^* = (x - c) - (x^* - c)$ changes (20.8) to

$$(x^* - c) \cdot ((x - c) - (x^* - c)) = (x^* - c) \cdot (x - c) - (x^* - c)^2 = 0.$$

Since $X^* \, \varepsilon \, \mathfrak{S}^n$, we have $-(x^* - c)^2 = -\rho^2$, and the theorem is proved.

We shall investigate next the meaning of (20.7) if the restriction is dropped that X^* be the point of contact.

Definition 20.2:   If (20.7) is meaningful for the Cartesian coordinates x^* of a point X^* (that is, if $x^* \neq c$), then its graph is called the *polar* (for $n = 2$) or *polar plane* (for $n = 3$) of X^* with respect to $\mathfrak{S}^n$. If the equation of a line (for $n = 2$) or plane (for $n = 3$) can be written in the form (20.7), then X^* is called *pole* of (the graph of) (20.7) with respect to $\mathfrak{S}^n$. A point is called *p-allowable* with respect to $\mathfrak{S}^n$ if it has a polar or polar plane. A line or plane is called *p-allowable* with respect to $\mathfrak{S}^n$ if it has a pole. The polar (for $n = 2$) or polar plane (for $n = 3$) of a *p*-allowable point P is denoted by $\mathfrak{P}$, and the pole of a *p*-allowable polar or polar plane $\mathfrak{Q}$ is denoted by Q.

It is easy to see that the only point that is not *p*-allowable is the center C, that the only lines or planes that are not *p*-allowable are those through the center, and that the pole of a *p*-allowable line or plane is a unique point (see exercise 6). From theorem 20.3 we conclude

Corollary 20.1:   *The polar (plane) of a point on $\mathfrak{S}^n$ is the tangent (plane) at that point, and the pole of a tangent (plane) of $\mathfrak{S}^n$ is the point of contact.*

The main property of the pole-polar relationship is given by

Theorem 20.4:   *If a p-allowable point P lies on the p-allowable point set $\mathfrak{Q}$, then Q lies on $\mathfrak{P}$.*

PROOF: Since $\mathfrak{Q}$ has the pole Q, its equation is given by

$$(q - c) \cdot (x - c) - \rho^2 = 0. \tag{20.9}$$

Since the coordinates p of the point P satisfy (20.9), we have

$$(q - c) \cdot (p - c) - \rho^2 = 0,$$

which can be written in the form

$$(p - c) \cdot (q - c) - \rho^2 = 0. \tag{20.10}$$

Hence, the coordinates q of the point Q satisfy

$$(p - c) \cdot (x - c) - \rho^2 = 0,$$

which is an equation of $\mathfrak{P}$. That is all. It is the *symmetry* of the inner product that allows this short proof.

Corollary 20.1 and theorem 20.4 make it possible to give a geometric construction of poles and polars with respect to a circle. We distinguish the following six cases:

Case 1.   Let P be a point on the circle. Construct the normal to the radius vector from the center to P, through P. This is the tangent at P, by theorem 20.1, and, hence, the polar $\mathfrak{P}$ of P, by corollary 20.1.

Case 2.   Let $\mathfrak{L}$ be a tangent of the circle. Then its pole L is the point of contact, by corollary 20.1.

Case 3.   Let P be a point outside the circle. Suppose that $\mathfrak{P}_1$ and $\mathfrak{P}_2$ are the tangents from P to the circle. Then $\mathfrak{P}$ passes through the poles P_1 and P_2, by theorem 20.4. As points of contact of two different tangents, P_1 and P_2 are two different points on the circle. Hence $\mathfrak{P}$ is the line through P_1 and P_2 (Fig. 20.4).

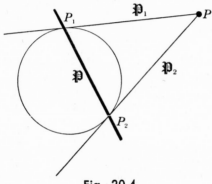

Fig. 20.4

Case 4.   Let $\mathfrak{P}$ be a line intersecting the circle in two distinct points P_1 and P_2 but not passing through its center. Then the tangents $\mathfrak{P}_1$ and $\mathfrak{P}_2$ at P_1 and P_2 respectively, are not parallel and, hence, have exactly one point in common. Since the pole P of $\mathfrak{P}$ must lie on the polars $\mathfrak{P}_1$ and $\mathfrak{P}_2$, it must be their point of intersection (Fig. 20.4).

Case 5.   Let P be a point inside the circle different from its center. Choose two distinct lines $\mathfrak{L}_1$ and $\mathfrak{L}_2$ through P that do not pass through the center. Use the method explained in case 4 to construct their poles L_1 and L_2, respectively. By theorem 20.4, the required polar $\mathfrak{P}$ of P must pass through L_1 and L_2. Since L_1 and L_2 are easily seen to be distinct points if $\mathfrak{L}_1$ and $\mathfrak{L}_2$ are distinct lines, the line through L_1 and L_2 is the polar $\mathfrak{P}$ of P (Fig. 20.5).

Case 6.   Let $\mathfrak{P}$ be a line not intersecting the circle. Choose two distinct points L_1 and L_2 on that line, and construct their respective polars $\mathfrak{L}_1$ and $\mathfrak{L}_2$ by the method of case 3. It is easy to see that $\mathfrak{L}_1$ and $\mathfrak{L}_2$ are not parallel; hence they have exactly one point in common, which must be the pole P of $\mathfrak{P}$, by theorem 20.4 (Fig. 20.5).

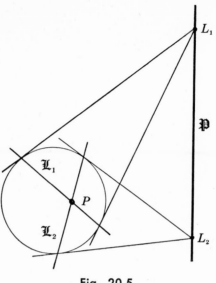

Fig. 20.5

A similar construction is possible in the three-dimensional case (see exercise 5).

So far, we have been concerned with one circle or sphere only. Let us now consider the graphs $\mathfrak{S}_1^n$ and $\mathfrak{S}_2^n$ of the two equations

$$(x - c^{(1)})^2 - \rho_1^2 = 0, \qquad \text{or} \qquad x^2 - 2c^{(1)} \cdot x + c^{(1)2} - \rho_1^2 = 0$$

$$\text{with} \qquad \rho_1 \neq 0; \qquad (20.11)$$

$$(x - c^{(2)})^2 - \rho_2^2 = 0, \qquad \text{or} \qquad x^2 - 2c^{(2)} \cdot x + c^{(2)2} - \rho_2^2 = 0$$

$$\text{with} \qquad \rho_2 \neq 0 \qquad (20.12)$$

in two or three unknowns *simultaneously*. We shall frequently suppress the upper index n to simplify the notation.

The first problem is to find all points that $\mathfrak{S}_1$ and $\mathfrak{S}_2$ have in common. Since the quadratic terms of all unknowns in (20.11) and (20.12) have the same coefficient, namely, $+1$, they can be eliminated by subtracting the second from the first equation. In this way we obtain

$$2(c^{(2)} - c^{(1)}) \cdot x + c^{(1)2} - c^{(2)2} + \rho_2^2 - \rho_1^2 = 0. \qquad (20.13)$$

If $c^{(1)} \neq c^{(2)}$, then (20.13) is the equation of a line (for $n = 2$) or of a plane (for $n = 3$). If $c^{(1)} = c^{(2)}$, then either $\rho_1 = \rho_2$, in which case $\mathfrak{S}_1 = \mathfrak{S}_2$, or $\rho_1 \neq \rho_2$, in which case the left-hand side of (20.13) reduces to a *nonzero* number. It is easily seen that (20.12) is a linear combination of (20.11) and (20.13). Hence, by lemma 8.1, $\mathfrak{S}_1$ and $\mathfrak{S}_2$ have a point in common if and only if (20.11) and (20.13) have a common solution. Thus the process of solving two equations of the form (20.11) and (20.12) can be reduced to that of solving one quadratic and one linear equation. This result can also be expressed as follows.

Lemma 20.1:   *The pencil of (20.11) and (20.12) is equal to the pencil of (20.11) and (20.13). If two distinct graphs of such a pencil have a point P in common, then every graph of the pencil passes through P.*

To formulate a stronger result, we introduce a definition.

Definition 20.3:   If in (20.13) $c^{(1)} \neq c^{(2)}$ then the graph of (20.13) is called the *radical axis* (for $n = 2$) or the *radical plane* (for $n = 3$) of the pencil of (20.11) and (20.12).

Theorem 20.5:   *Let $\mathfrak{I}$ be the intersection of the graphs of (20.11) and (20.12). If $\mathfrak{I}$ consists of more than one point, then the pencil of (20.11) and (20.12) consists of all circles (for $n = 2$) passing through $\mathfrak{I}$ and of the radical axis, or of all spheres (for $n = 3$) passing through $\mathfrak{I}$ and of the radical plane. If $\mathfrak{I}$ consists of only one point P, then, for $n = 2$, the pencil consists of the radical axis and all circles that have this radical axis as a tangent at P, and, for $n = 3$, the pencil consists of the radical plane and all spheres having the radical plane as tangent plane at P.*

PROOF: Both parts of the theorem can be obtained from lemma 20.1 and

Lemma 20.2:   *If the pencil of (20.11) and (20.12) has a radical axis or radical plane, then the centers of all circles or spheres of the pencil lie on a normal of the radical axis or radical plane.*

PROOF: (20.13).

EXAMPLES OF PENCILS OF CIRCLES

1. The pencil of

$$x_1^2 + x_2^2 - 1 = 0$$
$$x_1^2 + x_2^2 - 2 = 0$$

consists of all circles with the origin as center (see Fig. 6.11).

2. The pencil of

$$x_1^2 + x_2^2 - 9 = 0$$
$$(x_1 - 4)^2 + x_2^2 - 25 = 0$$

consists of all circles passing through $(0, 3)$ and $(0, -3)$ and of the line through these two points (Fig. 20.6).

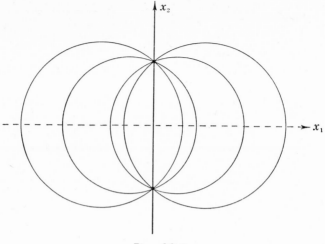

Fig. 20.6

3. The pencil of

$$(x_1 - 1)^2 + x_2^2 - 1 = 0$$
$$(x_1 + 1)^2 + x_2^2 - 1 = 0$$

consists of the graph of $x_1 = 0$ and all circles that have this line as a tangent with the origin as point of contact (Fig. 20.7).

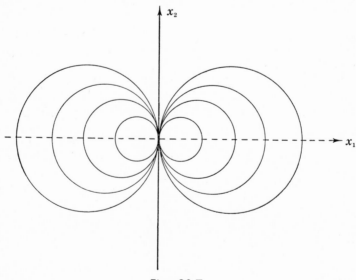

Fig. 20.7

4. The pencil of

$$(x_1 - 1)^2 + x_2^2 - \tfrac{1}{4} = 0$$

$$(x_1 + 1)^2 + x_2^2 - \tfrac{1}{4} = 0$$

consists also of the radical axis $x_1 = 0$ and of infinitely many circles having no points in common with one another or with the radical axis (Fig. 20.8).

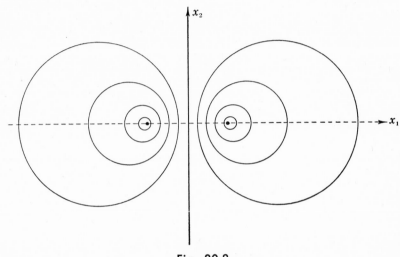

Fig. 20.8

In the three-dimensional case, similar cases can be distinguished (see exercise 20.10).

The results of this section can be generalized to Euclidean vector spaces with Cartesian bases as indicated in some of the exercises.

EXERCISES

1. Determine the distance between the point with Cartesian coordinates (8, 9) and the points of contact of the tangents from (8, 9) to the following circles:

(a) $x_1^2 + x_2^2 = 4$;

(b) $(x_1 - 1)^2 + (x_2 + 1)^2 = 1$;

(c) $x_1^2 + (x_2 - 2)^2 = 4$;

(d) $x_1^2 + (x_2 + 2)^2 = 4$;

(e) $(x_1 + 3)^2 + (x_2 + 1)^2 = 2$.

2. Determine the polar of the points (a) (2,1), (b) (1,2), (c) (0,0), and (d) (2,4) with respect to the circle $(x_1 - 1)^2 + (x_2 + 1)^2 = 4$.

3. Determine the polar plane of the points with Cartesian coordinates (a) (1,2,3), (b) (3,2,1) , (c) (0,0,0), and (d) (2,2,4) with respect to the sphere $(x_1 - 1)^2 + x_2^2 + (x_3 + 1)^2 = 9$.

4. Determine the pole of the lines (a) $x_1 + x_2 = 1$, (b) $x_1 - x_2 = 2$, and (c) $x_1 + 3x_2 = 1$ with respect to the circle $x_1^2 + x_2^2 = 4$.

5. Find a geometric construction for polar planes and poles with respect to a given sphere.

6. Prove: The pole of a p-allowable line or plane is a *unique* point.

7. Prove theorem 20.5.

8. Determine all degenerate circles belonging to any of the Examples of Pencils of Circles.

9. How is the radical axis of two nonintersecting circles with different centers constructed, and where does it cross the line of centers?

10. Discuss the different cases of pencils of spheres in analogy with the examples of pencils of circles.

11. Two circles are said to intersect *at right angles* if they intersect and if, at any such intersection point, the corresponding tangents are at right angles. Prove: If a circle intersects two distinct circles at right angles, then it also intersects all elements of their pencil at right angles.

Note. The following exercises concern Euclidean vector spaces $\{V, f\}$ of finite dimension n in which a Cartesian basis is chosen such that $f(x,y) = x \cdot y$ for the coordinate vectors x, y of any vectors **x** and **y**, respectively. The set of all vectors of **V** satisfying $(x - c)^2 - \rho^2 = 0$ for a given $c \in V$ and nonnegative $\rho \in R$, is called a *hypersphere* and is denoted by $\mathfrak{S}^n$. It is called *degenerate* if $\rho = 0$. A hyperplane of **V** that has exactly one point in common with a hypersphere is called a *tangent hyperplane* of this hypersphere. *Radius, radius vector, point of contact, poles, polar hyperplanes*, and so forth, are all defined as in the two- or three-dimensional case.

12. Prove: The set of all points that a hypersphere of **V** and a hyperplane **H** of **V** have in common is, if $\neq \varnothing$, a hypersphere of **H** (if **H** is considered as a Euclidean vector space of dimension $n - 1$).

13. Formulate and prove the extension of theorem 20.1 to **V**.

14. Prove the generalizations to **V** of theorems 20.2, 20.3, and 20.4 and corollary 20.1.

15. Prove: (a) If n p-allowable points $\mathbf{p}^{(i)}(i = 1,2,\cdots,n)$ generate an $(n - 1)$-dimensional p-allowable hyperplane $\mathfrak{Q}$, then the pole

q of $\mathfrak{Q}$ is the intersection of the polar hyperplanes $\mathfrak{P}^{(i)} (i = 1, \cdots, n)$ of the $p^{(i)}$, respectively. (b) If $\mathfrak{P}^{(i)} (i = 1, \cdots, n)$ are n p-allowable hyperplanes whose equations are linearly independent and which all pass through a p-allowable point q, then the polar hyperplane $\mathfrak{Q}$ of q is the flock generated by the poles $p^{(i)}$ $(i = 1, \cdots, n)$ of the $\mathfrak{P}^{(i)}$.

Hints: The flock generated by $\{p^{(i)}\}_{1 \le i \le n}$ is the *set of all flock combinations* of the $p^{(i)}$ $(i = 1, 2, \cdots, n)$. Assume that the origin is the center of the hypersphere. Choose in the first part your coordinate system so that $\mathfrak{Q}$ is represented by the equation $x_1 = c (\ne 0)$.

16. Generalize theorem 20.5 to **V**.

21

The Classical Conic Sections

In this chapter we shall investigate, in $\mathfrak{R}^2$, three types of curves, namely ellipses, hyperbolas, and parabolas. Their equations are quadratic in the variables but more complicated than the equation of a circle. Since these curves are often called *classical conic sections*, it will be shown at the end of this chapter that they occur as intersections of cones with planes.

Definition 21.1: The set $\mathfrak{E}$ of all points X of $\mathfrak{R}^2$ for which the sum of the distances from X to two fixed points $F^{(1)}$ and $F^{(2)}$ is a constant $2a_1$, greater than the distance $2e$ between $F^{(1)}$ and $F^{(2)}$, is called an *ellipse*. Every $F^{(i)}$ is called a *focus of* $\mathfrak{E}$, and the midpoint of $F^{(1)}F^{(2)}$ is called the *center of* $\mathfrak{E}$. The positive real numbers a_1 and $a_2 = \sqrt{a_1^2 - e^2}$ are called *the lengths of the major and minor semi-axes of* $\mathfrak{E}$, respectively.

Suppose we have an ellipse with center at the origin of a Cartesian coordinate system whose foci have coordinates $(e,0)$ and $(-e,0)$(Fig. 21.1). If X is a point on the ellipse, then we must have $|F^{(1)}X| + |F^{(2)}X| = |\mathbf{x} - \mathbf{f}^{(1)}| + |\mathbf{x} - \mathbf{f}^{(2)}| = 2a_1$, by definition of the ellipse, or, in terms of coordinate vectors,

$$\sqrt{(x_1 - e)^2 + x_2^2} + \sqrt{(x_1 + e)^2 + x_2^2} = 2a_1. \qquad (21.1)$$

By transferring the second square root to the right-hand side and squaring the equation so obtained, we get

$$(x_1 - e)^2 + x_2^2 = 4a_1^2 - 4a_1 \sqrt{(x_1 + e)^2 + x_2^2} + (x_1 + e)^2 + x_2^2,$$

which can be simplified to $\sqrt{(x_1 + e)^2 + x_2^2} = a_1 + \dfrac{e}{a_1} x_1$. By renewed

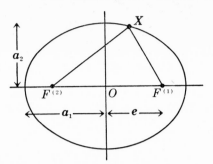

Fig. 21.1

squaring we obtain the relation

$$\left(1 - \frac{e^2}{a_1^2}\right)x_1^2 + x_2^2 = a_1^2 - e^2,$$

which can be simplified to

$$\frac{x_1^2}{a_1^2} + \frac{x_2^2}{a_2^2} = 1 \qquad (21.2)$$

by introduction of the minor semi-axis $a_2 = \sqrt{a_1^2 - e^2}$. Hence, the Cartesian coordinates of every point X on the described ellipse satisfy (21.2). On the other hand, it can be shown that all couples of real numbers that satisfy (21.2) must likewise satisfy (21.1). Consequently, we may state

Theorem 21.1: *The ellipse with center at the origin of a Cartesian coordinate system, with foci $(e,0)$ and $(-e,0)$, and with lengths of semi-axes a_1 and a_2, respectively, is the graph of equation* (21.2).

Note: 1.   From equation (21.2) it can be seen that the points $(\pm a_1, 0)$ and $(0, \pm a_2)$ lie on the ellipse and that they are the points of maximum and minimum distance from the center. This remark explains the names for a_1 and a_2. Consequently, the ellipse is a curve all of whose points lie in the inside or on the boundary of a rectangle with vertices $(\pm a_1, \pm a_2)$. 2. If $e = 0$, then the ellipse is a circle with radius $a_1 = a_2$.

Definition 21.2:   The set $\mathfrak{H}$ of all points X of $\mathfrak{R}^2$ for which the absolute value of the difference between the distances from X to two fixed points $F^{(1)} \neq F^{(2)}$ is a constant $2a_1$, less than the distance $2e$ between $F^{(1)}$ and $F^{(2)}$, is called a *hyperbola*. Every $F^{(i)}$ is called a *focus of* $\mathfrak{H}$, and the midpoint of $F^{(1)} F^{(2)}$ is called the *center of* $\mathfrak{H}$. The positive real numbers a_1 and $a_2 = \sqrt{e^2 - a_1^2}$ are called the *lengths of the transverse and conjugate semi-axes of* $\mathfrak{H}$, respectively.

Suppose we have a hyperbola with center at the origin of a Cartesian coordinate system whose foci have coordinates $(e,0)$ and $(-e,0)$ (Fig. 21.2). If X is a point on the hyperbola, then we must have $|F^{(1)}X| - |F^{(2)}X| = |\mathbf{x} - \mathbf{f}^{(1)}| - |\mathbf{x} - \mathbf{f}^{(2)}| = \pm\,2a_1$, by definition of the hyperbola. As in the case of the ellipse, it can be shown that this equation is equivalent to the condition

$$\frac{x_1^2}{a_1^2} - \frac{x_2^2}{a_2^2} = 1. \tag{21.3}$$

Hence, we may state

Theorem 21.2: *The hyperbola with center at the origin of a Cartesian coordinate system, with foci $(e,0)$ and $(-e,0)$, and with lengths of semi-axes a_1 and a_2, respectively, is the graph of equation (21.3).*

Note: From (21.3) it can be seen that the points $(\pm a_1,0)$ lie on the hyperbola and that they are the points of minimum distance from the center. It is also obvious that the hyperbola has no point in common with the line $x_1 = 0$; hence, it must consist of two separate branches. Their respective equations

$$x_1 = (a_1/a_2)x_2\sqrt{1 + a_2^2/x_2^2}$$
$$x_1 = -(a_1/a_2)x_2\sqrt{1 + a_2^2/x_2^2}$$

are obtained by solving (21.3) with respect to x_1. Furthermore, there exist points on the hyperbola whose distance from the center is as great as desired; hence the point set is unbounded in the sense of definition 10.4.

A line through the center of the hyperbola may or may not intersect the hyperbola. If $x_1 = \alpha x_2$ is the equation of such a line, then by substitution, we obtain, for the second coordinate of the possible intersection

$$\left(\frac{\alpha^2}{a_1^2} - \frac{1}{a_2^2}\right)x_2^2 = 1.$$

This equation does not have a *real* solution if $|\alpha| < a_1/a_2$, *and it does not even have a complex solution if* $\alpha = \pm a_1/a_2$. The two lines with $|\alpha| = a_1/a_2$, which do not have "even imaginary points in common with the hyperbola," are known as *asymptotes*.

It can be shown that there are points on both branches of the hyperbola that come "arbitrarily close" to one of the asymptotes, although the distance zero is excluded. For example, take the asymptote $x_1 = (a_1/a_2)x_2$ and the branch of the hyperbola whose coordinates satisfy

$$x_1 = (a_1/a_2)x_2\,\sqrt{1 + a_2^2/x_2^2}.$$

Then the difference between the first coordinate of the asymptote and the first coordinate of the hyperbola is given by

$$(a_1/a_2)x_2\,(1 - \sqrt{1 + a_2^2/x_2^2})$$

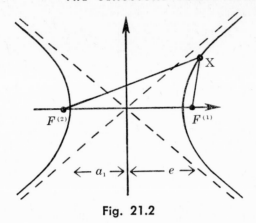

Fig. 21.2

for a fixed second coordinate x_2. For sufficiently large x_2, the expression $\sqrt{1 + a_2^2/x_2^2}$ can be made arbitrarily close to 1; hence, the difference between the first coordinates approaches zero if x_2 tends to infinity (Fig. 21.3).

Definition 21.3: The set $\mathfrak{P}$ of all points X of $\mathfrak{R}^2$ for which the distance from X to a fixed point F is equal to the distance from X to a fixed line $\mathfrak{D}$ is called a *parabola* if $F \not\subset \mathfrak{D}$. F is called the *focus* and $\mathfrak{D}$ the *directrix* of P. If p is the distance of F from $\mathfrak{D}$, it is called the *parameter* of $\mathfrak{P}$.

Suppose that the focus of a parabola has the Cartesian coordinates $(p/2, 0)$ and that the equation of the directrix is given by $x_1 = -p/2$ (Fig. 21.4). Then the distance of a point X from F is equal to

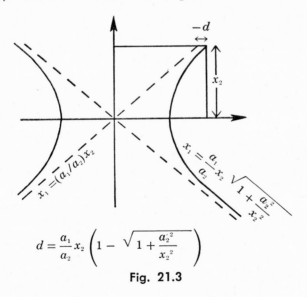

$$d = \frac{a_1}{a_2} x_2 \left(1 - \sqrt{1 + \frac{a_2^2}{x_2^2}} \right)$$

Fig. 21.3

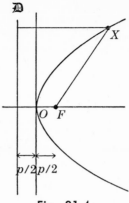

Fig. 21.4

$\sqrt{(x_1 - p/2)^2 + x_2^2}$, and the distance of X from $\mathfrak{D}$ is equal to $x_1 + p/2$. Consequently, for all points X on the parabola in question, we have the equation

$$\sqrt{\left(x_1 - \frac{p}{2}\right)^2 + x_2^2} = x_1 + \frac{p}{2},$$

which is easily seen to be equivalent to

$$x_2^2 = 2px_1. \tag{21.4}$$

Hence we may state

Theorem 21.3: *The parabola whose focus has the Cartesian coordinates $(p/2,0)$ and whose directrix has the equation $x_1 = -p/2$ is the graph of equation (21.4).*

Note: From (21.4) it can be seen that this parabola passes through the origin and that all other points of this parabola lie on that side of the line $x_1 = 0$ to which the direction of the first base translation points.

Equations (21.2), (21.3), and (21.4) can all be brought to a common form if the origins of the coordinate systems are suitably changed. In the case of the *ellipse* we substitute $(\bar{x}_1,\bar{x}_2) = (x_1 + a_1,x_2)$ and after a short computation, obtain,

$$\bar{x}_2^2 = 2\frac{a_2^2}{a_1}\bar{x}_1 - \frac{a_2^2}{a_1^2}\bar{x}_1^2 \tag{21.5}$$

as the equation of the ellipse in the new coordinates. In the case of the *hyperbola*, we substitute $(\bar{x}_1,\bar{x}_2) = (x_1 - a_1,x_2)$ and obtain in a similar manner

$$\bar{x}_2^2 = 2\frac{a_2^2}{a_1}\bar{x}_1 + \frac{a_2^2}{a_1^2}\bar{x}_1^2 \tag{21.6}$$

as the equation of the hyperbola in the new coordinates. Now (21.4), (21.5), and (21.6)(without the bars) are all special cases of the equation

$$x_2^2 = 2px_1 + (\epsilon^2 - 1)x_1^2 \quad \text{with} \quad p > 0 \quad \text{and} \quad \epsilon \geq 0. \quad (21.7)$$

If $\epsilon = 1$, we have the case of the *parabola*.

If $\epsilon > 1$ in (21.7), we can compute positive real numbers a_1 and a_2 *uniquely* from the conditions

$$p = \frac{a_2^2}{a_1} \quad \text{and} \quad \epsilon^2 = 1 + \frac{a_2^2}{a_1^2} = \frac{a_1^2 + a_2^2}{a_1^2}. \quad (21.8)$$

Hence, for $\epsilon > 1$, (21.7) is the equation of a hyperbola with a_1 and a_2 as lengths of the respective semi-axes and with center $(-a_1, 0)$.

If $\epsilon < 1$ in (21.7), we can compute positive real numbers a_1 and a_2 *uniquely* from the conditions

$$p = \frac{a_2^2}{a_1} \quad \text{and} \quad \epsilon^2 = 1 - \frac{a_2^2}{a_1^2} = \frac{a_1^2 - a_2^2}{a_1^2} \quad \text{with} \quad a_2 \leq a_1. \quad (21.9)$$

Hence, for $\epsilon < 1$, (21.7) is the equation of an ellipse with center $(a_1, 0)$.

Since, for $\epsilon = 0$, the ellipse (21.7) becomes a circle, ϵ is a sort of measure for the "deviation" of the curve from a circle. From definitions 21.1 and 21.2 it follows that $e^2 = a_1^2 + a_2^2$ for a hyperbola and $e^2 = a_1^2 - a_2^2$ for an ellipse. Therefore, we see from (21.8) and (21.9) that $\epsilon = e/a_1$ holds for both types of curves. Hence, one usually defines the eccentricity as follows:

Definition 21.4: The ratio e/a_1 is called the *eccentricity* in the case of an ellipse or a hyperbola. The eccentricity of a parabola is said to be the number 1.

Figure 21.5 shows some curves defined by equation (21.7) for different eccentricities ϵ.

The concept of a *tangent*, as introduced for the circle in the previous chapter, can be defined for "reasonable" curves at "reasonable" points; but in general a knowledge of the calculus is required for a rigorous defini-

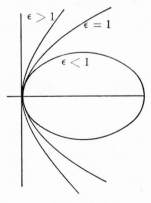

Fig. 21.5

tion. The idea is that a tangent "touches" the curve at a certain point or "has the same direction as the curve at a certain point." However, in the special cases of the ellipse and the hyperbola, the tangent at X^* may again be characterized as the line that has X^* but no other point in common with the curve. The graph of the equation

$$b_1 x_1 + b_2 x_2 + b_3 = 0 \quad \text{with} \quad (b_1, b_2) \neq (0,0) \quad (21.10)$$

has exactly one point in common with the ellipse (21.2) or the hyperbola (21.3) if and only if the quadratic equation for any coordinate of a common solution obtained by elimination of the other coordinate has only *double roots*. Thus, from an algebraic standpoint, the unique intersection point "counts twice."

With the parabola the situation is more complicated. The elimination of one unknown from the system consisting of (21.10) and (21.4) may still lead to a quadratic equation in the other unknown with double roots. But it may also happen that the elimination of one variable leads to a *linear* equation in the other variable. For example, take the system

$$x_2^2 = 2px_1$$

$$x_2 = c$$

where c is any real number. x_1 is eliminated in the second equation from the beginning. The elimination of x_2 in the first equation gives $x_1 = c^2/2p$. Hence, the equations for the coordinates of the possible points of intersection are both linear; there is only one point "with multiplicity 1" that line and curve have in common. From Fig. 21.6 it is clear that these lines could not possibly be called tangents. Thus, the condition that a line have only one point in common with a parabola cannot be used to define the concept of a tangent.

Therefore, we shall look to theorem 20.3 (for $n = 2$) for guidance in constructing formally the equation of a tangent. For $n = 2$, $c = (p,0)$, and $\rho = p$, equation (20.1) defines the same curve as (21.7) for $\epsilon = 0$,

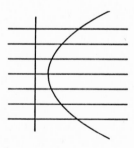

Fig. 21.6

and (20.7) defines the same curve as

$$x_2^* x_2 = p(x_1^* + x_1) + (\epsilon^2 - 1)x_1^* x_1 \qquad (21.11)$$

with $\epsilon = 0$. This equation (21.11) we shall later *define* as the equation of the tangent of the curve (21.7) at the point X^*, even in the case where ϵ does not vanish; that is, where (21.7) does not define a circle. We can then show that such a definition makes sense, namely, by proving that (21.7) and (21.11) have only one common solution and that the elimination of one variable x_i from (21.7) and (21.11) yields, for at least one variable, a *quadratic* equation in the other variable. But, as in the previous chapter, we shall also consider the graph of (21.11) for a point X^* *not* on the graph of (21.7), provided that (21.11) then defines a line at all. This leads again to a pole-polar theory, and the tangents will again be considered to be special polars. Accordingly, we define as follows:

Definition 21.5:   A set of points of $\mathfrak{R}^2$ is called a *classical conic section* if it is a graph of an equation (21.7) relative to a suitable Cartesian coordinate system. If the graph of (21.11) is a line for the coordinates x^* of a point X^*, it is called the *polar of X^** [*with respect to* (21.7)]. If the equation of a line can be written in the form (21.11), then X^* is called the *pole of that line* [*with respect to* (21.7)]. The polar of a point P of the graph of (21.7) is called the *tangent* of (21.7) *at P*, and its pole is called the *point of contact of the tangent* with the curve. Points and lines are called *p-allowable* if they have polars and poles, respectively. A line that is not *p*-allowable is called a *diameter* of the curve.

Theorem 21.4:   *A line is p-allowable with respect to an ellipse or hyperbola if and only if it does not pass through its center, and with respect to a parabola if and only if it is not perpendicular to its directrix. A p-allowable line has a unique pole. Every point is p-allowable with respect to a parabola, and every point different from the center is p-allowable with respect to an ellipse or hyperbola.*

PROOF: (21.11) can be written in the form

$$(p + (\epsilon^2 - 1)x_1^*)x_1 - x_2^* x_2 + px_1^* = 0. \qquad (21.12)$$

The graph of this line is equal to the graph of the equation

$$\alpha_1 x_1 + \alpha_2 x_2 + \alpha_0 = 0 \qquad (21.13)$$

if and only if (21.12) is a multiple of (21.13) by some scalar γ^*; that is, if and only if the nonhomogeneous system

$$p + (\epsilon^2 - 1)x_1^* = \gamma^* \alpha_1$$

$$-x_2^* = \gamma^* \alpha_2 \qquad (21.14)$$

$$px_1^* = \gamma^* \alpha_0,$$

or

$$\begin{bmatrix} \epsilon^2 - 1 & 0 & -\alpha_1 \\ 0 & -1 & -\alpha_2 \\ p & 0 & -\alpha_0 \end{bmatrix} \begin{bmatrix} x_1^* \\ x_2^* \\ \gamma^* \end{bmatrix} = \begin{bmatrix} -p \\ 0 \\ 0 \end{bmatrix} \tag{21.15}$$

has a solution (x_1^*, x_2^*, γ^*). If the determinant

$$\begin{vmatrix} \epsilon^2 - 1 & 0 & -\alpha_1 \\ 0 & -1 & -\alpha_2 \\ p & 0 & -\alpha_0 \end{vmatrix} = \begin{vmatrix} \epsilon^2 - 1 & \alpha_1 \\ p & \alpha_0 \end{vmatrix} \tag{21.16}$$

is not equal to zero, then there exists a *unique solution* of (21.14), by corollary 18.4. If the determinant (21.16) is equal to zero, then the rank of the coefficient matrix of (21.15) is less than 3, and the rank of the extended coefficient matrix

$$\begin{vmatrix} \epsilon^2 - 1 & 0 & -\alpha_1 & -p \\ 0 & -1 & -\alpha_2 & 0 \\ p & 0 & -\alpha_0 & 0 \end{vmatrix}$$

is equal to 3, because

$$\begin{vmatrix} \epsilon^2 - 1 & 0 & -p \\ 0 & -1 & 0 \\ p & 0 & 0 \end{vmatrix} = -p^2 < 0.$$

By corollary 14.5, (21.14) is *not solvable* in this case. In other words, the graph of (21.13) is the polar of some point with respect to (21.7) if and only if the determinant (21.16) is not equal to zero.

This argument shows also that (x_1^*, x_2^*) is determined *uniquely* by (21.14), provided that this system is solvable at all; that is, if a pole exists it is a *unique* point.

If (21.7) stands for an ellipse, then p and $\epsilon^2 - 1$ can be expressed in terms of a_1 and a_2 by (21.9); so (21.16) reduces to

$$\begin{vmatrix} -\dfrac{a_2^2}{a_1^2} & \alpha_1 \\ \dfrac{a_2^2}{a_1} & \alpha_0 \end{vmatrix} = \dfrac{a_2^2}{a_1^2} \begin{vmatrix} -1 & \alpha_1 \\ a_1 & \alpha_0 \end{vmatrix}.$$

Hence, every equation (21.13) for which $\alpha_0 \neq -\alpha_1 a_1$ and no other equation is the equation of some polar with respect to the ellipse in question. If and only if $\alpha_0 = -\alpha_1 a_1$, (21.13) reduces to

$$\alpha_1 x_1 + \alpha_2 x_2 - \alpha_1 a_1 = 0, \quad \text{or} \quad \alpha_1 (x_1 - a_1) + \alpha_2 x_2 = 0,$$

whose graph is a line through the center $(a_1, 0)$ of the ellipse.

Similarly it can be seen that, in the case of a hyperbola, (21.16) reduces to

$$\frac{a_2^2}{a_1^2} \begin{vmatrix} 1 & \alpha_1 \\ a_1 & \alpha_0 \end{vmatrix}.$$

Hence, (21.13) is the equation of a polar with respect to the hyperbola in question if and only if this determinant does not vanish; that is, if and only if (21.13) is *not* of the form $\alpha_1 (x_1 + a_1) + \alpha_2 x_2 = 0$ of a line through the center $(-a_1, 0)$ of the hyperbola.

If (21.7) stands for a parabola, then $\epsilon^2 - 1 = 0$; hence (21.16) reduces to

$$\begin{vmatrix} 0 & \alpha_1 \\ p & \alpha_0 \end{vmatrix}.$$

Since $p \neq 0$, this determinant is equal to zero if and only if $\alpha_1 = 0$. Hence, it is only the graphs of the form $\alpha_2 x_2 + \alpha_0 = 0$ that are not polars with respect to the parabola in question; these are the lines perpendicular to the directrix $x_1 = -p/2$.

This completes the proof of the part of theorem 21.4 that deals with p-allowable lines.

A point X^* with coordinates (x_1^*, x_2^*) is p-allowable if α_1, α_2, α_0 can be found such that (21.14) holds and $(\alpha_1, \alpha_2) \neq (0,0)$. This last inequality is the critical condition. It is never violated in the case of a parabola because $p \neq 0$, and it is violated in the case of an ellipse or hyperbola exactly if $(x_1^*, x_2^*) = (p/(1 - \epsilon^2), 0)$, which is the center of either curve.

Corollary 21.1: *A conic section and a tangent to it have only the point of contact in common.*

PROOF: The pole (x_1^*, x_2^*) of the graph of (21.11) lies on that line if and only if it lies on the curve (21.7). Now let Y^* and Z^* be two distinct points on the conic section. Then the tangents at these points have the equations

$$y_2^* x_2 = p(y_1^* + x_1) + (\epsilon^2 - 1) y_1^* x_1,$$

$$z_2^* x_2 = p(z_1^* + x_1) + (\epsilon^2 - 1) z_1^* x_1.$$

If the tangent at Y^* passed through Z^*, we would have

$$z_2^* y_2^* = p(z_1^* + y_1^*) + (\epsilon^2 - 1) z_1^* y_1^* \tag{21.17}$$

which is also the condition that the tangent at Z^* pass through Y^*. Thus, if the tangent at Y^* were to intersect the conic section at another point

Z^*, the tangent at Z^* would coincide with the tangent at Y^*, and this line would have two distinct poles: Y^* and Z^*. This is impossible, by theorem 21.4.

Corollary 21.2:   *If a p-allowable point Y lies on the p-allowable line $\mathbf{Z}$, then the pole Z of $\mathbf{Z}$ lies on the polar $\mathbf{D}$ of Y.*

PROOF: Both hypothesis and assertion are given by (21.17) without stars. That is all.

In the previous chapter it was shown how the corresponding theorem 20.4 for the circle can be applied to construct polars, provided that the construction of tangents is somehow known. A similar method can be applied in the cases of ellipses, hyperbolas, and parabolas.

We conclude this chapter with a motivation for the name *classical conic sections*. We first establish the equation of a (circular) *cone* in Cartesian coordinates. Let a fixed point F and a nondegenerate circle with center C be given in $\mathbf{R}^3$ such that FC does not have length zero and is perpendicular to the plane defined by the circle. Then the set of all points on all lines passing through F and some point on the circle is a *cone*. We take for F the origin, and we take the circle with equation $\bar{x}_1^2 + \bar{x}_2^2 = 1$ on the plane $\bar{x}_3 = 1$ (see Fig. 21.7). Now the radii r of the circular sections of a cone for a fixed plane $\bar{x}_3 = $ constant are proportional to the distance of the intersecting plane from the vertex of the cone, that is, proportional to $\bar{x}_3$. Since our circle with radius 1 lies on the plane having distance 1 from the vertex, a circular section on a plane having distance r from the vertex will have radius r. Hence the equation of our cone is simply

$$\bar{x}_1^2 + \bar{x}_2^2 = \bar{x}_3^2. \tag{21.18}$$

This cone will now be intersected by a plane. To facilitate the computing,

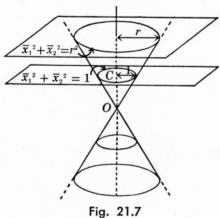

Fig. 21.7

we change the coordinate system so that, in the *new* system (*without bars*), the intersecting plane will have the simple form

$$x_3 = c. \tag{21.19}$$

There is no need to visualize the new base translations. All we have to do is carry out a substitution $\bar{x} = Ax$, where A is an orthogonal matrix, so that the coordinate system remains Cartesian by corollary 15.2. We take

$$\bar{x}_1 = x_1$$

$$\bar{x}_2 = \quad \alpha x_2 + \beta x_3 \qquad \text{with } \alpha^2 + \beta^2 = 1. \tag{21.20}$$

$$\bar{x}_3 = -\beta x_2 + \alpha x_3$$

Equation (21.18) is transformed by (21.20) into

$$x_1^2 + (\alpha^2 - \beta^2)x_2^2 + (\beta^2 - \alpha^2)x_3^2 + 4\alpha\beta x_2 x_3 = 0. \tag{21.21}$$

We shall now look for the possible intersections of this cone with any plane (21.19). Several cases will have to be distinguished:

Case 1. $\alpha^2 \neq \beta^2$ and $c \neq 0$. For $x_3 = c \neq 0$; we obtain

$$x_1^2 + (\alpha^2 - \beta^2)x_2^2 + (\beta^2 - \alpha^2)c^2 + 4\alpha\beta c x_2 = 0. \tag{21.22}$$

By completing the square in (21.22) with respect to x_2, we obtain

$$x_1^2 + (\alpha^2 - \beta^2)\left(x_2 + \frac{2\alpha\beta c}{\alpha^2 - \beta^2}\right)^2 = -(\beta^2 - \alpha^2)c^2 + \frac{4\alpha^2\beta^2 c^2}{\alpha^2 - \beta^2}$$

or, by applying $\alpha^2 + \beta^2 = 1$ and simplifying the right-hand side,

$$x_1^2 + (\alpha^2 - \beta^2)\left(x_2 + \frac{2\alpha\beta c}{\alpha^2 - \beta^2}\right)^2 = \frac{c^2}{\alpha^2 - \beta^2}. \tag{21.23}$$

This is an ellipse or hyperbola according as $\alpha^2 - \beta^2 > 0$ or $\alpha^2 - \beta^2 < 0$.

Case 2. $\alpha^2 \neq \beta^2$ and $c = 0$. Then we simply obtain

$$x_1^2 + (\alpha^2 - \beta^2)x_2^2 = 0. \tag{21.24}$$

If $\alpha^2 - \beta^2 > 0$, then *the origin* (0,0) *alone* is the only real solution of (21.24). If $\alpha^2 - \beta^2 < 0$, then the left-hand side of (21.24) can be decomposed into two linear polynomials with real coefficients; so in this case we get two *distinct lines*. Since (0,0) satisfies (21.24) in any case, these two lines must intersect.

Case 3. $\alpha^2 = \beta^2$ and $c \neq 0$. We obtain the parabola

$$x_1^2 = -4\alpha\beta c x_2. \tag{21.25}$$

Case 4. $\alpha^2 = \beta^2$ and $c = 0$. We get $x_1^2 = 0$. As this equation can be split into $x_1 = 0$ and again $x_1 = 0$, we shall speak of *two coinciding lines*.

This proves that ellipse, hyperbola, and parabola can be constructed as intersections of a cone by suitable planes. But, besides these curves, we also obtained two intersecting lines, two coinciding lines, or the origin alone. In all cases the algebraic expressions on the left-hand sides were quadratic. We may now reverse the question and ask whether the graph of any solvable quadratic equation in x_1 and x_2 is obtainable as the intersection of a cone with a plane. This problem will be dealt with in the next chapter. We shall see that among the quadratic equations in x_1 and x_2 there exists the type

$$x_1^2 + c = 0 \quad \text{with} \quad c \neq 0, \qquad (21.26)$$

which represents *two distinct parallel lines* and which did not occur in our previous discussion. Indeed, in order to obtain the graph of (21.26) in a similar way, the cone has to be "deformed" into a cylinder.

EXERCISES

1. Find the center, the foci, and the lengths of the semi-axes of each of the following ellipses:

   (a) $x_1^2 + 8x_1 + x_2^2 + 6x_2 - 26 = 0$;

   (b) $x_1^2 - 2x_1 + x_2^2 - 4x_2 - 25 = 0$;

   (c) $3x_1^2 - x_1 + 3x_2^2 - 3x_2 - 36 = 0$.

2. Prove in detail that (21.2) implies (21.1).

3. Find the center, the foci, and the lengths of the semi-axes of each of the following hyperbolas:

   (a) $x_1^2 + 8x_1 - x_2^2 - 6x_2 - 26 = 0$;

   (b) $2x_1^2 + 2x_1 - 2x_2^2 + 2x_2 + 1 = 0$;

   (c) $x_1^2 - x_1 - x_2^2 + 3x_2 + 11 = 0$.

4. Prove that the graph of $x_1 x_2 = 1$ is a hyperbola.

5. Find the focus, directrix, and parameter of each of the following parabolas:

   (a) $x_1^2 + 2x_2 + 3 = 0$;

   (b) $x_2^2 - 2x_1 - 3 = 0$;

   (c) $x_1^2 + 2x_1 - 2x_2 + 6 = 0$.

6. Prove theorem 21.2 and 21.3.

7. Show how (21.11) with $\epsilon = 0$ and $p = \rho$ is obtained from (20.7).

8. Give the equations for the polars of a point X^* with respect to the ellipse (21.2), hyperbola (21.3), and parabola (21.4).

Hint: Reverse the transformations by which the general form (21.7) was obtained.

9. Explain the proof of corollary 21.2 in detail.

10. Prove: Not both the equations obtained from the system (21.7) and (21.11) by elimination of one variable are linear.

   Hint: Apply exercise 8.

11. Draw an ellipse, a hyperbola, and a parabola, and show how polars and poles can be constructed geometrically if the construction of a tangent is supposed to be known.

12. Prove that (21.22) is the equation of an ellipse if $\alpha^2 - \beta^2 > 0$. Compute the lengths of the semi-axes and the coordinates of the center.

13. Prove that (21.22) is the equation of a hyperbola if $\alpha^2 - \beta^2 < 0$. Compute the lengths of the semi-axes and the coordinates of the center.

22

Reduction of Quadratic Polynomials

In this chapter it will be shown how quadratic polynomials can be simplified by substitutions of the variables induced by orthogonal matrices or by changes of the origin. The results will be applied in the next chapter in classifying the graphs of quadratic polynomials in two and in three dimensions.

We shall begin with a study of homogeneous quadratic polynomials with real coefficients, that is, real quadratic polynomials that have neither linear nor constant terms. It is possible to write every real homogeneous quadratic polynomal in n variables $x_1, \cdots, x_n$ in the form

$$\sum_{i=1}^{n} \sum_{j=1}^{n} a_{ij}x_i x_j, \tag{22.1}$$

but not in a unique way. For example, if a quadratic polynomial contains the term $3x_1x_2$, this term can be decomposed into the sum of two terms, one in x_1x_2 and the other in x_2x_1 in infinitely many ways: $3x_1x_2 = 2x_1x_2 + 1x_2x_1$, $3x_1x_2 = 5x_1x_2 - 2x_2x_1$, and so on. To obtain uniqueness of such a representation one may demand in (22.1) the additional condition

$$a_{ij} = a_{ji} \qquad \text{for every} \qquad i, j = 1, 2, \cdots, n. \tag{22.2}$$

This is not a restriction; for, if a homogeneous quadratic polynomial contains the term $\cdots + cx_ix_j + \cdots$, we may simply put $a_{ij} = a_{ji} = c/2$. In this way every homogeneous quadratic real ploynomial is connected with a real symmetric matrix

$$A = \begin{bmatrix} a_{11} & a_{12} & \cdots & a_{1n} \\ a_{21} & a_{22} & \cdots & a_{2n} \\ \vdots & \vdots & & \vdots \\ a_{n1} & a_{n2} & \cdots & a_{nn} \end{bmatrix} \quad \text{with} \quad A = A', \qquad (22.3)$$

namely, the matrix of all coefficients of (22.1) if (22.2) is satisfied. If the sequence of the variables is written as a column

$$x = \begin{bmatrix} x_1 \\ x_2 \\ \vdots \\ x_n \end{bmatrix}, \qquad (22.4)$$

then $x' = (x_1, x_2, \cdots, x_n)$, and it follows that we have

$$\sum_{i=1}^{n} \sum_{j=1}^{n} a_{ij} x_i x_j = x' A x, \qquad A' = A, \qquad (22.5)$$

because the variables commute with the elements of A.

The real zeros of (22.5) may be interpreted as elements of R^n or as Cartesian coordinates of an n-dimensional Euclidean vector space $\{V^n, \mathbf{f}\}$. A change of the basis of the vector space considered will, in general, change the coordinates of the zeros of (22.5), and the changed n-tuples will, in general, be the zeros of a polynomial other than (22.5). If the change in the basis is defined by

$$\bar{x} = \Omega x, \qquad (22.6)$$

where Ω is a real regular matrix, then the changed coordinate vectors of the old zeros must be zeros of the polynomial

$$\bar{x}'(\Omega^{-1})' A \Omega^{-1} \bar{x}, \qquad (22.7)$$

because $x = \Omega^{-1} \bar{x}$ and $x' = \bar{x}'(\Omega^{-1})'$.

We shall introduce a new basis in such a way as to meet two conditions: (1) that the new basis be again Cartesian; that is, the new base vectors still have length 1 and are perpendicular in pairs; (2) that the substitution of the new coordinates change (22.5) into a homogeneous quadratic real polynomial *without mixed terms*; that is, $a_{ij} = 0$ for all $i \neq j$. By exercises 15.8 and 16.3, the first condition is satisfied if and only if Ω is orthogonal. The second condition demands that (22.7) should reduce to $\bar{x}' \Lambda \bar{x}$ where Λ is a diagonal matrix. Hence, the two conditions together pose the problem of finding a *real orthogonal* matrix Ω such that, for a given *real symmetric* matrix A,

$$\Omega A \Omega' = \Lambda, \quad \Omega' = \Omega^{-1}, \quad A = A', \quad \Lambda = \begin{bmatrix} \lambda_1 & & & \text{O} \\ & \lambda_2 & & \\ & & \ddots & \\ \text{O} & & & \lambda_n \end{bmatrix}. \tag{22.8}$$

We shall see first that this is equivalent to an eigenvector problem of A.

Theorem 22.1: *(22.8) is satisfied if and only if the rows of Ω are unit eigenvectors of A perpendicular in pairs. If the ith row of Ω is an eigenvector of A, then λ_i is the eigenvalue for it.*

For typographical reasons we shall split up Ω' in columns:

$$\Omega' = (\omega_{\downarrow}^{(1)}, \omega_{\downarrow}^{(2)}, \cdots, \omega_{\downarrow}^{(n)}). \tag{22.9}$$

PROOF OF THE THEOREM: Because $\Omega^{-1} = \Omega'$, (22.8) is satisfied if and only if $A\Omega' = \Omega'\Lambda$. Applying (22.9), this can be written in the form

$$(A\omega^{(1)}, A\omega^{(2)}, \cdots, A\omega^{(n)}) = (\lambda_1 \omega^{(1)}, \lambda_2 \omega^{(2)}, \cdots, \lambda_n \omega^{(n)}). \tag{22.10}$$

Hence, (22.8) holds if and only if the columns of Ω' are eigenvectors of A, which, because Ω is orthogonal, must be unit vectors perpendicular in pairs by exercise 13.17.

Since the eigenvalues of A are solutions of an *algebraic* equation $|A - \lambda I| = 0$, it is possible that some may be (nonreal) complex numbers. In this case the corresponding eigenvectors may have complex coordinates, as indicated in chapter 18. But we shall see that this cannot happen for real symmetric matrices A.

Theorem 22.2: *Every real symmetric matrix of order n has n real unit eigenvectors perpendicular in pairs.*

This theorem is a consequence of the following three lemmas.

Lemma 22.1: *Every eigenvalue of a real symmetric matrix is real.*

This will assure us that we can find real eigenvectors.

Lemma 22.2: *Eigenvectors for two distinct eigenvalues of a real symmetric matrix are perpendicular in pairs.*

These two lemmas suffice to prove theorem 22.2 *if* the real symmetric matrix has n *distinct* eigenvalues. But an algebraic equation may have *multiple* roots, and in that case there may be fewer than n distinct eigenvalues.

Lemma 22.3: *If an eigenvalue of a real symmetric matrix has multiplicity m, then there exist m eigenvectors for this eigenvalue which, for $m > 1$, are perpendicular in pairs.*

From the two last lemmas it can be concluded easily that it is always possible to find n eigenvectors $x^{(1)}$, $x^{(2)}$, $\cdots$, $x^{(n)}$ of a real symmetric matrix of order n that are perpendicular in pairs. But then

$$\omega^{(i)} = \frac{1}{|x^{(i)}|} x^{(i)} \qquad i = 1, 2, \cdots, n$$

are n unit eigenvectors of that matrix that are perpendicular in pairs.

We turn first to the proof of the second lemma 22.2 because it will be needed to prove the first (lemma 22.1).

PROOF OF LEMMA 22.2:   Let λ^* and λ^{**} be two *distinct* eigenvalues of a real symmetric matrix A, and let ω^* and ω^{**} be eigenvectors for λ^* and λ^{**}, respectively. If ω^* and ω^{**} are written as columns, then we have

$$A\omega^* = \lambda^*\omega^*, \tag{22.11}$$

$$A\omega^{**} = \lambda^{**}\omega^{**}. \tag{22.12}$$

Let us evaluate the bilinear expression

$$(A\omega^*)'\omega^{**} = \omega^{*\prime}A'\omega^{**} = \omega^{*\prime}A\omega^{**} = \omega^{*\prime}(A\omega^{**}) \tag{22.13}$$

in two different ways. If (22.11) is applied, then (22.13) reduces to $\lambda^*\omega^{*\prime}\omega^{**}$ (because λ^* is a scalar). If (22.12) is applied, then (22.13) reduces to $\lambda^{**}\omega^{*\prime}\omega^{**}$. Hence $\lambda^{**}\omega^{*\prime}\omega^{**} = \lambda^*\omega^{*\prime}\omega^{**}$, or $(\lambda^* - \lambda^{**})\omega^{*\prime}\omega^{**} = 0$. Since $\lambda^* - \lambda^{**} \neq 0$, this last equation means that ω^* and ω^{**} are perpendicular.

PROOF OF LEMMA 22.1:   We shall use overbars *temporarily* to denote complex conjugates. If A has a (nonreal) complex eigenvalue λ^*, then it must also have its complex conjugate number $\bar{\lambda}^*$ as an eigenvalue, because the coefficients of $|A - \lambda I| = 0$ are real. If ω^* is an eigenvector for λ^*, then we denote by $\bar{\omega}^*$ the column of complex numbers obtained from ω^* by replacing $+i$ by $-i$ ($i = \sqrt{-1}$) in every coordinate. Then $\bar{\omega}^*$ must be an eigenvector for the eigenvalue $\bar{\lambda}^*$, because all algebraic relations remain unaltered if $+i$ is consistently replaced by $-i$. Lemma 22.2 was proved *without* the assumption that the n-tuples occurring in it were *real* numbers. If λ^* is not real, then $\lambda^* \neq \bar{\lambda}^*$; hence, $\omega^{*\prime}\bar{\omega}^* = 0$, by lemma 22.2. This means, in detail,

$$\omega_1^*\bar{\omega}_1^* + \omega_2^*\bar{\omega}_2^* + \cdots + \omega_n^*\bar{\omega}_n^* = 0. \tag{22.14}$$

If the complex numbers ω_j are written in the form $\omega_j = \alpha_j + \beta_j i$ (with α_j and β_j *real*), then $\omega_j^*\bar{\omega}_j^* = \alpha_j^2 + \beta_j^2$. Hence, (22.14) implies $\sum_{j=1}^{n} (\alpha_j^2 + \beta_j^2) = 0$. But a sum of squares of *real* numbers is equal to zero only if *every* square is itself equal to zero. Hence *all* $\alpha_j (j = 1, \cdots, n)$ and *all* $\beta_j (j = 1, \cdots, n)$ must be equal to zero. In other words, the column ω^* (and, likewise, the column $\bar{\omega}^*$) must be the zero vector. This contradicts the assumption that

ω^* was an eigenvector, that is, a *nonzero* vector. Consequently, λ^* cannot be complex.

PROOF OF LEMMA 22.3:   Let A be a real symmetric matrix of order n, which has an eigenvalue λ^* of multiplicity $m > 1$. We shall construct an orthogonal matrix B such that $B^{-1}AB$ has the form (22.16), and deal with this matrix which facilitates a proof by induction on the order. At the end we shall reinterpret our result in terms of the matrix A.

Suppose that $b^{(1)}$ is a unit eigenvector of the matrix A for the eigenvalue λ^*. Choose $n - 1$ columns $b^{(2)}, b^{(3)}, \cdots, b^{(n)}$ of real numbers such that, in the set $\{b^{(1)}, b^{(2)}, \cdots, b^{(n)}\}$, every vector has length 1 and any two are perpendicular. By theorem 16.3, this is always possible; for we have only to construct a Cartesian basis of R^n, starting with $b^{(1)}$ (see proof of theorem 16.3 and pp. 229–230 for a construction). Then the matrix

$$B = (b^{(1)}, b^{(2)}, \cdots, b^{(n)}) \tag{22.15}$$

is obviously orthogonal. B is so constructed that in $B'AB$ all elements of the first row and column vanish *except* the element in the principal diagonal that is equal to the eigenvalue (see exercise 18.28). Thus we have

$$B'AB = \begin{pmatrix} \lambda^* & 0 & \cdots & 0 \\ 0 & & & \\ \vdots & & R & \\ 0 & & & \end{pmatrix} \tag{22.16}$$

with the abbreviation $(B'AB)^{1;1} = R$, where R is also symmetric, because $B'AB$ is symmetric. The characteristic polynomial of (22.16) is equal to

$$|B'AB - \lambda I| = \begin{vmatrix} \lambda^* - \lambda & 0 & \cdots & 0 \\ 0 & & & \\ \vdots & & R - \lambda I & \\ 0 & & & \end{vmatrix} = (\lambda^* - \lambda)\,|R - \lambda I|.$$

Since $B' = B^{-1}$, this must be equal to the characteristic polynomial of A, by exercise 18.23; hence,

$$|A - \lambda I| = (\lambda^* - \lambda)\,|R - \lambda I|. \tag{22.17}$$

Now it follows from the theory of equations that λ^* is a zero of $|R - \lambda I|$ *of multiplicity* $m - 1$, provided that λ^* is an eigenvalue of A of multiplicity $m > 1$.

Lemma 22.3 is trivially true for matrices of order 1. Suppose it is also true for all real symmetric matrices of order $< n$. Then, in particular, it holds for a real symmetric matrix R of order $n - 1$ with eigenvalue λ^* of multiplicity $m - 1$. Hence, there must exist $m - 1$ unit eigenvectors of R

$$\begin{bmatrix} c_{11} \\ c_{21} \\ \vdots \\ c_{n-1,1} \end{bmatrix}, \quad \begin{bmatrix} c_{12} \\ c_{22} \\ \vdots \\ c_{n-1,2} \end{bmatrix}, \quad \cdots, \quad \begin{bmatrix} c_{1\,m-1} \\ c_{2\,m-1} \\ \vdots \\ c_{n-1,\,m-1} \end{bmatrix}$$

for the eigenvalue λ^*, perpendicular in pairs if $m > 2$. Therefore,

$$c^{(1)} = \begin{bmatrix} 0 \\ c_{11} \\ c_{21} \\ \vdots \\ c_{n-1,1} \end{bmatrix}, \quad c^{(2)} = \begin{bmatrix} 0 \\ c_{12} \\ c_{22} \\ \vdots \\ c_{n-1,2} \end{bmatrix}, \cdots, \quad c^{(m-1)} = \begin{bmatrix} 0 \\ c_{1,\,m-1} \\ c_{2,\,m-1} \\ \vdots \\ c_{n-1,\,m-1} \end{bmatrix}, \quad c^{(m)} = \begin{bmatrix} 1 \\ 0 \\ 0 \\ \vdots \\ 0 \end{bmatrix}$$

are m unit eigenvectors of the matrix (22.16), perpendicular in pairs, for λ^*. Since $B'ABc^{(i)} = \lambda^* c^{(i)}$ implies $A(Bc^{(i)}) = \lambda^*(Bc^{(i)})$,

$$Bc^{(1)}, \qquad Bc^{(2)}, \qquad \cdots, \qquad Bc^{(m-1)}, \qquad Bc^{(m)} = b^{(1)}$$

are m unit eigenvectors of the real symmetric matrix A of order n for the eigenvalue λ^* of multiplicity m, and the induction proof is completed.

Corollary 22.1: *If a real homogeneous quadratic polynomial (22.5) is given, there exists an orthogonal matrix M such that the substitution $x \to Mx$ reduces the polynomial to*

$$\sum_{j=1}^{n} \lambda_j x_j^2 \tag{22.18}$$

where $\lambda_1, \lambda_2, \cdots, \lambda_n$ are the eigenvalues of A counted as often as their multiplicity demands.

PROOF: This is an immediate consequence of theorem 22.2 in conjunction with theorem 22.1.

Corollary 22.2: *If A and B are two real symmetric matrices, then there exists an orthogonal matrix X such that $X^{-1}AX = B$ if and only if A and B have the same eigenvalues with the same multiplicities.*

PROOF: (1) If A and B have the same eigenvalues with the same multiplicities, then orthogonal matrices Y and Z can be found such that $YAY' = \Lambda = ZBZ'$, hence $B = Z'YAY'Z$ where $X = Y'Z$. (2) If $B =$

$X^{-1}AX$ then B and A have the same eigenvalues with the same multiplicities by exercise 18.24.

So far, only homogeneous quadratic polynomials have been considered. We turn now to quadratic polynomials in general and extend our matrix methods to this case. In order to obtain a representation similar to that of (22.5) for a polynomial in n variables $x_1, x_2, \cdots, x_n$, we introduce an additional "dummy variable" x_{n+1} used as an *alternative* symbol for the *number* 1. Moreover, the abbreviation x or $\bar{x}$ will now stand for the column of all variables, including the dummy variable in the old as well as in the new coordinate system:

$$
x = \begin{bmatrix} x_1 \\ x_2 \\ \vdots \\ x_n \\ x_{n+1} \end{bmatrix} = \begin{bmatrix} x_1 \\ x_2 \\ \vdots \\ x_n \\ 1 \end{bmatrix}, \qquad \bar{x} = \begin{bmatrix} \bar{x}_1 \\ \bar{x}_2 \\ \vdots \\ \bar{x}_n \\ \bar{x}_{n+1} \end{bmatrix} = \begin{bmatrix} \bar{x}_1 \\ \bar{x}_2 \\ \vdots \\ \bar{x}_n \\ 1 \end{bmatrix}. \tag{22.19}
$$

As before, every quadratic polynomial can now be written uniquely in the form

$$
\sum_{i=1}^{n+1} \sum_{j=1}^{n+1} a_{ij} x_i x_j, \qquad x_{n+1} = 1, \qquad a_{ij} = a_{ji}. \tag{22.20}
$$

In this way every quadratic polynomial in n variables is connected with a symmetric matrix A *of order* $n+1$, defined by

$$
A = \begin{bmatrix} a_{11} & \cdots & a_{1,n+1} \\ \vdots & & \vdots \\ a_{n+1,1} & \cdots & a_{n+1,n+1} \end{bmatrix}. \tag{22.21}
$$

Again it follows from the matrix multiplication that

$$
\sum_{i=1}^{n+1} \sum_{j=1}^{n+1} a_{ij} x_i x_j = x'Ax \qquad \text{with} \qquad A' = A \quad \text{and} \quad x_{n+1} = 1 \tag{22.22}
$$

holds.

In our new notation (22.6) takes the form

$$
\begin{bmatrix} \bar{x}_1 \\ \bar{x}_2 \\ \vdots \\ \bar{x}_n \\ 1 \end{bmatrix} = \begin{bmatrix} & & & 0 \\ & \Omega & & \vdots \\ & & & 0 \\ 0 & \cdots & 0 & 1 \end{bmatrix} \begin{bmatrix} x_1 \\ x_2 \\ \vdots \\ x_n \\ 1 \end{bmatrix} \tag{22.23}
$$

because the number 1 in the $(n + 1)$th coordinate has to remain the same.

Suppose now that, by a suitable substitution of the form (22.23), the polynomial (22.20) has been changed to a polynomial *without mixed quadratic terms*, that is, to a polynomial of which the corresponding symmetric matrix has the form

$$
A = \begin{bmatrix}
\lambda_1 & & & & a_{1,n+1} \\
& \lambda_2 & & & a_{2,n+1} \\
& & \ddots & & \vdots \\
& & & \lambda_n & a_{n,n+1} \\
a_{n+1,1} & a_{n+1,2} & \cdots & & a_{n+1,n+1}
\end{bmatrix}.
\tag{22.24}
$$

Then, by a simple change of the origin, we can eliminate all *linear terms* $(a_{i,n+1} + a_{n+1,i})x_i$ for those integers i for which $\lambda_i \neq 0$. For suppose we have in (22.20), with A defined by (22.24), the terms

$$
\cdots + \lambda_i x_i^2 + 2a_{i,n+1}x_i + \cdots \quad \text{with} \quad \lambda_i \neq 0 \quad \text{and} \quad a_{i,n+1} \neq 0.
$$

Then, "by completing the square," we can replace these terms by

$$
\lambda_i \left(x_i + \frac{a_{i,n+1}}{\lambda_i} \right)^2 - \frac{a_{i,n+1}^2}{\lambda_i}.
$$

Consequently, the substitution

$$
\bar{x}_i = x_i + \frac{a_{i,n+1}}{\lambda_i}, \qquad \bar{x}_j = x_j \qquad \text{for all} \quad j \neq i \tag{22.25}
$$

will eliminate the *linear* terms in x_i. Equation (22.25) moves the origin to the point whose *old* coordinates are

$$
\left(0, \cdots, 0, -\frac{a_{i,n+1}}{\lambda_i}, 0, \cdots, 0\right)
$$

with the nonzero element as the ith coordinate. By making use of the convention $x_{n+1} = 1$ and formula (13.4) where $\alpha = a_{i,n+1}/\lambda_i$, we can express equation (22.25) in the following matrix form:

$$
\bar{x} = M_{i,n+1}\left(\frac{a_{i,n+1}}{\lambda_i}\right)x. \tag{22.26}
$$

Suppose for convenience that the eigenvalues λ_i have been so numbered that

$$
\lambda_1 \neq 0, \lambda_2 \neq 0, \cdots, \lambda_k \neq 0; \qquad \lambda_{k+1} = \lambda_{k+2} = \cdots = \lambda_n = 0. \tag{22.27}
$$

Then, by a number of substitutions of the form (22.26)(for different i's), (22.20) can be reduced to a quadratic polynomial in which not only the *mixed* quadratic terms are eliminated but also all linear terms *in those variables x_i whose quadratic terms are different from zero*:

$$\sum_{i=1}^{k} \lambda_i x_i^2 + \sum_{i=k+1}^{n} \mu_i x_i + \gamma, \qquad \lambda_i \neq 0 \quad \text{for} \quad i = 1, 2, \cdots, k. \qquad (22.28)$$

Either all μ_i vanish, or there exists at least one μ_i different from zero. In this case we can still eliminate all but (at most) one of the remaining linear terms by a substitution involving only the last $n - k$ coordinates induced by an orthogonal matrix. Let $\varphi^{(1)}$ be the following $(n - k)$-tuple of coefficients of the linear terms in (22.28), written as a *row*

$$\varphi^{(1)} = \frac{1}{\sqrt{\mu_{k+1}^2 + \mu_{k+2}^2 + \cdots + \mu_n^2}} (\mu_{k+1}, \mu_{k+2}, \cdots, \mu_n).$$

By theorem 16.3, it is possible to find $n - k - 1$ other $(n - k)$-tuples of real numbers, written as *rows* $\varphi^{(2)}, \varphi^{(3)}, \cdots, \varphi^{(n-k)}$, that have length 1 and are perpendicular in pairs and to $\varphi^{(1)}$. Then the square matrix of order $n - k$

$$\Phi = \begin{pmatrix} \varphi^{(1)} \\ \varphi^{(2)} \\ \cdot \\ \cdot \\ \cdot \\ \varphi^{(n-k)} \end{pmatrix}$$

is orthogonal.

Now, consider the matrix Ψ *of order $n + 1$* defined by

$$\Psi = \begin{bmatrix} I_k & 0 & 0 \\ & & \vdots \\ 0 & \Phi & 0 \\ & & \\ 0 & \cdots & 0 & 1 \end{bmatrix}.$$

It is easy to check that *both* Ψ itself and the submatrix $\Psi^{n+1;n+1}$ of Ψ are orthogonal, provided that Φ is orthogonal. Now, consider the change in the coordinate system defined by

$$\bar{x} = \Psi x. \qquad (22.29)$$

As $\Psi^{n+1;n+1}$ is orthogonal, the new coordinate system defined by (22.29) is Cartesian, too. But, by the substitution (22.29), the quadratic polynomial (22.28) is reduced to a polynomial of the form†

$$\sum_{i=1}^{k} \lambda_i x_i^2 + \mu x_{k+1} + \gamma \quad \text{with} \quad \lambda_i \neq 0 \quad \text{for} \quad i = 1, 2, \cdots, k, \qquad (22.30)$$

where

$$\mu = \sqrt{\sum_{i=k+1}^{n} \mu_i^2}$$

† Where we deleted the bar for simplification.

because (22.29) implies

$$\bar{x}_{k+1} = \frac{1}{\sqrt{\sum\limits_{i=k+1}^{n} \mu_i^2}} \sum_{i=k+1}^{n} \mu_i x_i.$$

If $\mu\gamma \neq 0$, we can simplify (22.30) by the further change

$$\bar{x}_{k+1} = x_{k+1} + \frac{\gamma}{\mu}, \qquad \bar{x}_i = x_i \qquad \text{for all} \qquad i \neq k+1,$$

which will eliminate the constant term γ. By making use of our convention $x_{n+1} = 1$ and of (13.4) where $\alpha = \frac{\gamma}{\mu}$, we can express this change in the matrix form

$$\bar{x} = M_{k+1,n+1}\left(\frac{\gamma}{\mu}\right) x. \tag{22.31}$$

To summarize the results of our investigations, we state

Theorem 22.3: *Any real quadratic polynomial (22.22) can be reduced to one of the three forms:*

$$\sum_{i=1}^{k} \lambda_i x_i^2 \tag{22.32}$$

$$\sum_{i=1}^{k} \lambda_i x_i^2 + \gamma \qquad \text{with} \qquad \gamma \neq 0 \tag{22.33}$$

$$\sum_{i=1}^{k} \lambda_i x_i^2 + \mu x_{k+1} \qquad \text{with} \qquad \mu \neq 0 \tag{22.34}$$

$$\text{with} \qquad \lambda_1 \neq 0, \cdots, \lambda_k \neq 0 \qquad \text{and} \qquad 0 < k \leq n$$

by consecutive substitutions of the form (22.23), (22.26), (22.29) and (22.31). Let the symmetric matrix

$$\tag{22.35}$$

represent one of the reduced polynomials (22.32), (22.33), and (22.34).

There are only three choices for the rank of (22.35): *It may be* (1) *equal to k if it represents* (22.32); *that is, if* $\gamma = \mu = 0$; (2) *equal to* $k + 1$ *if it represents* (22.33); *that is, if* $\gamma \neq 0$ *but* $\mu = 0$; *or* (3) *equal to* $k + 2$ *if it represents* (22.34); *that is, if* $\gamma = 0$ *but* $\mu \neq 0$.

By theorem 14.3, the rank of the matrix (22.21) is not altered by any of the substitutions listed in theorem 22.3. Therefore, we have

Corollary 22.3: *If the real symmetric matrix A of order* $n + 1$ *represents a real quadratic polynomial in n variables and if the symmetric submatrix* $A^{n+1;n+1}$ *possesses k nonzero eigenvalues counted as often as their multiplicity demands, then the rank of A is k, k + 1, or k + 2, depending on whether the polynomial reduces to* (22.32), (22.33), *or* (22.34), *respectively.*

As the rank of A is not altered by our reduction process, the corollary also shows that it is not possible to transform any of the three forms (22.32), (22.33), and (22.34) into either of the other two *by a change of the Cartesian coordinate system.*

In comparison with the preceding part of this chapter, the following proposition is now easy to prove:

Theorem 22.4: *Let A and B be two real symmetric matrices of order* $n + 1$, *corresponding to two real quadratic polynomials in n variables that define the same point set, but relative to different Cartesian coordinate systems. Then*

$$\rho(A) = \rho(B) \tag{22.36}$$

$$|A| = |B| \tag{22.37}$$

$$|A^{n+1;n+1} - \lambda I| = |B^{n+1;n+1} - \lambda I|. \tag{22.38}$$

Note: By exercise 18.30, (22.38) implies in particular

$$\tau(A^{n+1;n+1}) = \tau(B^{n+1;n+1}). \tag{22.39}$$

Although the main results of this chapter have been obtained only for quadratic polynomials with *real* coefficients, they remain valid for *complex* coefficients, provided that "real symmetric" and "orthogonal" are consistently replaced in the theorems by "Hermitian" and "unitary" (see exercise 16.7), respectively. For the details we refer the reader to some of the following exercises.

EXERCISES

1. Prove: If Φ is orthogonal, then $\begin{bmatrix} I & \mathbf{O} & 0 \\ & & \vdots \\ \mathbf{O} & \Phi & 0 \\ 0 & \cdots & 0 & 1 \end{bmatrix}$

is also orthogonal.

2. Determine the three choices for the rank of (22.35) explicitly.

3. Prove theorem 22.4.

4. Prove: $\rho(A) = \rho(Y'AY)$ if Y is one of the substitution matrices in (22.23), (22.26), (22.29), and (22.31).

5. Prove: If A is a real symmetric matrix of order n with eigenvalues $\lambda_1, \lambda_2, \cdots \lambda_n$ (counted as their multiplicity demands), then

$$\sum_{i=1}^{n} a_{ii} = \sum_{i=1}^{n} \lambda_i.$$

Hint: Use (22.39).

6. Prove: Every polynomial (22.1) with *complex* coefficients can be uniquely written as $x'Ax$, where A is a Hermitian matrix (that is, where $A = \bar{A}'$).

7. Prove the complex analog of theorem 22.1; that is, prove that $\Omega A \Omega' = \Lambda$, for Hermitian A, unitary Ω, and diagonal Λ, if and only if the rows of Ω are unit eigenvectors of A perpendicular in pairs [that is, having *complex* inner products (definition 16.3) equal to zero].

8. Prove the *complex* analog of lemma 22.1: Every eigenvalue of a Hermitian matrix is *real*.

9. Construct and prove the *complex* analogs of lemmas 22.2 and 22.3.

10. Construct and prove the *complex* analog of corollary 22.1.

Note: The λ_i are *real* (by exercise 8).

23

Classification of Conics and Quadrics

After the n-dimensional investigations of the last chapter we return to two- and three-dimensional point space, and apply the general results for $n = 2$ and $n = 3$. We shall explore the question of what point sets are defined by quadratic equations in two or three unknowns. All coordinate systems will be *Cartesian*.

As the reader knows from algebra, it may happen that a quadratic equation has no solutions with real coordinates, but only solutions with nonreal complex coordinates. Obviously, those solutions do not correspond to points of $\Re^2$ or $\Re^3$. But, in order to avoid tedious listing of exceptional cases and to indicate the *algebraic reason* for the nonexistence of certain graphs defined by quadratic equations, we shall make the following formal definition.

Definition 23.1: An n-tuple of complex numbers in which at least one coordinate is not a real number is said to define an *imaginary point* or an *imaginary translation*. A set of such n-tuples is said to define an *imaginary graph*.

In chapter 21 it was shown that the intersections of cones with planes can be ellipses, hyperbolas, parabolas, pairs of intersecting lines, pairs of coinciding lines, and single points (= degenerate circles). In modern terminology the following algebraic generalization of the notion of conic section is customary.

Definition 23.2: The graph of a proper quadratic equation in two unknowns is called a *conic* and in three unknowns a *quadric*.

The qualification *proper* is to mean that the coefficient of at least one quadratic term in the quadratic equation does not vanish; that is, that the *formally quadratic* equation does not really reduce to a *linear* equation.

By theorem 22.3, any conic must be the graph of one of the following equations, relative to a suitable Cartesian coordinate system:

$$\lambda_1 x_1^2 + \lambda_2 x_2^2 + \gamma = 0, \qquad \lambda_1 \lambda_2 \gamma \neq 0, \qquad (23.1)$$

$$\lambda_1 x_1^2 + \lambda_2 x_2^2 \qquad = 0, \qquad \lambda_1 \lambda_2 \neq 0, \qquad (23.2)$$

$$\lambda_1 x_1^2 + \mu x_2 \qquad = 0, \qquad \lambda_1 \mu \neq 0, \qquad (23.3)$$

$$\lambda_1 x_1^2 \qquad + \gamma = 0, \qquad \lambda_1 \gamma \neq 0, \qquad (23.4)$$

$$\lambda_1^2 x_1^2 \qquad = 0, \qquad \lambda_1 \neq 0. \qquad (23.5)$$

The assumption is made that no coefficient occurring in the above equations vanishes. As in chapter 22, we shall sometimes abbreviate any of these five forms by the equation

$$x'Bx = 0, \qquad B = B', \qquad x = \begin{bmatrix} x_1 \\ x_2 \\ 1 \end{bmatrix}, \qquad (23.6)$$

where B is a symmetric matrix and x is the column with coordinates $x_1, x_2, 1$.

Case (23.1): A comparison with chapter 21 shows that we obtain a *hyperbola* if the two eigenvalues λ_1 and λ_2 have different signs and an *ellipse* if the two eigenvalues have the same sign and this sign is opposite to that of γ. If λ_1, λ_2, and γ all have the same sign, then the equation does not define a real point; but, in analogy with definition 21.1, its imaginary graph is frequently called an *imaginary ellipse*.

Case (23.2): If the eigenvalues have opposite signs, condition (23.2) can be rewritten in the form

$$p^2 x_1^2 - q^2 x_2^2 = (px_1 + qx_2)(px_1 - qx_2) = 0, \qquad p \cdot q \neq 0,$$

with suitable real numbers p and q. Hence we obtain *two intersecting lines*. If the eigenvalues have equal signs, we may rewrite condition (23.2) in the form

$$p^2 x_1^2 + q^2 x_2^2 = (px_1 + (qi)x_2)(px_1 - (qi)x_2) = 0, \quad p \cdot q \neq 0, \quad i = \sqrt{-1}.$$

For $p = q$, this defines a degenerate circle, that is, a *single point*. But, because of the decomposition of (23.2) into the product of two linear equations with complex coefficients, this conic is usually called *two imaginary intersecting lines with real intersection*. It is clear that the origin satisfies the equation as the only real point and that it belongs to both imaginary lines.

Case (23.3): This is obviously a parabola.

Case (23.4): If λ_1 and γ have opposite signs, then condition (23.4) can be rewritten in the form

$$(px_1 + q)(px_1 - q) = 0, \qquad p, q \, \varepsilon \, R,$$

with suitable real numbers p and q. Hence, we obtain *two distinct parallel lines*. If λ_1 and γ have the same sign, then the left-hand side is either always positive or always negative and, hence, cannot define a real point. But, in this case, condition (23.4) can be expressed in the form

$$(px_1 + qi)(px_1 - qi) = 0, \qquad p, q \, \varepsilon \, R;$$

therefore, this imaginary conic is called *two distinct imaginary parallel lines*.

Case (23.5): All points on the line $x_1 = 0$ and only those points have coordinates that satisfy (23.5). In analogy with cases (23.2) and (23.4), this conic is called *two coinciding lines*.

From this list we see that, apart from imaginary lines, the only conic that cannot be obtained as the intersection of a cone with a plane is the point set of two distinct parallel lines. As mentioned in the previous chapter, this conic can be obtained as a *cylindric section*.

After these preparations we turn to the problem of finding, *with as little computation as possible*, the type of conic that is represented by a given quadratic equation

$$x' A x = 0, \qquad A = A', \qquad x = \begin{bmatrix} x_1 \\ x_2 \\ 1 \end{bmatrix}. \tag{23.7}$$

By theorem 22.3, the point set defined by (23.7) must be equal to the point set defined by (23.6), which stands for exactly one of the five equations (23.1) to (23.5) if a suitable Cartesian coordinate system is chosen. From theorem 22.4 we know that $|A| = |B|$ and $|A^{3;3}| = |B^{3;3}|$ hold. The determinants of B and of $B^{3;3}$ can be computed immediately from equations (23.1) to (23.5). We obtain

$$|A| = |B| = \begin{cases} \lambda_1 \lambda_2 \gamma & \text{in case (23.1)}, \\[2mm] -\dfrac{\lambda_1 \mu^2}{4} & \text{in case (23.3)}, \\[2mm] 0 & \text{in all other cases;} \end{cases}$$

and, similarly,

$$|A^{3;3}| = |B^{3;3}| = \begin{cases} \lambda_1\lambda_2 & \text{in cases (23.1) and (23.2),} \\ 0 & \text{in all other cases.} \end{cases}$$

We summarize the results in the following table.

Theorem 23.1: *The graph of the proper quadratic equation (23.7) is the following conic*:

Conic	If $|A|$	& if $|A^{3;3}|$
Ellipse (possibly imaginary)	$\neq 0$	> 0
Hyperbola	$\neq 0$	< 0
Parabola	$\neq 0$	$= 0$
2 intersecting lines	$= 0$	< 0
2 imaginary lines with real intersection	$= 0$	> 0
2 parallel lines (possibly coinciding or imaginary)	$= 0$	$= 0$

This table does not provide a rule for distinguishing between an ellipse and an imaginary ellipse. An ellipse is imaginary if and only if $\lambda_1 + \lambda_2$ and γ have the same sign. But $\lambda_1 + \lambda_2 = \tau(A^{3;3})$, by exercise 22.5, and

$$\gamma = \frac{|A|}{|A^{3;3}|},$$

hence,

$$\frac{\tau(A^{3;3})\,|A|}{|A^{3;3}|} < 0$$

is necessary and sufficient for an ellipse to be *real*.

We turn now to the investigation of quadrics of which the spheres of chapter 20 are a very special case. To visualize the shape of a given quadric, we shall check the shape of its intersections with all planes perpendicular to base translations.

By theorem 22.3, any quadric must be the graph of any of the following equations, provided that a suitable Cartesian coordinate system is chosen:

$$\lambda_1 x_1^2 + \lambda_2 x_2^2 + \lambda_3 x_3^2 + \gamma = 0, \qquad \lambda_1\lambda_2\lambda_3\gamma \neq 0, \qquad (23.8)$$

$$\lambda_1 x_1^2 + \lambda_2 x_2^2 + \lambda_3 x_3^2 \phantom{{}+\gamma} = 0, \qquad \lambda_1\lambda_2\lambda_3 \neq 0, \qquad (23.9)$$

$$\lambda_1 x_1^2 + \lambda_2 x_2^2 + \mu x_3 \phantom{{}+\gamma} = 0, \qquad \lambda_1\lambda_2\mu \neq 0, \qquad (23.10)$$

$$\lambda_1 x_1^2 + \lambda_2 x_2^2 \phantom{{}+ \mu x_3} + \gamma = 0, \qquad \lambda_1\lambda_2\gamma \neq 0, \qquad (23.11)$$

$$\lambda_1 x_1^2 + \lambda_2 x_2^2 \phantom{{}+ \mu x_3 + \gamma} = 0, \qquad \lambda_1\lambda_2 \neq 0, \qquad (23.12)$$

$$\lambda_1 x_1^2 + \mu x_2 \phantom{{}+ \lambda_2 x_2^2 + \gamma} = 0, \qquad \lambda_1\mu \neq 0, \qquad (23.13)$$

$$\lambda_1 x_1^2 \qquad\qquad\qquad + \gamma = 0, \quad \lambda_1 \gamma \quad \neq 0, \qquad (23.14)$$

$$\lambda_1 x_1^2 \qquad\qquad\qquad = 0, \quad \lambda_1 \quad \neq 0. \qquad (23.15)$$

Again the assumption is made that no coefficient occurring in the above equations vanishes. By the proof of corollary 22.3, it is not possible to transform any of these eight forms into any of the other seven by a suitable change in the Cartesian coordinate system. Again, any of these eight forms will be abbreviated by the equation

$$x'Bx = 0, \qquad B = B', \qquad x = \begin{bmatrix} x_1 \\ x_2 \\ x_3 \\ 1 \end{bmatrix}, \qquad (23.16)$$

where B is a symmetric matrix of order 4 and x the column with coordinates x_1, x_2, x_3, and 1.

Case (23.8): As in the corresponding situation for conics, the type of quadric obtained depends on the signs of the coefficients in (23.8). Here there are four possibilities for the distribution of signs:

E_1: The λ_i have the same sign; the constant γ has the opposite sign.

E_2: The λ_i and the constant γ have the same sign.

H_1: The λ_i do not have the same sign, but exactly one of them has the same sign as the constant γ.

H_2: The λ_i do not have the same sign, but exactly two of them have the same sign as the constant γ.

Subcase E_1: All quotients $\lambda_j / -\gamma$ ($j = 1, 2, 3$) are positive. Dividing (23.8) by $-\gamma$, and substituting

$$\sqrt{\frac{\lambda_i}{-\gamma}} = \frac{1}{a_i}, \qquad i = 1, 2, 3,$$

in the resulting equation, and rearranging, we obtain

$$\frac{x_1^2}{a_1^2} + \frac{x_2^2}{a_2^2} + \frac{x_3^2}{a_3^2} = 1. \qquad (23.17)$$

Let us see what point set the quadric defined by (23.17) has in common with the plane

$$x_i = c \qquad \text{for} \qquad i = 1 \quad \text{or} \quad = 2 \quad \text{or} \quad = 3. \qquad (23.18)$$

By substituting c for this x_i in (23.17), we obtain an *ellipse* (on that plane) if $|c| < a_i$, a *point* on that plane (= *two imaginary lines with real intersection*) if $|c| = a_i$, and *no point* (= *an imaginary ellipse*) if $|c| > a_i$, as can be shown by theorem 23.1 (see Fig. 23.1). The graph of (23.17) is called an *ellipsoid*. The sphere is a special ellipsoid.

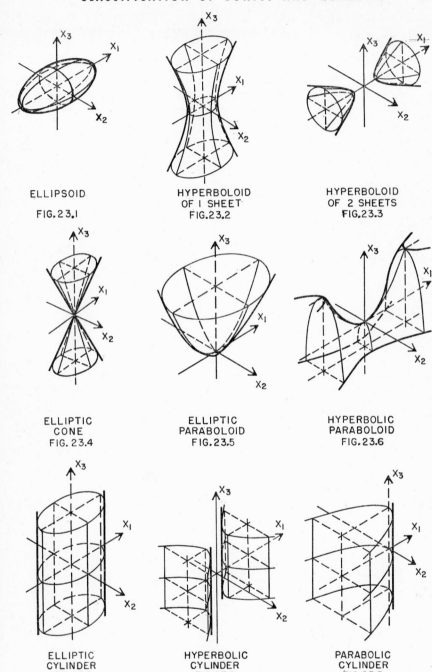

ELLIPSOID
FIG. 23.1

HYPERBOLOID
OF I SHEET
FIG. 23.2

HYPERBOLOID
OF 2 SHEETS
FIG. 23.3

ELLIPTIC
CONE
FIG. 23.4

ELLIPTIC
PARABOLOID
FIG. 23.5

HYPERBOLIC
PARABOLOID
FIG. 23.6

ELLIPTIC
CYLINDER
FIG. 23.7

HYPERBOLIC
CYLINDER
FIG. 23.8

PARABOLIC
CYLINDER
FIG. 23.9

Subcase E_2: All quotients λ_j/γ $(j = 1,2,3)$ are positive. Dividing (23.8) by γ, substituting

$$\sqrt{\frac{\lambda_i}{\gamma}} = \frac{1}{a_i}, \quad i = 1, 2, 3,$$

in the resulting equation, and rearranging, we obtain

$$\frac{x_1^2}{a_1^2} + \frac{x_2^2}{a_2^2} + \frac{x_3^2}{a_3^2} = -1. \tag{23.19}$$

Obviously, no real point can satisfy this equation. Because of its formal analogy with (23.17), this graph is called an *imaginary ellipsoid*.

Subcase H_1: Let us so order the base translations that λ_1 and λ_2 have the same sign and λ_3 and γ have the other sign. Then the quotients $\lambda_1/-\gamma$, $\lambda_2/-\gamma$, and λ_3/γ are all positive. Dividing (23.8) by $-\gamma$, substituting

$$\sqrt{\frac{\lambda_1}{-\gamma}} = \frac{1}{a_1}, \qquad \sqrt{\frac{\lambda_2}{-\gamma}} = \frac{1}{a_2}, \qquad \sqrt{\frac{\lambda_3}{\gamma}} = \frac{1}{a_3}$$

in the resulting equation, and rearranging, we obtain

$$\frac{x_1^2}{a_1^2} + \frac{x_2^2}{a_2^2} - \frac{x_3^2}{a_3^2} = 1. \tag{23.20}$$

Let us substitute (23.18) for some fixed i in (23.20), to see what points this quadric has in common with the plane (23.18). For $i = 1$ we obtain a *hyperbola*, except when $|c| = a_1$, in which case we obtain *two* (real) *intersecting lines*. For $i = 2$ the situation is similar; here the two intersecting lines occur for $|c| = a_2$. But for $i = 3$ we always obtain *ellipses* with increasing principal axes for increasing absolute value of c. Hence this quadric has the form indicated in Fig. 23.2; it is called a *hyperboloid of one sheet*.

Subcase H_2: By a procedure similar to that used in the previous subcases, the equation of the quadric may be written in the form

$$\frac{x_1^2}{a_1^2} - \frac{x_2^2}{a_2^2} - \frac{x_3^2}{a_3^2} = 1. \tag{23.21}$$

Again we substitute (23.18) for some fixed i in (23.21), to find the points of intersection of our quadric with the plane (23.18). For $i = 1$ we obtain *no points* (= an imaginary ellipse) as long as $|c| < a_1$, exactly *one point* (= two imaginary lines with real intersection) if $|c| = a_1$, and *ellipses* if $|c| > a_1$. Hence, this quadric must consist of at least two separate pieces (divided by the plane $x_1 = 0$). For $i = 2$ and $i = 3$ we always obtain *hyperbolas*. Therefore this quadric must have the form indicated in Fig. 23.3; it is called a *hyperboloid of two sheets*.

This finishes the discussion of case (23.8).

Case (23.9):   The following two subcases will be distinguished:

C_1:   Not all λ_i have the same sign.

C_2:   All λ_i do have the same sign.

Subcase C_1:   It is easily seen that, for a suitable numbering of the base translations and with substitutions similar to those in the previous cases, this quadric (23.9) may be written in the form

$$\frac{x_1^2}{a_1^2} + \frac{x_2^2}{a_2^2} - \frac{x_3^2}{a_3^2} = 0. \tag{23.22}$$

For every $c \neq 0$, the substitution $x_3 = c$ reduces (23.22) to the graph of an *ellipse*; for $x_3 = 0$ we obtain a single *point*. Let X^* be some point on some fixed ellipse on that quadric with coordinate vector x^*. Then, with x^* also every scalar multiple αx^* satisfies (23.22). But the points X whose coordinates x satisfy $x = \alpha x^*$ form the line through the origin O and the point X^* (see Fig. 23.4). Thus, this quadric contains all points on all lines through O and any point on some fixed ellipse obtained as intersection of that quadric with a plane $x_3 = c \neq 0$. It is not hard to see that the quadric cannot contain any other points. It is called a (an elliptic) *cone*. The cone of chapter 21 is a special case.

Subcase C_2:   Except for the zero vector, no triple of real numbers can satisfy (23.9). Hence this quadric has only the origin as a real point. Since the equation of this quadric can be brought to the form

$$\frac{x_1^2}{a_1^2} + \frac{x_2^2}{a_2^2} + \frac{x_3^2}{a_3^2} = 0, \tag{23.23}$$

it is called an *imaginary cone (with real vertex)*.

Case (23.10):   The following subcases will be distinguished:

P_1: λ_1 and λ_2 have the same sign.

P_2: λ_1 and λ_2 have opposite signs.

Subcase P_1:   The equation of this quadric can be brought to the form

$$\frac{x_1^2}{a_1^2} + \frac{x_2^2}{a_2^2} + px_3 = 0. \tag{23.24}$$

The intersections with every plane perpendicular to the first or second base translation turn out to be parabolas. The intersections with a plane perpendicular to the third base translation are *ellipses*, a *single point*, or *imaginary ellipses*. The quadric has the shape indicated in Fig. 23.5; it is called an *elliptic paraboloid*.

Subcase P_2:   The equation of this quadric can be brought to the form

$$\frac{x_1^2}{a_1^2} - \frac{x_2^2}{a_2^2} + px_3 = 0. \tag{23.25}$$

The intersections with every plane perpendicular to the first or second base translation again turn out to be *parabolas*. But the intersections with planes perpendicular to the third base translation are *hyperbolas* or (for $x_3 = 0$) *two intersecting lines*. The quadric has the form indicated in Fig. 23.6; it is called a *hyperbolic paraboloid*. As this quadric is somewhat difficult to visualize, looking at a three-dimensional model is recommended.

Cases (23.11) *and* (23.13): Since x_3 does not occur in (23.11) or (23.13), the intersection of any of these quadrics with any plane $x_3 = c$ is the *same* curve (but, of course, in different positions). If we take the set of all points on the plane $x_3 = 0$ as the two-dimensional point space $\mathfrak{R}^2$, then the intersection curve is given by the same equation (23.11) or (23.13). From theorem 23.1 it follows that it is an *ellipse*, an *imaginary ellipse*, a *hyperbola*, or a *parabola*. Suppose that a point X^* with coordinate vector x^* lies on the intersection of the plane $x_3 = 0$ with the quadric (23.11) or (23.13) we are investigating. Then all points X whose coordinate vectors x satisfy $x = x^* + \alpha(0,0,1)$ for every scalar α also lie on the quadric. Since $(0,0,1)$ is perpendicular to the plane $x_3 = 0$, this equation defines a normal to that plane. In other words, every normal of the plane $x_3 = 0$ through a point on the intersection curve consists of points that all belong to the quadric being investigated. According to the four kinds of intersection curves, these types of quadrics are called *elliptic cylinders, imaginary elliptic cylinders, hyperbolic cylinders,* and *parabolic cylinders*. Except for the imaginary graph, these quadrics are sketched in Figs. 23.7, 23.8, and 23.9. They can be distinguished by the following criteria:

For equation (23.11):

Z_1: λ_1 and λ_2 have the same sign; γ has the opposite sign.

Z_2: λ_1, λ_2, and γ have the same sign.

Z_3: λ_1 and λ_2 have opposite signs.

Z_4: Equation (23.13).

Cases (23.12), (23.14), *and* (23.15): These quadrics consist of *two planes* whose normals are perpendicular to the third base translation. We distinguish the following five subcases:

T_1: Equation (23.12); λ_1 and λ_2 have opposite signs.

T_2: Equation (23.12); λ_1 and λ_2 have the same sign.

T_3: Equation (23.14); λ_1 and γ have opposite signs.

T_4: Equation (23.14); λ_1 and γ have the same sign.

T_5: Equation (23.15).

The graphs of these five equations are called, respectively: *two intersecting planes, two imaginary planes with real intersection line, two distinct parallel planes, two distinct imaginary parallel planes,* and *two coinciding planes*.

This finishes the list of all possible types of quadrics. Now we turn again to the problem of finding an easy classification of the quadric represented by a given proper quadratic equation

$$x' A x = 0, \quad A = A', \quad x = \begin{bmatrix} x_1 \\ x_2 \\ x_3 \\ 1 \end{bmatrix}, \qquad (23.26)$$

with as little computation as possible. As in the case of conics, theorems 22.3 and 22.4 give the key to verification of the following classification table:

Theorem 23.2: *The graph of the proper quadratic equation* (23.26) *is the following quadric:*

	Quadric	If the number of nonzero eigenvalues of $A^{4;4}$ is	& if the signs of the nonzero eigenvalues of $A^{4;4}$ are	& if $|A|$
E_1	Ellipsoid	3	Equal	< 0
E_2	Imaginary ellipsoid	3	Equal	> 0
H_1	Hyperboloid of 1 sheet	3	Different	> 0
H_2	Hyperboloid of 2 sheets	3	Different	< 0
P_1	Elliptic paraboloid	2	Equal	< 0
P_2	Hyperbolic paraboloid	2	Different	> 0

	Quadric	If the number of nonzero eigenvalues of $A^{4;4}$ is	& if the signs of the nonzero eigenvalues of $A^{4;4}$ are	& if $\rho(A) =$
C_1	Cone	3	Different	3
C_2	Imaginary cone	3	Equal	3
Z_1, Z_2	Elliptic cylinder (possibly imaginary)	2	Equal	3
Z_3	Hyperbolic cylinder	2	Different	3
Z_4	Parabolic cylinder	1	. . .	3
T_1	2 intersecting planes	2	Different	2
T_2	2 imaginary planes (with real line)	2	Equal	2
T_3, T_4	2 distinct parallel planes (possibly imaginary)	1	. . .	2
T_5	2 coinciding planes	1	. . .	1

EXERCISES

1. Write down *explicitly* the symmetric matrix B, defined by (23.6), in cases (23.1) to (23.5).

2. Write down *explicitly* the symmetric matrix B, defined by (23.16), in cases (23.8) to (23.15).
3. Use exercise 2 to prove theorem 23.2 for $A = B$.
4. Show that the intersection of any quadric with any plane is a conic on that plane (but possibly an *imaginary* one).
5. Show that the equations of the quadrics of the subcases H_2, C_1, C_2, P_1, and P_2 can be brought into the forms (23.21) to (23.25), respectively.
6. Show that subcase C_1 does not contain any points other than those described in the paragraph on C_1.
7. If A has order 4, then the determinant $|A^{4;4} - \lambda I|$ is a polynomial in λ of third degree and, hence, can be written in the form

$$|A^{4;4} - \lambda I| = \alpha_0 + \alpha_1 \lambda + \alpha_2 \lambda^2 + \alpha_3 \lambda^3.$$

Compute the coefficients of the right-hand side in terms of sub-determinants of A.

8. Show that it is not necessary to compute the eigenvalues of $A^{4;4}$ *explicitly* in order to find whether they have equal or different signs and how many are different from zero.

   Hint: Apply Descartes' rule of signs and the previous exercise. Hence construct criteria, involving subdeterminants of A only, to replace the criteria in theorem 23.2 involving the signs of the eigenvalues of $A^{4;4}$.

9. If P and Q are two distinct points, denote by $L(P,Q) = 0$ an equation of the straight line through P and Q. Let U, V, Y, Z be four points of $\mathbf{R}^2$ chosen in such a way that no three of them are collinear. Then both quadratic equations $L(U,V)L(Y,Z) = 0$ and $L(U,Y)L(V,Z) = 0$ define conics (namely, in every case two distinct real lines). Show: The pencil of conics defined by

$$\alpha L(U, V)L(Y, Z) + \beta L(U, Y)L(V, Z) = 0$$

is the set of *all* conics passing through the four given points.

10. Use the previous exercise to prove: Given five points of $\mathbf{R}^2$ of which no three are collinear; there exists *one and only one* conic passing through these five points.

11. Generalize the propositions made in the two previous exercises to the three-dimensional case of quadrics.

12. Find criteria to determine whether an elliptic cylinder or two distinct parallel planes are imaginary or not.

13. Develop a pole-polar theory for ellipsoids and hyperboloids.

    Hint: If the quadric is represented by equation (23.26), *define* the graph of $x^{*\prime} A x = 0$ as the polar plane of the point X^* with respect to the quadric, if possible.

Comments on the Axiomatic Treatment of Analytic Geometry

To make sure that any science, branch of science, or scientific theory is complete and logically sound, one has to develop it from the very beginning. In the development the concepts have to be introduced in such sequence that, in every definition, only concepts that have been defined earlier are used. But regardless of how the presentation is made, there is always one principal difficulty: To state the *first* definition of a scientific field we still need a vocabulary of terms standing for the concepts that enter that definition. These initial concepts cannot be defined later in the sequence, because later their meaning is assumed to be *known,* and a definition that presupposes knowledge of what is to be defined is no definition at all. Consequently, every theory has to be started with a number of *undefined* concepts, that is, concepts that are undefined within that theory.

In order not to confuse the freshman by starting with undefined terms and complicated abstractions in addition to the heavy reading, we choose in this textbook to consider analytic geometry as a part of geometry that comes after elementary geometry. Such questions as: What is a point? or What is a direction? have been shifted to elementary geometry. But the questions exist there just the same. Although it is not necessary, it is very natural and practical to consider the concept *point* as the most basic concept in geometry, because, in the language of elementary set theory, all geometric figures can be expressed in terms of points. If this viewpoint is taken, then the concept of a point cannot be defined *within geometry.* Yet if we consider *point* a *geometric* concept, then it cannot be defined *outside of geometry*, either; that is, *before* geometry is introduced in that sequence of scientific fields that we call mathematics. Thus, in such a presentation, we have to take *point* as the first undefined term of geometry. But, to consider *several points together*, or a whole *line* or *curve*, we need the language of elementary set theory, which is introduced in chapter 2 in a most simple form.

Now an analysis of geometry has shown that it is possible and convenient to develop its elementary parts *from linear algebra*. If we assume (as we did in this textbook) that we know the most elementary set theory and the definition and handling of real numbers, then we can construct a substantial part of linear algebra. We start with the concept of a three-dimensional vector space $\mathbf{R}^3$ over the real numbers, and we can show that there exists such an object, namely, the set of all triples of real numbers together with (4.1) and (4.2). We can then introduce such concepts as linear combination, linear dependence, subspace, and so forth.

After linear algebra is developed we start to build up geometry. We take the set of elements of such a three-dimensional vector space $\mathbf{R}^3$ and construct a second set, to be denoted by $\mathfrak{R}^3$, in such a way that there exists a one-to-one correspondence between $\mathbf{R}^3$ and $\mathfrak{R}^3$. The easiest method is to take *two copies* of the set $\mathbf{R}^3$ and *denote the elements of the second copy differently*, for example, by using a different alphabet (as we did) or distinguishing marks, such as dashes, bars, or tildes. The second set will now be called *three-dimensional point space*, and its elements will be called *points*. This is the first step into geometry. Note that *point* is not defined by any geometric means, but simply introduced as a *name* for the elements of a certain set in one-to-one correspondence with a three-dimensional vector space.

In the next step we fix one point O at our pleasure and call it the *origin*. Now the elements of $\mathbf{R}^3$ can be brought into our theory. We call them *translations* and define them to be mappings of $\mathfrak{R}^3$ into itself with the property that every element $\mathbf{t}$ of $\mathbf{R}^3$ maps the origin on its copy T in $\mathfrak{R}^3$ $t(O) = T$ (p. 62). Thereafter we define two nonzero translations as having the *same* or *opposite direction* according as they are positive or negative multiples of each other. Then the qualification "not the same or opposite direction" is synonymous with "not a nonzero multiple." If we have $\mathbf{u} = \alpha\mathbf{v}$ for two translations $\mathbf{u}$ and $\mathbf{v}$ and a positive real number α, then we say that $\mathbf{u}$ *has α times the length of* $\mathbf{v}$.

Turning back to $\mathfrak{R}^3$, we define *lines* and *planes* as the sets of all images of the origin under the translations of a one- or two-dimensional subspace of $\mathbf{R}^3$. With any two points on a line we can associate a translation, namely, that which maps the first point on the second. Now distances between points *on the same line* can be compared by means of the ratios of the lengths of the associated translations.

But, in order to introduce *distances* as well as (cosines of) *angles* in

$\mathfrak{R}^3$ in general, we choose a positive definite symmetric bilinear mapping of $\mathbf{R}^3$ into R as in chapter 16; that is, we make $\mathbf{R}^3$ into a *Euclidean vector space*. We can then define in $\mathbf{R}^3$ *unit translations* and *perpendicularity* of two nonzero translations, and in $\mathfrak{R}^3$ *distance* between two points, *perpendicularity* of two lines, *normal* of a plane, and so forth. As we can always find a Cartesian basis in a Euclidean vector space, according to theorem 16.3, we may alternatively introduce distances and angles by picking out any three linearly independent translations from $\mathfrak{R}^3$ and *defining* them to be a Cartesian basis.

If we have chosen any basis for $\mathbf{R}^3$, we can introduce coordinates for the translations and thence for the points in the manner of definitions 6.3 and 6.4. Note that, in the statement of definition 6.3, the distinction between boldface and italic letters is not essentially a distinction between geometry and algebra, but rather a distinction between vectors considered as abstract quantities, namely, as elements of a vector space, and vectors in relation to a basis of the vector space. Once we have coordinates, it is advisable to take them to be Cartesian, since then the bilinear mapping reduces to the *inner product*.

Finally, we may define *volume* of a tetrahedron and compare the *orientation* of an arbitary nonzero triple of translations with that of the base translations as in chapter 19.

In this way we can build up the most elementary part of three-dimensional geometry. Similarly, we can construct a two-dimensional geometry. On the other hand, we have seen in this textbook that we can develop the theory of three-dimensional translation and point spaces from elementary geometry. Thus, a basic part of elementary geometry is, *in its structure*, identical with the theory of vector spaces of at most three dimensions. Because of this close relationship, it is quite natural to combine analytic geometry and linear algebra in a single text.

Since this textbook is intended for undergraduates, it contains only a selection of the more elementary parts of geometry and algebra. We have considered only those point sets whose coordinates satisfy linear or quadratic equations or systems of them. To investigate point sets defined by *algebraic* equations in general, a much more advanced algebraic theory is needed, which is known as *algebraic geometry*. The introduction of the idea of *points at infinity* as *points* (better: *directions*) where parallel lines "intersect" leads to *projective geometry*, which combines ordinary geometric results in more general and very symmetric theorems and gives excellent insight into the structure of geometry. The application of (advanced) calculus to geometry brings about *vector analysis* and *differential geometry*.

In abstract algebra one considers the general theory of *vector spaces*, whereas in this text we dealt only with vector spaces that have real or complex numbers as scalars. For example, one may admit any set of numbers or abstract quantities with which one can add, subtract, multiply, and divide "as with the real numbers." To introduce an analog of the inner product for infinite-dimensional vector spaces, additional tools from the calculus are needed; the theory so obtained is known as *Hilbert spaces*. There are also a number of further types of vector spaces with additional properties, of which probably the most important are the *Banach spaces*. All these fields are related to the *theory of matrices*, which gives methods for *practical* computation; there the elements of a matrix can be much more general quantities than real numbers, and the number of rows and columns can also be infinite, with certain restrictions.

None of the follow-up fields mentioned—and the list is not intended to be complete— is isolated, but all are interrelated with one another and with other fields. This overlapping is so pronounced in several instances that, properly speaking, one cannot claim any more that there exist separate branches of mathematics called "geometry" or "algebra." Any such division, although it may be needed for convenience in teaching and filing, is artificial and dependent on personal interpretation and taste. A genuine separation is today impossible.

Guide to Further Reading

For the reader whose appetite has been whetted by the ideas in this introductory text, and for the teacher who wants to have background information, the following more detailed or advanced treatises, or relevant parts of them, can be recommended. The list is by no means complete and may partly reflect the author's personal tastes, but may serve as a good starting point. Further references, also to easy introductory texts, will be found in some of these books. For a more advanced presentation, a knowledge of the simple properties of *rings, fields, quotient structures*, and other algebraic concepts, which are explained in modern books on algebra, will be needed. A more unified and global treatment is contained in modern books on projective geometry.

E. Artin, *Geometric Algebra*, New York, Interscience Publishers, 1957.

R. Baer, *Linear Algebra and Projective Geometry*, New York, Academic Press, 1952.

R. Bellman, *Introduction to Matrix Analysis*, New York, McGraw-Hill, 1960.

G. Birkhoff and S. MacLane, *A Survey of Modern Algebra*, New York, Macmillan, 1953.

N. Bourbaki, *Algèbre*, Paris, Hermann, 1951– .

H. Buseman and P. J. Kelly, *Projective Geometry and Projective Metrics*, New York, Academic Press, 1953.

C. Chevalley, *Fundamental Concepts of Algebra*, New York, Academic Press, 1956.

F. R. Gantmacher, *The Theory of Matrices*, New York, Chelsea, 1959.

P. R. Halmos, *Finite-dimensional Vector Spaces*, Princeton, Van Nostrand, 1958.

H. Hasse, *Higher Algebra*, New York, Ungar, 1954.

N. Jacobson, *Lectures in Abstract Algebra*, Princeton, Van Nostrand, 1951, 1953.

H. W. Kuhn and A. W. Tucker, *Linear Inequalities and Related Systems*, Princeton University Press, 1956.

H. K. Nickerson, D. C. Spencer, and N. E. Steenrod, *Advanced Calculus*, Princeton, Van Nostrand, 1959.

G. Pickert, *Analytische Geometrie*, Leipzig, Akademische Verlagsgesellschaft, 1953.

O. Schreier and E. Sperner, *An Introduction to Modern Algebra and Matrix Theory*, New York, Chelsea, 1952.

E. Sperner, *Einführung in die analytische Geometrie und Algebra*, Göttingen, Vandenhoek und Ruprecht, 1948, 1951.

R. R. Stoll, *Linear Algebra and Matrix Theory*, New York, McGraw-Hill, 1952.

R. M. Thrall and L. Tornheim, *Vector Spaces and Matrices*, New York, Wiley, 1957.

B. L. van der Waerden, *Modern Algebra*, New York, Ungar, 1949, 1950; *Algebra*, Berlin, Springer, 1955.

Index of Examples

Index of Symbols

δ_{ij}	Kronecker delta, 216
E_{ij}	(special matrix), 165
$\mathfrak{E}$	ellipse, 250
f_S	restriction of a mapping to a subset S, 20
$\mathbf{f}$	multilinear (bilinear) mapping, 195
$\{G,*\}$	group under composition law $*$, 38
Hom $(\mathbf{V},\mathbf{W})$	vector space of homomorphisms of $\mathbf{V}$ into $\mathbf{W}$, 59
$\mathfrak{H}$	hyperbola, 251
I	set of integers, 9; $= I_n$ identity matrix of order n, 163
I^*	set of non-zero integers, 9
I^+	set of positive integers, 9
i	(occasionally) $= \sqrt{-1}$, 5
$M_{ij}(\alpha)$	(special matrix), 164
$|\mathbf{m}|$	length of translation $\mathbf{m}$, 28
$N_i(\alpha)$	(special matrix), 165
$\nu(M)$	nullity of matrix M, 178
$\nu(\mathbf{M})$	nullity of linear mapping $\mathbf{M}$, 178
$P(A)$	power set of a set A, 11
$\mathfrak{P}$	parabola, 253
R	set of real numbers, 9
R^*	set of non-zero real numbers, 9
R^+	set of positive real numbers, 9
R^2	set of real couples (pairs), 9
R^3	set of real triples, 9
R^n	real n-tuples, additive group of, 39; vector space of, 48
$R[x]$	vector space of real polynomials, 48
$R[x]_L$	vector space of real linear polynomials, 48
$R[x]_{LH}$	vector space of real linear homogeneous polynomials, 48
$r\mathbf{a}$	multiple of vector $\mathbf{a}$ by scalar r, 32
$r(a_1,a_2,\cdots,a_n)$	multiple of sequence $(a_1,\cdots,a_n)$ by scalar r, 37
$\mathbf{R}^1$	set of translations of line $\mathfrak{R}^1$, 48
$\mathbf{R}^2$	set of translations of plane $\mathfrak{R}^2$, 48
$\mathbf{R}^3$	set of translations of space $\mathfrak{R}^3$, 47
$\mathfrak{R}^1$	line, 8
$\mathfrak{R}^2$	plane, 8
$\mathfrak{R}^3$	three-dimensional geometric space, 8
$\rho(A)$	rank of a matrix A, 178

$\rho(\mathbf{A})$	rank of a linear mapping $\mathbf{A}$, 178
$\hat{S}$	subspace orthogonal to subspace S, 113
$\bar{s}$	opposite element of s, 39
s^2	inner square of n-tuple, 148
$\mathbf{s}^2$	inner square of translation, 185
$\mathfrak{S}^n$	circle, sphere, 239
$\mathfrak{T}^n_{\mathfrak{S}}$	tangent (plane) to circle (sphere) $\mathfrak{S}^n$, 239
$\tau(A)$	trace of matrix A, 163
$\mathbf{V}^*$	dual of vector space $\mathbf{V}$, 60
$|\mathbf{v}|$	length of $\mathbf{v}$ in a Euclidean vector space
ε	element of, 7
$\not\varepsilon$	not element of, 7
$\cap$	intersection, 9
$\cup$	union, 9
$\times$	Cartesian product, 9; vector product, 231
$\{,\cdots,\}$	set of listed elements, 10
$\{\ |\cdots\}$	set defined by properties of its elements, 10
$\varnothing$	empty (null) set, 10
$\subset, \supset$	set inclusion, 10
$\rightarrow$	assignment defining a mapping, 12
$\circ$	composition of mappings, 18
$+$	addition of translations, 30; in the abstract case, 35; of n-tuples, 36; of matrices, 151
$-$	subtraction of translations, 30; in vector spaces, 47
$\sum$	summation convention for translations, 31; in vector spaces, 47; for linear combinations, 49
$*$	composition law, 35
$\cdot$	multiplication, 35; inner multiplication for sequences, 148, for translations, 185; complex inner product, 200
1	identity, 39
0	zero, 39
$[\ ]$	span, 49
O	zeros omitted in indicated area, 95
$'$	transposition of matrices, 169
$\leq, <$	inequalities for n-tuples, 114

Index of Terms